# ADDICTION AND OPIATES

# ADDICTION
# AND OPIATES

ALFRED R. LINDESMITH
*Indiana University*

ALDINE PUBLISHING COMPANY
CHICAGO

First published 1968 by ALDINE Publishing Company
529 South Wabash Avenue, Chicago, Ill. 60605

Library of Congress Catalog Card Number 68–19870

Designed by Miles Zimmerman

Printed in the United States of America

Second printing, 1970

# PREFACE

This revision of my 1947 book, *Opiate Addiction*, has been prompted primarily by continued interest in and debate concerning the theory of addiction that was elaborated in it. The first part of the book, which presents a theoretical discussion of the social psychology of opiate addiction, has been extensively revised to incorporate new evidence and arguments, to make the theoretical position more clear, and to take negative criticisms into account.

The second part deals with the social problem of addiction and is relatively brief. Because I have analyzed the policy and problem aspects of addiction in some detail in my 1965 book, *The Addict and the Law*, I have simply reproduced my 1947 analysis with only a very few minor editorial changes and a brief postscript. The bibliography and the glossary of the addict's argot have been expanded and updated.

# CONTENTS

PREFACE                V

PART I   The Nature of the Opiate Habit

| | | |
|---|---|---|
| *Chapter 1* | Method and Problem | 3 |
| *Chapter 2* | The Effects of Opiates | 23 |
| *Chapter 3* | Habituation and Addiction | 47 |
| *Chapter 4* | The Nature of Addiction | 69 |
| *Chapter 5* | Processes in Addiction | 97 |
| *Chapter 6* | Cure and Relapse | 129 |
| *Chapter 7* | A Critique of Current Views of Addiction | 157 |
| *Chapter 8* | Conclusions, Implications, Problems | 191 |

PART II   Opiate Addiction as a Social Problem

| | | |
|---|---|---|
| *Chapter 9* | The Problem in the United States during the Nineteenth Century | 207 |
| *Chapter 10* | Federal Anti-Narcotics Legislation | 217 |
| *Chapter 11* | The Effects of World War II | 225 |
| *Chapter 12* | Needed Reforms | 233 |
| *Chapter 13* | Postscript—1968 | 239 |

APPENDIX *Kinds of Drugs and Methods of Use*            243

GLOSSARY OF ADDICT ARGOT                               249

SELECTED BIBLIOGRAPHY                                  267

INDEX                                                  289

# PART I

## The Nature of the Opiate Habit

# 1

# METHOD AND PROBLEM

The present study is directly concerned only with addiction to the opiate-type drugs and their synthetic equivalents. A rational, general theoretical account of the nature of the experiences which generate the addict's characteristic craving for drugs is proposed and systematically elaborated. While this theoretical position has obvious implications for other addictions which resemble opiate addiction in that they also involve drugs which produce physical dependence and withdrawal distress, an extension of the theory to these other forms of addiction, such as alcoholism, is not attempted here. This is a matter which requires specific empirical investigation of a comparative nature.

The central theoretical problem of this investigation is posed by the fact that some persons who experience the effects of opiate-type drugs and use them for a period sufficient to establish physical dependence do not become addicts while others under what appear to be the same conditions do become addicted. The attempt to account for this differential reaction requires a specification of the circumstances under which physical dependence results in addiction and in the absence of which it does not. It also requires a careful consideration of the meaning of "addiction" spelled out in terms of behavior and attitudes characteristic of opiate addicts everywhere. The theory that is developed is a general one; its applicability is not limited to American addicts, to lower-class users, to twentieth-century addiction, to any restricted segment of the problem, or to any specific historical period. Consequently, the focus of theoretical attention must be on those aspects of addiction which may reasonably be regarded as basic or essential in the sense that they are invariably manifested by all types of addicts regardless of place, time, method of use, social class, and other similar variable circumstances.

The second part of the study consists of a brief statement of a view of current public policy concerning addiction in the United States, with proposals for reform which, it is believed, would substantially reduce the evils now associated with addiction and the large illicit traffic in drugs. Since the original publication of this book in 1947 there has been a widespread public realization that the American program of dealing with addicts is both cruel and ineffective and that it compares unfavorably in these respects with the programs of most European countries in which opiate addiction is handled primarily as a medical rather than as a police problem.

It should be kept in mind that when I use such terms as "narcotics," "drugs," "drug addict," and "drug users," I will be referring to drugs that are commonly classified as opiates and their synthetic equivalents and to persons addicted to drugs in this class. Common and well-known examples are opium, heroin, morphine, methadone, and demerol. Marihuana and cocaine do not belong to this category, and only incidental reference will be made to them. While alcohol is addicting in approximately the same sense that heroin is, it will also be referred to only incidentally. The fact that marihuana, cocaine, and heroin and other opiate-type drugs are covered in the same anti-narcotics legislation is a fertile source of confused thinking because it obscures the facts that the use of marihuana is totally unlike heroin or morphine addiction and that alcoholism, which is not covered by the legislation and is not popularly thought of as a form of narcotic addiction, actually has very much in common with opiate addiction.

The theory that is proposed in this book, in its earliest stages, was derived from observing addicts and conversing with them. The later development of the theoretical framework of the study was also significantly influenced by data available in the extensive literature. Approximately fifty addicts were interviewed over a fairly extended period of time sufficient to establish an informal, friendly relationship of mutual trust. In the case of twelve others there was at least one interview but the relationship was brief or occurred under circumstances that made it impossible to place much confidence in what was said or to obtain a full and consistent account of the person's addiction history. Since my contacts were usually with addicts who were using drugs it was unavoidable that some of them disappeared before I could learn much from them. On the other hand, there were some with whom I established relationships that lasted for several years covering periods of use, of temporary voluntary abstention, and of incarceration.

My principal assistance in becoming acquainted with new subjects came from "Broadway" Jones, officially known by the alias "Chic Conwell," which Sutherland gave to him in *The Professional Thief*.[1] Mr. Jones himself had had a long history of addiction that began in his late teens. He was an invaluable source of information. He also read and criticized my manuscript. Indeed, *he* initially suggested that I study drug addiction and offered his cooperation in the project. I remained in communication with him until his death, some years after that of Dr. Sutherland. Mr. Jones was not using drugs during most of the approximately twenty years that I knew him but did relapse some years before his death. On the advice of Sutherland he voluntarily committed himself to Lexington for withdrawal.

When I first began to talk to addicts with the idea of making a systematic analysis of the habit, I became fascinated by the theoretical problems it posed. I dreamed of basing my analysis on interviews with hundreds of addicts, perhaps even as many as a thousand. For this purpose, through the good offices of Professor Sutherland I obtained permission from the Federal Bureau of Prisons to interview addicts at the Lexington Public Health Serv-

1. E. H. Sutherland, *The Professional Thief* (Chicago: University of Chicago Press, 1937).

ice Hospital and the annex of the Federal Penitentiary at Leavenworth, which at that time specialized in handling drug offenders. However, the Public Health Service, which also exercised authority in these two establishments, refused to give me this permission on the grounds that what I proposed to do was already being done by their personnel. I was consequently compelled to rely on the costly, slow, and arduous techniques involved in picking up subjects from the Chicago streets, financing my research almost entirely from my own pocket.

Many but not all of my subjects were introduced to me by Broadway Jones, who briefed both them and me in advance. Most of them were experienced in criminal activity such as drug peddling, some form of theft, or the confidence game. Mr. Jones sometimes warned me that my new subject could not be trusted and that I should keep one hand on my billfold and the other on my watch when I was with him. In other instances the subject was characterized as an "honest thief" who could be trusted implicitly to steal only from strangers and whom I could safely take into my home. A substantial number of my subjects did in fact visit with me, my wife, and our daughter in our apartment. None of these ever pilfered anything; on the contrary, a number of them offered to provide us with stolen goods.

I ordinarily told each new subject that I was interested in studying the "psychology" of the habit and trying to understand it. This invariably satisfied them, and they asked no probing questions, perhaps because they felt that they knew a great deal more about the psychology of addiction than I ever would. It was thus unnecessary to explain the theoretical development of the study to them, and, indeed, they were not interested in it.

To encourage addicts to remain in contact with me I usually rewarded them by buying them a meal in a cheap restaurant or bar or by giving them fifty cents or a dollar after an interview. My conversations with them were held in bars and restaurants as a rule. Most of my subjects were very cooperative, in part perhaps because addicts talk and think about their addiction a great deal in any case, and also, in many instances, because they felt that an objective, non-moralistic study of addiction was needed and might benefit them by leading to a more rational public policy. There is a widespread feeling among addicts that addiction is not understood, that it is misrepresented in the mass media, and that it is dealt with in an inhumane and needlessly severe manner. Non-addicts who have dealings with known addicts generally deal with them in a condescending or authoritarian manner and often moralize with them. I consciously avoided all of this, even at times when I was repelled or shocked. I felt no condescension because I knew that my subjects had information which might be useful to me and that I was thus dependent on them. Finally, I was in no position to be authoritarian because my subjects were free to break off the relationship whenever they wished to.

The literature of drug addiction was at first not consulted for fear that the opinions expressed would introduce an initial and perhaps decisive bias into the investigation. The first temporary hypothesis was formulated exclusively on the basis of observation of and conversations with addicts, and it was only after the study had crystallized around a few central problems and theories that the literature was intensively examined. It was examined particularly with the view of uncovering negative evidence which would force revision of the theory and also of exploring as exhaustively as possible all relevant aspects of the subject and all implications of the theory.

The first tentative and obviously inadequate hypothesis formulated was that individuals who do not know what drug they are receiving do not become addicted and, on the positive side, that they become addicted when they know what they are getting and have taken it long enough to experience withdrawal distress when they stop. This hypothesis was destroyed almost at once by negative evidence. One of the first addicts to be interviewed, a doctor, had once received morphine for several weeks; he was fully aware of the fact, but he did not become addicted at that time. The difficulty presented by this case remained unresolved until my attention was attracted to a rather casual and incidental comment made by Dr. Albrecht Erlenmeyer in an article concerned mainly with the physiological effects of morphine. Speaking of withdrawal distress, Erlenmeyer said, "In such moments the *craving for morphine* is born and rapidly becomes insatiable, because the patient has learned during the period of habituation, when abstinence symptoms always set in after the effect of the last morphine dose has passed off, that those terrible symptoms are banished as if by magic by a sufficiently large dose of morphine."[2] In the light of this statement, the second hypothesis of the investigation was that persons become addicts when they recognize or perceive the significance of withdrawal distress which they are experiencing, and that if they do not recognize withdrawal distress they do not become addicts regardless of other considerations.

This formulation proved to be much more significant and useful than the first, but like the first it did not stand the test of evidence and had to be revised when cases were found in which individuals who had experienced and understood withdrawal distress, though not in its severest form, did not use the drug to alleviate the distress and never became addicts. The final revision of the hypothesis involved a shift in emphasis from the individual's recognition of withdrawal distress to his use of the drug to alleviate the distress after this insight has occurred. This hypothesis was found to be superior to the others. It had the advantage of attributing the origin of addiction, not to a single event, but to a series of events, thus implying that addiction is established in a learning process extending over a period of time.

If one thinks of the central problem of addiction as being that of isolating and describing the nature of the experience from which the fatal craving or "hook" is derived, the hypothesis stated above suggests that the critical experience in the fixation process is not the positive euphoria produced by the drug but rather the relief of the pain that invariably appears when a physically dependent person stops using the drug. This experience becomes critical, however, only when an additional indispensable element in the situation is taken into account, namely, a cognitive one. The individual not only must experience relief of withdrawal distress but must understand or conceptualize this experience in a particular way. He must realize that his distress is produced by the interruption of prior regular use of the drug.

It is evident that when a person becomes addicted to heroin or morphine the entire pattern of his social behavior is commonly altered to a pervasive degree and that his orientation toward the drug is radically altered. These drastic changes in behavior and

2. As quoted by Charles E. Terry and Mildred Pellens, *The Opium Problem* (New York: Committee on Drug Addictions and the Bureau of Social Hygiene, 1928), p. 602.

attitude are not of the kind that could reasonably be expected to occur in an instant. They are learned, according to the theory, in a gradual but rather rapid way as the withdrawal distress recurs and must repeatedly be banished by further use of the drug. Even though the beginner may like the effects of morphine or heroin, the prospects of becoming an addict are traumatic if they are actually fully understood. In this sense, the addict does not ordinarily become such voluntarily but is rather trapped "against his will" by the hook of withdrawal.

If one disregards the cognitive aspect, one can say of this hypothesis that it is a theory emphasizing negative rather than positive reinforcement as the basis of addiction. In psychological writings the term "negative reinforcement" is used to refer to a situation in which a given action is rewarded by the elimination of something unpleasant—an adverse stimulus. Thus, if a child is locked in his room until he masters his school assignment, his reward for doing it will be that he will be freed from confinement. This is negative reinforcement. If, on the other hand, the child is promised a much desired trip to the zoo when he completes his homework, this is called positive reinforcement.

It will be pointed out in a later chapter that psychologists have explored the theory advanced here, minus the cognitive feature, in ingenious experimental investigations of the effects of opiates on lower animals. Some of this work strongly suggests that insofar as lower animals are capable of matching the behavior of human subjects in becoming attached to drugs, their attachment also depends upon the negative reinforcement obtained from the relief of withdrawal rather than on positive reinforcement stemming from pleasurable effects of the drugs. Investigations of this type which necessarily ignore the differences between human beings and animals occasioned by the former's immense cognitive superiority leave open the question of the extent to which the responses of lower animals to opiates can be made to parallel those of human subjects. In a subsequent chapter attention will be given to the matter of determining whether it is justifiable or meaningful to assert, as some investigators do, that addiction can be induced in rats, monkeys, and other animals.

The hypothesis of this study was tested under the following assumptions: (1) the verification of a theory consists not in piling up selected instances which confirm it but in looking for evidence which contradicts clear logical implications which may be deduced from it; (2) a valid theory of addiction must account for the basic or essential aspects of addiction by indicating that they form a system or pattern which is logically implied or predicted by the theory. All of the evidence obtained from the literature and from conversations with all subjects was considered from this point of view. None of it seems to me to contradict the theory. On the contrary, the theory seems to make sense of a number of aspects of addiction which have usually been regarded as paradoxical or puzzling from other points of view. It also suggests a simple unitary explanation of a central theoretical problem, that of accounting for the fact that physical dependence on opiates is sometimes followed by addiction and sometimes is not.

The fact that the hypothesis of the study was revised a number of times in the course of the investigation suggests that further evidence or the extension of the theory to other forms of addiction may necessitate further reformulations. This is a probability rather than a mere possibility and seems to me to constitute an advantage rather than a weakness. It is characteristic of all genuine scientific systems that they evolve as they are confronted with new evidence that does not fit the old theories. The prime virtue of a general theory is that it stimulates the search for negative evidence and challenges its critics to construct a better one.

It may be asked whether the search for negative cases was properly conducted and if the observer has not neglected evidence of a contradictory character. To this, of course, there is no final answer. It is probable that somewhere in the course of any study unconscious distortion takes place. Concerning the central hypothesis and the direct lines of evidence, however, certain procedures were followed which may be said to exclude bias. For example, when the theory had been stated in an approximation of its final form it occurred to me that it could be tested in cases where an individual had had two separate experiences with morphine or opiates, each of which was sufficiently prolonged to produce withdrawal distress but with addiction following only the second episode. Case 3 in Chapter 4 is an example. It was concluded that if the theory was valid, the person would report that he had failed to realize the nature of the withdrawal in that experience from which he had escaped without becoming addicted. Thereupon a thorough search was made for cases in which an individual had undergone such an experience with the drug prior to becoming an addict. All cases of this kind which could be found, or of which any record could be located, were taken into account. Any of these cases might have contradicted the final hypothesis, but none did so. The inference or prediction which had been drawn on the basis of the theory was thus fully borne out. This procedure was followed throughout the study wherever possible and, as will be seen, is implicit in the form in which the theory is stated.

As previously mentioned, I scrupulously refrained from informing the addict of any theories which I held or of the exact reasons for my inquiries. Thus when an addict was asked about his experience during gradual withdrawal cures he was not told that an attempt was being made to check the implications of the theory. It was inferred that if addicts feel approximately normal between shots as they maintain they do, it should be possible to deceive them as to whether they are really getting the drug. During the discussion of such gradual withdrawal cures, the information was often volunteered by the addict that he himself had been deceived at some time into believing that he was getting the drug when he actually was not, or vice versa. This information was usually introduced with the remark that he did not expect to be believed, whereupon he would proceed to give the facts which corroborated the theory and which had been anticipated. In none of these cases, however, did the addict know when he gave the information that it had any significance for a theory of addiction.

It has often been said that testimony of addicts is virtually worthless because of the secrecy surrounding addiction and the tendency of drug users to distort and falsify. I have found that this view is incorrect. The addict lies and distorts not because he has any indiscriminate urge to do so but in order to obtain certain definite and practical results. If it is clear to him that he has nothing to gain by lying and nothing to lose by telling the truth, he is as straightforward and honest as anyone else. Of course, he will rationalize and offer excuses, but in this sense he is no different from non-addicts.

It is true that there are certain areas in which the addict has very strong inhibitions against giving the unvarnished truth, but these inhibitions apply entirely to information which was not relevant to the central problem of the study. A drug user is particularly cautious about information concerning the sources of his supply, and if he is engaged in theft or other illegal activity he will be very reluctant to describe this activity. Since matters of this kind had no bearing on the central problem being investigated no special effort was made to obtain these data, although practically all the addicts who were interviewed eventually volunteered such information. The drug user has no special tendency to falsify concerning the nature of the drug habit. The fact that contact was maintained with some of the cases over a period of several years was a further insurance against deception. On the whole, once friendly contact is made, drug users are probably above average in cooperativeness, because many of them believe that they ought to be studied and better understood. The data which they provided me were found to be quite consistent with the material that the literature on opiate addiction offers.

This study might be criticized on the grounds that the addicts who were interviewed did not constitute a representative sampling of American drug users. Indeed, no effort whatever was made to secure a sample that was representative in a statistical sense because it was not the purpose of the study to make a statistical description of the variable attributes and characteristics of American addicts. The purpose was rather to try to find a plausible general theory of addiction, that is, to describe the nature of the experience from which the user's craving for the drug is derived.

The investigation of any subject necessarily proceeds on the basis of assumptions that cannot themselves be established as valid in the research in question. One such assumption which underlies the present study is that the scientist who studies social or other phenomena should, whenever possible, seek to formulate generalizations that apply to all of the instances of the problem with which he is concerned, rather than to most or some of them only. In other words, it is assumed that genuinely scientific causal propositions should be stated as universals. This does not imply a belief in absolute truth as is sometimes erroneously assumed, since it is anticipated that all such generalizations will be accepted provisionally only, as long as no contradictory evidence is available or no better theory is at hand. This assumption implies the belief that it is possible for the social scientist as well as for the natural scientist to state theories in such a form as to suggest crucial instances testing the theory and to permit the search for negative cases. It is assumed, in other words, that the exceptional instance is the growing point of science and that cumulative growth and progressive development of theory is obtained by formulating generalizations in such a way that negative cases force us either to reject or to revise them.[3]

The methodological orientation of this study is deterministic rather than statistical. Applied to the study of narcotics addiction, each of these orientations has its own characteristic goals, methodological assumptions, and analytical procedures, and neither can be judged by the standards of the other. Failure to distinguish between them leads to intellectual confusion.

The assumption made at the outset of this investigation—that the craving for drugs is generated in one identifiable, unitary type of experience—is deterministic in nature. The research problem it poses is that of identifying or discovering and describing such an experience and indicating how and why the patterns of behavior called addiction follow from it. It is incongruous and illogical to consider such an experience as a "variable" to be handled by statistical methods. This is because an "experience" is a complex interactional process involving many elements or variables in a series of happenings or events. Moreover, if one insists on speaking of such a sequential process as a variable, it must be noted that it is not at hand at the outset of the study since it has not yet been identified and described. From the deterministic viewpoint the whole trick consists of finding or identifying it. To suggest that this identification be made by statistical methods presupposes the knowledge that is being sought.

It is more appropriate to consider the statistical approach to drug addiction within its own frame of reference as a technique of describing average behavior of aggregates of individuals or of

3. George H. Mead, "Scientific Method and Individual Thinker," in John Dewey (Ed.), *Creative Intelligence* (New York: Henry Holt, 1917); A. D. Ritchie, *Scientific Method: An Inquiry into the Character and Validity of Natural Laws* (New York: Harcourt, Brace, 1923), pp. 53–83.

making mass comparisons between groups of addicts and non-addicts. Such comparisons and descriptions have dealt with a wide variety of attributes, characteristics, and background factors such as those of age, sex, social status, place of residence, occupation, and personality attributes. These investigations have their own particular kind of merit or significance. They may, for example, illuminate such matters as why addiction rates are higher in one segment of the population than in another; they may indicate that certain identifiable personality traits increase the probability of addiction; they may suggest that public policies of dealing with addiction have important consequences on the prevalence of addiction and on variations in its incidence. Such studies are often of great practical importance. They may also be of theoretical significance at their own level—that of broad "social system" or societal analysis. They may suggest ideas to the determinist, and their findings must be taken into account, but they do not have a direct bearing on the determinist's search for the causal process or processes that always and everywhere generate addiction. The difference between these two types of enterprise is analogous to that between explaining malaria and explaining malaria rates, or crime and crime rates. From a deterministic standpoint, conclusions derived from statistical comparisons of addicts with non-addicts which assert as a "theory" that a given attribute is significantly more frequent among drug users than in the general population are simply not theories at all.

The attempt to identify causal relationships and the assumption that such relationships can be found dictate that all relevant and available evidence, including the results of statistical studies, be taken into consideration. In particular, this methodological stance requires intensive, exhaustive probing of individual cases and comparison of certain crucial types of cases. Thus, when it was noted that some non-addicts receive drugs regularly for long periods of time in hospitals without becoming addicts, I was compelled to compare them with addicts in order to isolate and describe the causal processes which were present in the cases of addiction and absent among the non-addicted hospital patients. No tabulations were necessary in making this comparison because it was assumed that the essential causal process of addiction would be found in all cases of addiction and that it would not be found in any case of non-addiction.

The addicts who were interviewed contributed very unequally to the final theoretical formulation. As already indicated, some were not seen often enough. Others were inarticulate or lacked the necessary intelligence or interest to provide coherent accounts of their initial experiences with drugs. Many who were interviewed in the later stages of the investigation provided data of relatively little theoretical import because the information they gave followed a pattern made familiar by earlier cases without adding new elements or posing new problems. Only a relatively small proportion of the addicts interviewed, consisting mainly of intelligent, articulate, experienced, and self-observant users, made important contributions to the formulation of the theory. Some of these crucial cases forced the abandonment of provisional hypotheses that had been entertained up to the time they were encountered. Others seemed to bring out in a striking and obvious way the nature of the process in which addiction is established. This was because they were departures from the standard and familiar pattern, presenting combinations of circumstances and conditions of the type which one would wish to have in an experimental test of the theory. After familiarity with the general characteristics of the addict's behavior had been acquired from the initial conversations with users, the subsequent progress of the study seemed to depend upon the analysis of a series of crucial cases which led to successive revisions of the guiding ideas of the study and to broader perceptions of the logical implications and ramifications of these ideas. As the analysis progressed the various aspects of addiction behavior, which had at first seemed to be isolated, discrete bits of information or even paradoxical in nature, fell into place to form integral parts of what eventually seemed to me to be a consistent and logical whole.

The literature of addiction is highly repetitive, sometimes unreliable, and often based on misinformation. In the later stages of the study, however, it probably became my most important source of data. The interviews with addicts and observations of them provided standards for judging the literature and enabled me to understand the sources of error and distortion. The evidence available in books and articles served the vital function of providing a broad, world-wide perspective, limited by neither space nor time. Without such a perspective it would have been easy to fall into the error of taking the part for the whole, that is, of assuming that a particular manifestation or form of addiction limited to a particular time or place was the prototype of all addiction. Thus, no general theory of opiate addiction can be based on effects which are produced only when heroin is injected intravenously, as it usually is at present in this country, since opiate addiction existed many thousands of years before heroin or the intravenous method of injection were known.

The strategy of the research was one of focusing on a strictly limited and specific problem, analyzing it as exhaustively as possible, and leaving out of consideration a great many other matters that might be of interest and significance in connection with other types of theories or interests.

This study, it will be observed, is not a study in motivation and therefore does not propose an explanation of addiction in terms of the motives or purposes that people have for trying drugs. It began as a search for the experience or process in which addiction is invariably generated, without any prejudgments concerning the motivation question. As it progressed it seemed evident that no general theory of addiction in terms of motives was possible. This was because: (1) hospital patients sometimes become addicted when doctors prescribe drugs for them without the patient ever voluntarily administering the drug to himself; (2) motives or verbal rationalizations of drug users vary widely from person to person, from culture to culture, and from time to time, and they are often contradictory and inconsistent; and (3) while initial use of the drug is often but not always voluntary, nonaddicts are rarely motivated to become addicts, but are rather trapped by the drug, often unwittingly or against their wills. As will be indicated later, the initial effects of drugs upon the beginner are not at all comparable to the effects of the same drug upon the habitual user, and, by the same token, explaining the first trial is a separate and distinct problem from that of accounting for addiction.

While motives are not considered as causes of addiction in this inquiry they are not altogether irrelevant, since the study might be characterized as being concerned with the origins of the addict's drive to obtain and use drugs. Once established, this drive becomes a dominant feature of the user's motivational life and tends to extend its influence to virtually all of his behavior. The intricacies of this revolutionary change in personality are an appropriate subject for psychiatric exploration and beyond the limits of this investigation.

The conventional view of addiction is that it is an escape mechanism for defective persons, variously characterized as "inadequate," "inferior," "frustrated," or "psychopathic." It is assumed that persons become addicts for the "purpose" or "motive" of escaping from or alleviating their psychic troubles. This confusion of "cause" and "motive" leads to difficulty because of two stubborn facts which cannot be ignored or explained away: (1) some persons become addicts as a consequence of medical practice under conditions which preclude the influence of their motives on any part of the process of becoming addicted, and (2) a substantial percentage of addicts are admittedly "normal" prior to addiction; that is, no evidence of defects, inferiority feelings, inadequacy, etc., can be found. The proponents of this conventional view satisfy themselves in this situation by asserting that *most* addicts are abnormal prior to addiction and ignore or write off in advance a considerable body of exceptional cases. No satisfactory explanation is offered for the fact that "normal" individuals become addicts. It is even admitted sometimes that the generalization probably does not apply even to *most* addicts in some parts of the world.

Since exactly the same explanation is applied to many other forms of undesirable behavior, it has no particular or specific explanatory power with regard to any of them. The defective individual is sometimes pictured as one who casts about, reviewing alternative forms of deviant behavior and choosing one more or less at random or on the basis of availability. A theory of this sort has the attraction of seeming to explain much with little investigative effort. Applied to drug addiction it has the added charm of making it superfluous to bother about examining the actual mechanisms involved.

The logical inadequacies of this type of approach are obvious. If the validity of a theory is defined in terms of the empirical evidence that might demonstrate its falsity but does not, this theory is unverifiable, since the exceptions that negate it are admitted in advance. If one is concerned only with some, many, or most addicts, there are many variables in addition to personality factors that are positively associated with addiction rates. These variables differ from one country to another; they differ from one group to another and from one place to another; and they change with time even in the same country. It is therefore possible to formulate a series of theories, each of them applicable to some addicts in some place at some time, and none of them applicable to all addicts anywhere. Under such circumstances no grounds exist for saying any such theory is wrong, that one is right and the others wrong, or that one is any better than another. Acceptance of one above the others becomes a matter of personal taste or professional prejudice.

The point of view under consideration is based on preoccupation with variability and with statistical techniques of dealing with it. It involves a fundamentally skeptical or negative attitude toward the possibility of discovering ordered patterns in the behavior of the individual. Human behavior is said to be too complex, too dynamic, too indeterminate, and to vary too much from culture to culture and from person to person to be dealt with in any other way than in the aggregate or on the average. Kurt Lewin characterizes this viewpoint as Aristotelian, contrasting it with the Galilean position, which he views as characteristic of modern science:

> The conviction that it is impossible wholly to comprehend the individual case as such implies . . . a certain laxity of research: it is satisfied with setting forth mere regularities. The demands of psychology upon the stringency of its propositions go no further than to require a validity "in general" or "on the average" or "as a rule." The "complexity" and "transitory nature" of life processes make it unreasonable, it is said, to require complete, exceptionless validity. According to the old saw that "the exception proves the rule," *psychology does not regard exceptions as counter-arguments so long as their frequency is not too great.*
>
> The attitude of psychology toward the concept of lawfulness also shows clearly and strikingly the Aristotelian character of its mode of thought. It is founded on a very meager confidence in the lawful-

ness of psychological events and has for the investigator the added charm of not requiring too high a standard of validity in his propositions or in his proofs of them. . . .

Methodologically also the thesis of the exceptionless validity of psychological laws has a far-reaching significance. It leads to an extraordinary increase in the demands made upon proof. It is no longer possible to take exceptions lightly. They do not in any way "prove the rule," but on the contrary are completely valid disproofs, even though they are rare; indeed, so long as one single exception is demonstrable. The thesis of general validity permits of no exceptions in the entire realm of the psychic, whether of child or adult, whether in normal or pathological psychology.[4]

Writing on the nature of scientific systems, Braithwaite makes the following comment:

The one thing upon which everyone agrees is that it [a scientific law] always includes a generalization, i.e., a proposition asserting a universal connexion between properties. It always includes a proposition stating that every event or thing of a certain sort either has a certain property or stands in certain relations to other events or things, having certain properties.[5]

The significance of theories formulated in universal form, as emphasized by Lewin, Braithwaite, and many others who have concerned themselves with the logic of science, depends less on their truth than on the functions they perform in guiding the search for evidence, providing guidelines in the analytical process, and providing means for testing theories. A proposition or theory which affirms an invariable or universal connection between events, unlike one which affirms the connection in only some of the instances, lends itself much more readily than the latter to deductive elaboration and hence to falsification by negative evidence. Because it claims much, it is easily disproved if it is in fact false.

Once a beginning has been made in the construction of theories of this type there is a built-in guarantee of progressive evolution,

4. Kurt Lewin, *A Dynamic Theory of Personality* (New York: McGraw-Hill, 1935), pp. 18–19, 24.
5. R. B. Braithwaite, *Scientific Explanation: A Study of the Function of Theory, Probability and Law in Science* (New York: Harper Torchbooks, 1960), p. 9.

since evidence not consistent with the existing theoretical structure forces changes in the structure, improving and broadening it. The progressive refinement of theory that is brought about by the necessity of taking negative instances seriously regardless of their frequency also makes for a progressively closer articulation of theory with the empirical evidence generated by research.

Another important function of theory couched in the universal form is that it directs research efforts to the problematic areas in which its validity may be in doubt. Because the verification of a scientific theory consists primarily in the failure to prove that it is wrong, it is most effectively tested by the close examination of precisely those areas in which it seems the weakest or of the instances which appear to contradict it. This is why, in the advanced sciences, investigators do not simply go on replicating endlessly the experiments on which the established theories are based. Instead, new logical implications of the currently accepted scheme are traced into new areas where they are confronted by new evidence and tested by new techniques.

Writing of a method which he called "analytic induction," Znaniecki said:

> The only reason for the existence of this method (analytic induction) is, as we have seen, the impossibility of arriving by enumerative induction at judgments of the type "All S are P," or rather "if p then 2." Whenever such judgments can be formulated, the use of the statistical method is precluded. Now everybody knows that in physical and biological sciences there are innumerable judgments bearing upon empirical reality which have this form. Every botanist or zoologist in describing a species means to characterize all the living beings of this species; every physicist or chemist in formulating a law claims that the law is applicable to all the processes of a certain kind. Does this mean that the reality with which the botanist or the physicist is dealing is so uniform empirically that no exceptions, no deviations from the type can ever be observed? Of course not; the botanist or the physicist well knows that cases may be discovered which will contradict his generalization. But he is not afraid of them. He is ready to grant any exception as raising a problem and thus stimulating new research. The research may enlarge and confirm his theory by helping to discover a new species or a new law definitely connected with his previous generalization—which will mean that the exception was only apparent. Or further research may invalidate

his former generalization and force him to reach wider and deeper in creating a new and more efficient theory.[6]

It should be observed that Znaniecki neither invented this method nor was he by any means the first to describe it. The distinction between enumerative and analytical induction is derived from one of the oldest and thorniest problems in the logic of induction and is made by numerous writers, including for example, John M. Keynes, who grappled with it using the terms "pure induction" and "induction by analogy." The distinction arises from the fact that some of the relatively secure conclusions of science have been derived from the examination of very few instances, as for example, from a few repetitions of a crucial experiment or even from one such experiment. On the other hand, highly questionable, unreliable, and even false propositions have been based on the examination of very many instances. "Pure" or "enumerative" induction refers to the type of analysis in which the dependability of one's inferences depends solely on the number of instances examined. "Induction by analogy" or "analytic induction" refers to another mode in which the validity of conclusions depends on something other than the sheer number of examined instances, such as their variety, the extent of one's knowledge of each of them, and the circumstances presented by each. The crucial experiment of the classical form may be taken as a prototype of the latter mode.

Such terms as "cause" and "causal process" have been used as a matter of convenience in this discussion and will be used repeatedly in subsequent pages to refer to the special kind of relationships that are affirmed by universal theories. The substance of the methodological position that has been briefly sketched here could have been described without the use of these terms, just as there are many inquiries made within the deterministic framework which never make use of them.

On the other side of the fence, some social science statisticians have recently made considerable use of the concept "cause," giving it a very different meaning from that which it has traditionally had or that it has here. Others reject the concept altogether and

6. Florian Znaniecki, *The Method of Sociology* (New York: Rinehart, 1934), pp. 232–33.

urge that the latest developments in sub-atomic physics have totally discredited it along with the entire logic and philosophy of nonstatistical determinism. Since this drastic conclusion is currently under debate and is rejected by many eminent natural scientists and logicians, it is premature for social scientists to accept it as given. Considering the vast differences between the theoretical sophistication of modern physics and modern sociology, the rejection of causality and determinism by the latter looks more like an attempt to dodge problems than to solve them.

It is possible that the lesson which the social scientist might learn from these statistical theories of modern physics is the more modest one that strict causality and determinism are inappropriate concepts at that level of analysis in which individual instances are lost sight of and are merged in the description of aggregates. Since individual human beings, unlike electrons, are accessible to direct observation it is unnecessary to study them only in the aggregate.

CHAPTER

2

# THE EFFECTS OF OPIATES

A nondrinker engaged in the study of alcoholics might deliberately get drunk once himself in order to understand his subjects better. There are, however, two excellent arguments for not doing this in the case of opiates. First, the effects of a small amount of drugs upon a non-addict are in almost no sense comparable to their effects upon an addict; indeed, in many respects, they are quite the opposite, and the difference not only is one of degree but is definitely qualitative as well. Second, the experiment would be too dangerous. Under normal circumstances a man can deliberately make himself drunk and can be none the worse when he recovers. But it is doubtful whether anyone can use morphine long enough to acquire the same experiences as an addict without himself becoming one.

Since the first injections of morphine which a non-addict receives are usually gratifying, either in a positive sense or because of the relief from pain afforded, it is the popular impression that the pleasure of the addict must be immensely greater, especially in view of the enormous sacrifices that he makes to keep himself supplied with the drug. Plausible as this notion seems, it is nevertheless fallacious.

The effect of opiates upon the human organism constitutes a

problem for physiologists and biochemists. We are here concerned mainly with the question of how the physiological and psychological effects of the drug are perceived by the addict.

## Initial Effects

The first effects of injections of opiates administered to non-addicts are, as we have said, usually but not always pleasurable. The sensation or experience varies greatly depending upon the person, the setting, the mood of the user, and the size of the dose and the manner in which it is taken. The intravenous method of use produces the sharpest and most noticeable impact. In some instances, as Becker has reported with respect to marihuana, the beginner experiences effects which he does not recognize as being associated with the shot, no doubt because he anticipated something else.[1] Sometimes, even in the case of individuals who later become addicted, the initial injections may produce unpleasant sensations such as headache, dizziness, and nausea. There are also some persons who appear to have something like an opiate allergy, so that the drug, even with repeated use, does not produce pleasurable feelings but leads instead to increasing discomfort and distress. Such persons are very rare. They do not, of course, become addicted.

To the average person, however, the first dose may bring sleep, or it may, especially if it is small, stimulate him to extra activity or mental effort. Under different circumstances the same person will be variously affected, even though the dose is of the same strength. When the subject is depressed or fatigued the effects of a small dose are usually much more noticeable then when he is normal and in good spirits. In fact, the more closely he approximates a normal condition, the less likelihood there is of his noticing any reaction at all when he takes the first dose.

The learning processes involved in the first trials of the drug are illustrated by incidents related to me by addicts. For example, a man who experimented with opiates in the presence of two addicts reported that he felt nothing except nausea, which

---

1. Howard S. Becker, "Becoming a Marihuana User," *American Journal of Sociology* (1953), 59: 235–42.

occurred about half an hour after the injection. It took a number of repetitions and some instruction from his more sophisticated associates before this person learned to notice the euphoric effects. In another instance an individual who complained that she felt nothing from two closely spaced injections amused her addicted companions by rubbing her nose violently while she made her complaints. A tingling or itching sensation in the nose or other parts of the body is a common effect of a large initial dose.

Experiments made by Beecher[2] with non-addicted subjects who were given injections of various kinds of drugs, including heroin, along with placebos, provide a more sober perspective on initial effects of opiates than that which is often projected in the popular literature. Beecher's subjects did not know what particular drug they were given nor did those who received placebos know this fact. All were asked to report on the degree of pleasure or displeasure they felt after being given what they supposed to be a drug. Those who received placebos reported greater pleasure than those who were given heroin. This result may well have been produced by the unpleasant initial effects that sometimes occur and to which allusion has already been made. It is of interest that the addict redefines such effects as desirable and welcomes them because they are indications to him of good quality drugs.

The disagreeable effects that sometimes accompany the first few trials of the drug ordinarily disappear after a few or several repetitions of the dose. There then follows in most cases what has been called a "honeymoon" period during which the person on his way to addiction increases the size of his dose and for a time experiences a more intense euphoria. The latter has often been described in the popular literature. It appears to consist largely of a subtle feeling of being at home in the world and at peace with it. The effect is more marked if the individual is depressed, fatigued, or troubled when he takes his shot.

One of my addicted subjects commented as follows on the drug's effects:

> Contrary to the belief entertained by many, if not most, a dose or a series of doses of opium derivatives does not produce a super-

2. Henry K. Beecher, *Measurement of Subjective Responses* (New York: Oxford University Press, 1959), pp. 321–41.

normal state. It does not produce the ability to do things better, to think or reason with greater clearness than would be possible without the drug. It is true that in some conditions of mind or body, and perhaps during the short initial period of addiction, the drug will seemingly lift one up to a state where the perceptibilities are sharpened, where the senses are better able to cope with any given situation than would be the case without drugs. But a careful analysis of the condition of the individual would usually elicit the fact that he was considerably below par, in some respect, before he took the drug. All that it has done is to restore him to a normal, or nearly normal, state of mind and body.

Opiates do not produce spectacular or uncanny states of mind like those attributed to LSD. There are no hallucinations, waking dreams, illusions, or other psychotic-like effects associated with them. Popular writers have sometimes attributed such effects to heroin and other opiates probably because they have been influenced more by literary stereotypes or a desire to create a dramatic effect than by the actual testimony of addicts. The latter too is often colored by the user's craving for the drug, which leads him to retrospective exaggeration. Friedrich Chotzen observed in 1902:

> Nearly all authors agree that the chronic abuse of morphia in contra-distinction to other poisons gives rise to no special psychosis. . . . When mental disturbances occur in chronic users of morphine, these are referred for the most part to contemporary complicating poisoning by other poisons, especially alcohol, chloral hydrate, and cocaine.[3]

Along similar lines, Lawrence Kolb observed in 1925:

> There is no destruction of protoplasm such as follows prolonged excessive use of alcohol. Neither nerve cells nor fibers degenerate; consequently, the drug cannot produce diseases analogous to Korsakoff's psychosis, acute hallucinosis, or alcoholic multiple neuritis, and hospitals for the insane have remarkably few cases diagnosed as drug psychoses. Such psychoses are so rare that one is led to suspect

3. Quoted by Charles E. Terry and Mildred Pellens, *The Opium Problem* (New York: Committee on Drug Addictions and the Bureau of Social Hygiene, 1928) p. 186.

that case 72 is typical of most of those that do occur. [This was a case of the use of cocaine and morphine in combination.][4]

The initial effects then consist largely of a general dulling of sensibilities, accompanied by a pleasant though not sensational or uncanny state of mind which is characterized by freedom from pain and worry and by a quickened flow of ideas. It should be emphasized again that normal, healthy persons may fail to notice any initial effects whatsoever if they are not on the watch for them. As C. Edouard Sandoz has stated:

> The widely spread belief that morphine brings about an uncanny mental condition, accompanied by fantastic ideas, dreams and what-not, is wrong, notwithstanding certain popular literature on the subject. The most striking thing about morphine, taken in ordinary doses by one who is not an addict, is that it dulls general sensibility, allays or suppresses pain or discomfort, physical or mental, whatever its origin, and that disagreeable sensations of any kind, including unpleasurable states of mind are done away with. In fact, the suppression of pain is the only outstanding effect of morphine when given for that purpose. The more normal a person feels, the less marked, as a rule, the effects will be.[5]

Naturally, the evaluation of the first effects of opium will vary in accordance with the character of the individual. Thus a sensitive man, with certain neurotic ailments, may be tremendously impressed with the soothing qualities of the drug, and by contrast with his usual state of mind, may feel intense pleasure. On the other hand, a prosaic and stolid person, with no sense of strain or conflict, may be wholly unaffected.[6]

4. Lawrence Kolb, "Pleasure and Deterioration from Narcotic Addiction," *Mental Hygiene* (1925), 9: 704.

5. Edouard Sandoz, "Report on Morphinism to the Municipal Court of Boston," *Journal of Criminal Law and Criminology* (1922), 13: 13.

6. It is repeatedly said that certain psychoneurotic types are peculiarly susceptible to the pleasurable effects of narcotics. See, for example, *Report of the Departmental Committee on Morphine and Heroin Addiction* (London: British Ministry of Health, 1926); Lawrence Kolb, "Drug Addiction in Its Relation to Crime," *Mental Hygiene* (1925), 9: 74–89, and "Pleasure and Deterioration from Narcotic Addiction," *Mental Hygiene* (1925), 9: 699–724; Paul Sollier, "Hystérie et morphinomanie," *Revue Neurologique* (1903), 11: 855; and Terry and Pellens, *op. cit.*, Index entry, "psychopaths, predisposition of."

A good account of the most common initial effects was given by Louis Faucher, who experimented on himself while preparing a thesis on morphinism at the medical college of the University of Montpellier.[7]

He took one dose each day for six days, stopped for fifteen days, and then repeated the experiment. He wrote:

> The initial effects were pleasant. . . . Then, for a brief moment I noticed a feeling of unusual well-being; my bed was more pliable, the objects in my room seemed more familiar, my body seemed lighter. I also had at the same time two unpleasant experiences. . . . Then when everything became silent again I began to experience the euphoria of morphine. It made the night sweet for me; I can scarcely express in any other way the subtle pleasure that I experienced. It is true I noticed nothing extraordinary; I had no illusion or hallucinations. My breathing was easier and freer. I thought about my personal affairs, my work and my dislikes. Things that had seemed difficult now seemed easy. Some of the problems of real life appeared to me in a new guise, with their solutions perfectly obvious. . . . It was nothing. It was scarcely noticeable. But it was good.[8]

## Withdrawal Symptoms

The regular administration of opiates, extending over a period of time, creates a physiological need for its continuance. Once habitual use is stopped, a number of distressing symptoms appear, increasing in severity in proportion to the period of addiction and depending upon the size and frequency of the dosage. In fact, no matter why the drug was first taken, its continued use leads to a periodic, artificially produced depression and distress which disappear immediately upon repetition of the dosage. After about three weeks of regular daily use, the abstinence symptoms apparently increase at an accelerated tempo and rapidly become very severe and even dangerous. A discussion of almost any aspect of the drug habit invariably involves a consideration of these withdrawal symptoms, which are uniquely associated with the use of opiates. Animals and infants, as well as adults who unwittingly receive drugs, suffer withdrawal symptoms which are similar to

7. Louis Faucher, *Contribution à l'étude du rêve morphinique et de la morphinomanie* (thesis, University of Montpellier, no. 8, 1910–11).
8. *Ibid.*, p. 18 ff.

those of the addict. This fact demonstrates that the distress is not "imaginary" but is based upon disturbances of organic functions.

A. B. Light, E. G. Torrance, and their co-authors have provided an excellent chronological account of the withdrawal symptoms accompanying the discontinuance of opiates, based on observation and experimentation with American underworld addicts who submitted themselves for cure at the Philadelphia General Hospital. They described the behavior of their patients during withdrawal as follows:

As the time approaches for what would have been the addict's next administration of the drug, one notices that he glances frequently in the direction of the clock and manifests a certain degree of restlessness. If the administration is omitted, he begins to move about in a rather aimless way, failing to remain in one position long. He is either in bed, sitting on a chair, standing up, or walking about, constantly changing from one to another. With this restlessness, yawning soon appears, which becomes more and more violent. At the end of a period of about eight hours, restlessness becomes marked. He will throw himself onto a bed, curl up and wrap the blankets tightly around his shoulders, sometimes burying his head in the pillows. For a few minutes he will toss from side to side, and then suddenly jump out of the bed and start to walk back and forth, head bowed, shoulders stooping. This lasts only a few minutes. He may then lie on the floor close to the radiator, trying to keep warm. Even here he is not contented, and he either resumes his pacing about, or again throws himself onto the bed, wrapping himself under heavy blankets. At the same time he complains bitterly of suffering with cold and then hot flashes, but mostly chills. He breathes like a person who is cold, in short, jerky, powerful respirations. His skin shows the characteristic pilomotor activity well known to those persons as "cold turkey." The similarity of the skin at this stage to that of a plucked turkey is striking. Coincident with this feeling of chilliness, he complains of being unable to breathe through his nose. Nasal secretion is excessive. He has a most abject appearance, but is fairly docile in his behavior. This is a picture of his appearance during the first eight hours.

Often at the end of this period the addict may become extremely drowsy and unable to keep his eyes open. If he falls asleep, which is often the case, he falls into a deep slumber well known as the "yen" sleep. It takes unusual noises to awaken him. The sleep may last for as long as eight or twelve hours. On awakening, he is more restless than ever. Lacrimination, yawning, sneezing, and chilliness are extreme. A feeling of suffocation at the back of the throat is frequently mentioned. Usually at this stage, the addict complains of cramps, locating them most frequently in the abdomen, but often in the back and lower extremities. A right rectus rigidity with pain localized over the appendical region is not uncommon; one can easily be misled in the diagnosis, since at this stage a leucocytosis is frequently present. Vomiting and diarrhea appear. He may vomit large quantities of bile-stained fluid. Perspiration is excessive. The underwear and pajamas may become saturated with sweat. Muscular twitchings are commonly present; they may occur anywhere, but are most violent in the lower extremities. He may sit in bed with his leg flexed, grasping it tightly below the knee, fearing the twitch will suddenly throw it into a complete extension which he cannot control. If he is handed a cigarette to smoke, his hands tremble so violently that he may have difficulty in placing it in his mouth. The tremor is so marked that he is unable to light it himself. He refuses all food and water, and frequently sleep is unknown from this point. It is at this stage that he may one minute beg for a "shot" and the next minute threaten physical violence. Nothing can make him smile. He will beat his head against the wall, or throw himself violently on the floor. Any behavior which he thinks will bring about the administration of the drug will be resorted to. Occasionally he may complain of diplopia. Seminal emission in the male and orgasms in the female frequently occur.

We believe that the height of these withdrawal symptoms is reached somewhere between the period of forty-eight hours and seventy-two hours following the last dose of the drug taken. The readministration of the drug promptly brings about a dramatic change. The patient becomes exceedingly docile almost with the puncture of the hypodermic needle. In a few minutes he begins to feel warm, and the goose flesh and perspiration are no longer visible. He speaks about a "heaviness" in his stomach, but regards this as a welcome symptom presaging relief. In a period ranging from thirty minutes to one hour the tremors disappear. He has become strong and well. He no longer walks with bowed head and stooped shoulders. He stands erect, is quite cheerful, and lights his cigarette like any normal person. He becomes profuse in his apologies for his conduct during the abrupt withdrawal of the drug.[9]

9. A. B. Light, E. G. Torrance, W. G. Karr, Edith G. Fry, and W. A. Wolff, *Opium Addiction* (Chicago: American Medical Association, 1929), pp. 10–11. Reprinted by permission.

Mild withdrawal symptoms appear after a very few injections provided that the injections are sufficiently large and are spaced close enough to each other to produce a cumulative effect. As use continues, it becomes necessary, if the withdrawal symptoms are to be prevented from appearing, to increase the amounts taken and to take more doses per day. As the withdrawal symptoms become more intense, the effects of the injections that eliminate them become correspondingly more pronounced. In the earliest stages of use both withdrawal distress and euphoria may be so slight as to go unnoticed. With repeated and increased doses both the distress and the euphoria are greatly increased; the latter particularly by the fact that it is augmented by relief of withdrawal. Eventually, as will be indicated later, the positive euphoria obtainable from the drug diminishes or vanishes, leaving the addict with two main sources of gratification: (1) relief of withdrawal symptoms and (2) impact effects that are felt immediately after an injection for a period of perhaps five to ten minutes.

### Reversal of Effects

According to Sandoz, the continued administration of morphine causes the following changes in initial effects:

> The duration of the effect of the morphine is shortened. Whatever untoward effects were present at the beginning disappear. The same dose will become less and less effective, or must be increased in order to obtain the same effect. More than this, the original feeling of unusual well-being can no longer be obtained; under the influence of morphine the chronic user will simply feel "normal."[10]

In the beginning phases of addiction, the pleasurable effects of drugs, other than those that occur at the time of injection, tend to diminish and vanish. As this occurs, and as withdrawal distress increases, the psychological significance of the doses changes. Whereas they at first produced pleasure, their primary function becomes that of avoiding pain, that is, withdrawal. The addict

10. Sandoz, *op. cit.*, p. 13.

seems to continue the use of the drug to avoid the symptoms which he knows will appear if he stops using it.

This change or reversal of psychological effects appears to have its counterpart on the bodily level, for here too the effects of morphine and heroin upon the addict are very different from and in some respect the opposite of what they are on the non-addict. In the latter the first effects of the drug are to produce disturbances of normal bodily functions. With continued administrations as tolerance and physical dependence are established, most but not all of these disturbed functions seem to return to normal or nearly so. A new body equilibrium or "drug balance" is established and is upset only or primarily when the drug is stopped. Many biologically oriented investigators have noted this fact and pointed to the necessity of distinguishing between opiate effects observed in non-using subjects and those found in addicts. Erlenmeyer, a German investigator, wrote as follows on this point:

> The continued administration of morphine exerts an entirely different effect on a morphinist from that exerted by a single medium dose of morphine injected into a healthy person. While this latter causes nausea, even vomiting, feeling of faintness, heart weakness, pulse acceleration and lowering of the blood pressure, the former occasions just the opposite feelings, sensations and states . . . namely pleasant feeling, euphoria, increased power, and, in the heart and vessels, strengthening of the contraction, invigoration of the pulse, and rise of the blood pressure. Since every morphinist has once had the first morphine injection, there arises the question: by what means and at what time of the continued abuse does this reversal of effect take place? Is it brought about as follows: The morphine, originally foreign to the body, becomes an intrinsic part of the body as the union between it and the brain cells keeps growing stronger; it then acquires the significance and effectiveness of a heart tonic, of an indispensable element of nutrition and subsistence, of a means of carrying on the business of the entire organism. . . . This reversal does not occur abruptly, but very, very gradually. If morphine is withdrawn before this reversal, the abstinence symptoms do not appear.[11]

Although Erlenmeyer's apparent assumption that the initial effects of morphine are always or usually unpleasant may be

11. Quoted by Terry and Pellens, *op. cit.*, pp. 601–602.

incorrect, his main point is one that has been made in one form or another by many investigators. Amsler, for example, argued that morphine has two effects on a nontolerant individual: a narcotic or depressing one which lasts a relatively long time and is followed by a short period of stimulation. As addiction progresses, the stimulating phase gradually becomes dominant and reduces and finally eliminates the depressing phase.[12]

An explanation or theory of addiction cannot be based on the first effects of the drug on the beginner if these effects are reversed or vanish when addiction is established. Moreover, the initial effects of the drug may never be experienced at all by a hospital patient who is unconscious and they may be unnoticed by other patients who are seriously ill or in great pain. Addiction may nevertheless follow from these circumstances and from any others that involve regular use or administration over a sufficient period of time. The theoretical problem posed by addiction is therefore altogether separate and distinct from that of accounting for the initial use of drugs. Since an unconscious person may have drugs administered to him to the point of establishing physical dependence, it appears that mere *use* of drugs does not constitute a unitary or homogeneous pattern of behavior which could be accounted for by one general theory applicable to all such use. The central theoretical problem of addiction concerns, not the initial use, but the continued, voluntary and regular use of drugs after physical dependence has been built up.

Taking regular, closely spaced doses (for example, four hours apart), the beginner soon notes a feeling of slight depression before each shot, and a vague depletion of energy signaling the beginning of the withdrawal symptoms. Following the injection, his energy is revived, his efficiency, both mental and physical, is restored, and he is again prepared to go about his ordinary affairs. An injection delayed beyond the usual time will bring greater relief, varying according to the depression preceding it. Various methods of administering the drug produce different effects. For example, intravenous injection brings an intense physical thrill,

---

12. Cäsar Amsler, "Ueber Gewöhnung an narkotische Gifte und Entwöhnung davon, insbesondere ueber Morphingewöhnung und Entwöhnung," *Wiener Klinische Wochenschrift* (1935), 48: 815–18. See also on this point Terry and Pellens, *op. cit.*, pp. 233, 260.

sometimes compared by the addicts to sexual ecstasy. The sensation is momentary. On the other hand, oral use of opiates causes a gradual transition of feeling tone, with relief as the primary sensation. Some addicts find pleasure in making the puncture with the needle, and in playing with the injection; others who are "needle-shy" find the puncture distasteful and may avoid using the needle altogether.

Addicts almost invariably assert that, apart from the physical impact of injections, they feel "normal" or "usual" under the drug's influence. At the same time, with apparent inconsistency, they also extravagantly praise its effects upon them. To say that one *feels* normal is, of course, not entirely the same as saying that one *is* normal. American addicts, for example, are chronically afflicted by constipation, their appetites for sex and food are commonly reduced, and they have much more tooth decay than does the general population. Mortality rates of addicts are not exactly known, but they are undoubtedly high. These are items of which addicts are well aware, and they have many other troubles besides. When they say they feel normal they refer to a state of mind, not to the state of their bodies, their finances, or their social relations.

In the above sense, there is only one authoritative source on how a given addict feels, and that is the addict himself. The tendency of the outsider who learns about addiction from the mass media is to assume that the drug user who sacrifices so much and undergoes so many deprivations and miseries for the sake of his habit must obtain an extraordinary euphoria from it—in other words, that the drug must make him feel very extraordinary indeed. The idea that addicts experience uncanny psychological pleasures and live a life of ecstasy is false on the face of it and is denied by them. Their denial must be accepted unless evidence can be produced to discredit it. Available evidence, however, tends to confirm the user's view.

For example, it is conclusively established that under appropriate circumstances addicts can be deceived into believing that they are receiving drugs and are under their influence when in fact they are not. They may also be led to believe that they are not under the influence of drugs when they in fact are. An illustration is provided by a gradual reduction method of curing addicts that has been practiced in this country and that has also been used elsewhere. These cures involved gradual reduction of dosage with saline solution substituted gradually for the drug until after a period of time (such as two weeks) the patient was being given only saline and no drugs at all. In some of these systems the injections were continued on a regular basis for a period of time after complete withdrawal of the drug had been effected. The addicts, who were not told what the program was, often thought they were still getting drugs after it had been discontinued and others thought they were off drugs when in fact they were still receiving substantial doses.

I have interviewed ex-patients who sheepishly admitted that such deception had been successfully practiced on them for as long as ten days. One addict said that he knew of two women who had received water or saline for an entire month under the impression that it was morphine. It is also reported that addicts who demand drugs for insomnia can sometimes be put to sleep with a sterile hypodermic if they believe it is morphine. Conversely, when they have been given a morphine injection and have been told that it was a non-opiate drug, they may continue to complain. Instances of this kind have been so generally noted in the literature and reported so often by addicts that the possibility of such deception must be considered an established fact.

Dr. Charles Schultz performed an experiment in which half of a group of subjects were put on a seven-day reduction treatment, and the other half on a fourteen-day schedule; for the former, the daily dose was reduced by one-seventh, and for the latter by one-fourteenth.[13] As a result, some patients on the fourteen-day schedule thought they were receiving the seven-day treatment, and after the expiration of seven days began to show great nervousness and restlessness, one subject even resorting to an apparently simulated convulsion. When it was explained to them that they had been put on a fourteen-day course, and that they were still get-

13. "Report of the Mayor's Committee on Drug Addiction to the Honorable R. C. Patterson, Jr., Commissioner of Correction, New York City, *American Journal of Psychiatry* (1930–31), 10: 509. (Hereinafter referred to as "Report of Committee on Drug Addiction to Commissioner of Correction, New York City.") A portion of this report was written by Charles Schultz.

ting half of their beginning dosage, all symptoms disappeared at once.[14] A similar illustration is furnished by a former addict, a soldier who was wounded at the front and lay unconscious in a hospital for several days. Opiates were freely administered to him, but when he regained consciousness he did not realize that he was under the influence of drugs until the characteristic and unmistakable distress of withdrawal appeared.

In a personal communication to me, a physician reported that a woman patient about to undergo a painful operation had asked him not to administer opiates under any circumstances, explaining that, although an abstainer, she had once been addicted and that a single injection might cause a relapse. Even if it were a matter of life and death, she begged that no opiates be given her. The doctor agreed, but after the operation the patient suffered such intense pain that a narcotic prescription became absolutely necessary, and was administered orally disguised in liquid form. It made the patient more comfortable and relieved the pain. Since she was not aware that she had received the opiate there was no relapse into the former habit. Later she thanked the doctor for his support of her program of abstinence.

R. N. Chopra and his collaborator performed an ingenious experiment along the same lines. They disguised opium by administering it in oil of citronella as "tonic number X" to patients in a Calcutta hospital who complained of pain and demanded relief.[15] This device revealed the malingering addict, for he always continued to complain after the opium had been taken, while nonaddicts admitted that they felt relieved.

The absence of a distinctive or unusual state of mind produced by the drug is clearly revealed by another interesting phenomenon. The addict's common complaint during a cure of the gradual reduction type, is not that he suffers from withdrawal, but that he cannot "feel the shots." When such a point is reached many addicts demand that the drug be discontinued entirely, preferring not to prolong the suspense; since they cannot feel the injections,

14. *Ibid.*, p. 519.
15. R. N. Chopra and J. P. Bose, "Psychological Aspects of Opium Addiction," *Indian Medical Gazette* (1931), 66: 663–66.

they may as well not take them. In commenting on this attitude, Schultz observes:

> When they reach the end of the reduction, with complete withdrawal, there is not the same reaction of euphoria as after abrupt withdrawal, for several reasons. First, they are never really sure that they are getting less than they should anyway, and, in fact, they are always in a paranoid, suspicious state thinking they are not getting a square deal. They believe they are being fooled by sterile hypodermics and resent this idea because they often think they can detect when no more narcotics are given them, although they actually do not. When they are still getting opiates they sometimes believe they are getting sterile water (they call it "aqua" or "Swanee River" or "onion juice"); and, vice versa, they often think they are getting morphine when plain saline is given them.[16]

One addict reported to me that he had been similarly deceived in a hospital, and that when he discovered it he left at once, resenting "their making a fool of me." He had been getting sterile hypodermics for ten days and was feeling quite well until an attendant, whom he had bribed to find out how much morphine he was getting, disclosed the truth. Instances of this kind are quite common. Indeed, it is remarkable that veteran addicts who have run the gamut of experiments with the drug can be deceived about its effects. Needless to say, individuals who have not had previous experience are much more readily and completely deceived. The patient who receives therapeutic drug treatment, or who becomes dependent upon morphine, does not ordinarily report anything more than relief from pain. If he has withdrawal symptoms, the latter are usually identified as symptoms of his disease, the after-effects of surgery, and so on.

It seems evident that opiates do not produce an uncanny or extraordinary state of mind. In fact, if incidental events which serve as signs of the drug's presence are manipulated, the injection itself cannot even be recognized. In other words, nearly all the direct effects of the drug which last beyond a few minutes after the shot are such that they could easily be attributed to other

16. "Report of Committee on Drug Addiction to Commissioner of Correction, New York City," *op. cit.*, p. 518.

causes if they appeared in isolation. Knowing that he is addicted, the addict ascribes his mental changes to the drug, not because they are recognizable as such but because they always accompany the shot. The characteristic impact of the drug, coupled with the changes in feeling tone intimately associated with the injection, assures him that it was an opiate and nothing else. In addition, the withdrawal symptoms inevitably remind him of the need for a further supply. When all these incidental aspects of addiction are taken out of his control, the patient becomes uncertain of his feelings, and the psychological satisfaction derived from the *belief* that he is receiving morphine may closely simulate the cyclic changes that occur with actual injections. During an abrupt withdrawal, without substitute medication, it is quite impossible to deceive an addict into believing that his distress is due to any cause other than a shortage or absence of opiates in his system. It will be noted that all deception involves the suppression of the drug's physical impact and the absence of pronounced withdrawal symptoms. When either of these two factors is clearly identified, deception is no longer possible.

The point may be made in another way by comparing opiates with other drugs that do produce sensational and spectacular effects, such as LSD. It is impossible to imagine an LSD user going on a "trip" without realizing it, or experiencing the LSD effect from eating a cube of sugar which he erroneously believed to contain the drug.

While there has been considerable interesting research in recent years on the placebo effect in other areas, very little of it has been done with addicts or with the opiates. The unexploited possibilities of this sort of a research enterprise are suggested by certain events following World War II. It was reported by some investigators that a new form of addiction to heroin had been found among juveniles. Its peculiarity was that it involved no withdrawal symptoms. It later appeared that this idea was derived from the heavy dilution of the drugs sold by the peddlers, so that addicts who believed themselves to be addicted were in fact using such a heavily diluted product that they were not getting enough to maintain physical dependence. Some of these users were themselves surprised and humiliated, when, after claiming to have big habits, they experienced little distress upon withdrawal. The peddlers had, in effect, administered a gradual reduction cure without their customers realizing it!

## Direct and Indirect Effects

The addict's claim that he feels normal under the influence of drugs obtains further support from the fact that the study of the effects of opiates upon the body and bodily functions have uncovered either only minor injurious effects or none at all that can be traced directly to the drug. Allusion was made earlier to the prevalence of constipation, tooth decay, and reduced appetites among addicts. Some of these, such as tooth decay, for example, are not traceable directly to the drug. There are persons who have used drugs for long periods of time and who have no tooth decay at all. This suggests that this particular ailment is associated with some incidental aspect of the addict's way of life rather than with the drug *per se*. The same may be said of the depression of sex activity, since users sometimes report no such effect and may even regard the drug as an aphrodisiac.

Apart from the above considerations, if it is asked whether the regular use of drugs such as morphine and heroin produces any major bodily malfunction or destruction of tissue, the answer on the basis of available evidence must be that apparently it does not. W. G. Karr, professor of biochemistry at the University of Pennsylvania, commented as follows:

> The addict under his normal tolerance of morphine is medically a well man. Careful studies of all known medical tests for pathologic variation indicate, with a few minor exceptions, that the addict is a well individual when receiving satisfying quantities of the drug. He responds to work in the normal manner. His weight is normal. His cardiac and vascular system is normal. He is as agreeable a patient, or more so, than other hospital cases. When he is abruptly withdrawn from the drug he is most decidedly a sick individual.[17]

17. *Unpublished speech at the Fifth Annual Conference of Committees of the World Narcotic Defense Association and International Narcotic Education Association* (New York, 1932).

Light and Torrance reach a similar conclusion. They observe:

> . . . morphine addiction is not characterized by physical deterioration or impairment of physical fitness aside from the addiction *per se*. There is no evidence of change in the circulatory, hepatic, renal or endocrine functions. When it is considered that these subjects had been addicted for at least five years, some of them for as long as twenty years, these negative observations are highly significant.[18]

In view of such typical findings, any attempt to attribute decay of "character" or of "moral sense" to the drug must be regarded as unwarranted, since there are no known physiological or neurological changes to which they may conceivably be related. Moreover, in the therapeutic administration of opiates to patients who are unaware of what they are receiving, no such results have ever been reported. In fact, the trend has been in the opposite direction. After an exhaustive review of reports on the alleged effects of opiates, Terry and Pellens in 1928 concluded: "Wherever the truth may lie, the evidence submitted in support of statements . . . dealing with type predisposition and with the effects of opium use on mental and ethical characteristics is, in our opinion, insufficient to warrant the opinions expressed."[19] This conclusion still appears valid.

It was noted early in this chapter that the user who characteristically maintains that he feels normal under the drug's influence also characteristically describes the effects of the drug with great enthusiasm. This seeming inconsistency arises from the different points of reference in the two assertions. When the user says he feels normal he refers to the interval between shots, which may be taken as four hours here for illustrative purposes. The praise he bestows on the drug's effects refers to the sensations that occur when the injection is made and immediately after. These might be called "impact" effects. They may last for five to ten minutes in the case of intravenous injections. The intensity of the pleasure the addict obtains from them depends in considerable part on the intensity of distress or depression immediately preceding the shot.

It is from this contrast between the way the addict feels before and the way he feels after an injection that he derives his ideas of

18. Light, Torrance, *et al.*, *op. cit.*, p. 115.
19. Terry and Pellens, *op. cit.*, p. 515.

the desirable effects of the drug. Viewed in this light the apparent inconsistency of the addict's claims vanishes and the importance which he attaches to "feeling the shot," that is, the impact effect, is made more intelligible. When I confronted addicts with the inconsistency involved in simultaneously talking of the wonderful effects of drugs and of feeling normal under its influence, some were ready to concede that it was probably the relief of beginning withdrawal symptoms that created the favorable impression of the drug. Another idea was that it was simply a reflection of the intensity of the addict's craving; that he enjoys the drug so much because he desires it so intensely rather than because it is inherently enjoyable.

The ideas that the drug addict's inner life is serene and untroubled, that he lives in a world of drug-induced fantasy and dreams, or that his life is dominated by ecstasy are completely false. The average American addict is in fact a worried, troubled, and harried individual. Misery, alienation, and despair, rather than pleasure and ecstasy, are the key features of his life. After the honeymoon period, the user usually feels trapped by the inexorable rhythm of his habit and the heavy demands it makes upon him. In addition, he experiences more than his share of tragedy, frustration, and misfortune and is affected by them much as other people are except that there is superimposed on his reactions the artificial cyclic rhythm of addiction. Without the drug, life may seem intolerable; with it the user feels that he is in control and that he can face his problems. Misfortunes that occur when a user is suffering from drug deprivation seem to depress him more than they should. When he has an adequate supply, the addict feels that his reactions to misfortune are more nearly what they should be, more like those of the average, normal non-addict.

It is well known that many addicts have led useful and productive lives, relatively unaffected by their habit. Lawrence Kolb, in a study of 119 person addicted through medical practice, found that 90 had good industrial records and only 29 had poor ones. He comments:

> Judged by the output of labor and their own statements, none of the normal persons had their efficiency reduced by opium. Twenty-two of them worked regularly while taking opium for twenty-five years or more; one of them, a woman aged 81 and still alert men-

tally, had taken 3 grains of morphine daily for 65 years. She gave birth to and raised six children, and managed her household affairs with more than average efficiency. A widow, aged 66, had taken 17 grains of morphine daily for most of 37 years. She is alert mentally but is bent with age and rheumatism. However, she does physical labor every day and makes her own living.[20]

After three years of observation and tests upon 453 addicts in India, Chopra found changes in personality and social behavior in only one-third of the cases, and in only 3.6 per cent were these described as major changes.[21] The most usual were the acquisition of a sad expression, vacant look, bad memory, or tendency toward slow cerebration. About 60 per cent of his subjects had a healthy and normal appearance and were mentally unaffected by the habit. A notable case was that of a British army officer who, at the alleged age of 111, was said to have used opium or morphine in huge quantities for the preceding seventy years. His army career had been brilliant, and at his advanced age he was described as unusually active and alert.[22]

Chopra asked 1,070 addicts whether they regarded the habit as beneficial or harmful. Grouping the cases according to the size of the daily dosage, his investigation yielded the following principal findings:[23]

| Number of Addicts | Dose in Grains | Beneficial | | Harmful | |
|---|---|---|---|---|---|
| | | Number | % | Number | % |
| 255 | 1 to 5 | 165 | 65.0 | 90 | 35.0 |
| 247 | 6 to 10 | 137 | 55.6 | 110 | 44.4 |
| 287 | 11 to 20 | 142 | 49.6 | 145 | 50.4 |
| 281 | 21 and over | 100 | 35.6 | 181 | 64.4 |
| 1070 | | 544 | | 526 | |

20. Lawrence Kolb, "Drug Addiction—A Study of Some Medical Cases," *Archives of Neurology and Psychiatry* (1928), 20: 178.

21. R. N. Chopra, "The Present Position of the Opium Habit in India," *Indian Journal of Medical Research* (1928), 16: 389–439.

22. See "The Opium Habit," *Catholic World* (September, 1881), 33: 827–35.

23. Chopra, *loc. cit.*

Grouping the same cases according to the reason given for the original use of opium, he obtained the following results:

| Reason for use | Total Cases | Beneficial Number | % | Harmful Number | % |
|---|---|---|---|---|---|
| Disease | 416 | 309 | 75.8 | 107 | 24.2 |
| Fatigue, old age, worry, etc. | 126 | 85 | 67.2 | 41 | 32.8 |
| Association | 247 | 77 | 31.3 | 170 | 68.7 |
| Pleasure-euphoria | 222 | 56 | 25.2 | 166 | 74.8 |
| Replacement of alcohol or other addictions | 59 | 17 | 28.8 | 42 | 71.2 |
| | 1070 | 544 | | 526 | |

These data suggest that, disregarding social consequences, the effects are considered beneficial in inverse proportion to the size of the dose, and depending upon whether the drug is used to alleviate such conditions as old age, worry, fatigue, and disease, or for other reasons. This conclusion harmonizes with medical opinion. Although it may strike the reader as a paradox, the morphine habit may actually benefit particular individuals, such as the chronic alcoholic or the psychoneurotic. Drug addiction and drunkenness are incompatible vices—for liquor causes the addict's withdrawal symptoms to appear sooner than usual and morphine tends to make an intoxicated man sober. Neurotic symptoms may sometimes be suppressed by the regular use of opiates. Roger Dupouy describes a woman who took morphine for hysterical symptoms.[24] She used it for thirty years without any further seizures until the drug was removed, whereupon the paroxysms immediately returned.

The obvious deleterious effects which the drug habit usually has on the American addict's social life and personality, and even some of physical discomforts and disturbances associated with it, cannot be regarded as direct and necessary consequences of the pharmacological action of the drug. Addicts who are well-to-do

24. Roger Dupouy, "Morphinomanie familiale d'origine thérapeutique: deux morts; deux guérisons, après vingt ans de morphinisme continu," Encéphale (1912), 2: 499.

or who have an assured supply of drugs often avoid these consequences. Serious "character deterioration" often makes its appearance only when the user is apprehended by the police and
processed in the courts. There are vast differences between the
behavior of most American addicts and those of other countries
that handle the problem in different ways. The social behavior
of the addict everywhere depends upon the legal and social context in which it occurs, not on the biochemistry of the drug.

Ostromislensky has appropriately remarked that "the phenomenon of morphinism seems from the outside to be a chaotic mixture
of strange and apparently illogical facts, seeming nonsense and
various paradoxes."[25] If the user only succeeds in feeling normal,
one is compelled to wonder why he should go on spending twenty
to fifty dollars a day for this non-effect. Why, when he has been
extricated from this trap, is he so strongly impelled to resume his
habit? In view of his intense craving and his extravagant appraisal
of the drug's effects, how can it be possible to deceive him about
whether he is under its influence? In view of the catastrophic personal consequences of addiction of which the user is more keenly
aware than anyone else, why does the user not feel "normal"
when he is withdrawn from the drug? These paradoxical aspects
of the addict's behavior make it easy to understand the popular
impression that there is something sinister, mysterious, or uncanny
in a drug which has such devastating effects and is at the same
time such a great boon in medical practice.

## Conclusion

Three major points emerge from this discussion. First, that the
initial effects of opiates are not comparable to their effects upon
an addict and are indeed, in many respects, the opposite of them.
Second, the psychological effects of the drug upon the regular
user, apart from the impact effects, are not sufficiently marked to
provide any clue for an understanding of the power of the habit.
During addiction the drug seems to function to keep the user in a
psychological and physical state which is so close to what may be

25. Ivan Ostromislensky, "Morphinism," New York Medical Record (1935),
141: 556.

called normality that it is often extremely difficult or impossible to determine by simple external observation whether a given person is or is not actively using drugs. Third, the personal and social characteristics of the American addict are not directly determined by the pharmacological effects of the drug, but are consequences of the role which he is forced to adopt in our society, that is of his social, economic, and legal situation.

The reversal of effects which occurs during the process of establishing tolerance and physical dependence on opiates makes it impossible for non-addicts to share the experiences of the chronic user. The attempt to understand the addict from one or a few experiences with morphine inevitably produces only misunderstanding. The varied and paradoxical aspects of the opiate habit have long offered challenging theoretical problems to behavioral scientists and have generated theories which are about as varied, paradoxical, and inconsistent as is the behavior of addicts.

# 3

# HABITUATION AND ADDICTION

Not all persons receiving opiates regularly for long periods of time become addicted. Edouard Levinstein, a prominent nineteenth-century German authority, designated persons who were not addicted, but who were receiving the drug, as "morphinists," and applied the term "Morphiumsüchtiger" (morphine addict) to those who were addicted. French students made the same distinction. In this country, also, there have been attempts to introduce separate terms for the two conditions.[1] Patients who receive therapeutic doses of opiates for a period of time without becoming addicted do not, however, constitute a homogeneous group requiring separate conceptual consideration. There is no generally accepted term to differentiate the two conditions, and yet they need to be examined separately. One condition involves pharmacological tolerance and withdrawal distress upon removal of the drug, without the usual manifestations of intense desire that occur

1. See Albrecht Erlenmeyer, *Die Morphiumsucht* (3d ed.; Munich; Heuser, 1887); Edouard Levinstein, *Die Morphiumsucht* (Berlin; Hirschwald, 1880); F. McKelvey Bell, "Morphinism and Morphinomania," *New York Medical Journal* (1911) 93: 690–92; and Daniel Jouet, *Étude sur le morphinisme chronique* (thesis, University of Paris, 1883).

in addiction; the other concerns, in addition to these two symptoms, intense and persistent desire.

That morphine or some other opiate may be given to a patient over a long period of time without creating an independent craving is confirmed by many scientific reports. In a study of morphine use among ex-soldiers, Friedrich Dansauer and Adolf Rieth found many had been using the drug regularly for years, sometimes more than five, but were, nevertheless, not addicted. These users are designated as the "symptomatic type," and are not classified with true addicts, who are called "the idiopathic type." Classifying 240 of their cases in the former category, the authors give representative summaries of about 20.[2]

In the more recent literature, the distinction with which we are here concerned has been made by differentiating between drug users and drug addicts. Chein and his associates, for example, remark:

> It was not until this book was well under way that it dawned on us that even a person with a history of drug use and physiological dependence on the drug might conceivably not be an addict. Such a person might be lacking in what we now regard as an indispensable characteristic of a true addict—craving, that is, a powerful desire for the drug independent of the degree to which the drug has insinuated itself into the physiological workings of his body.[3]

In the discussion that follows, the term "habituation" will be used to refer to the state of the person who is physically dependent on the drug but not addicted to it. The term "addiction" will be reserved for those individuals who have the characteristic crav-

2. Friedrich Dansauer and Adolph Rieth, "Ueber Morphinismus bei Kriegsbeshädigten, *Arbeit und Gesundheit: Schriftenreihe zum Reichsarbeitsblatt* (1931), 18: 23. Cf. also Kurt Pohlisch, "Die Verbreitung des chronischen Opiatsmissbrauchs in Deutschland," *Monatschrift für Psychiatrie und Neurologie* (1931), 79 (1): 1–32. C. E. Terry in *Report to the Committee on Drug Addictions on the Legal Use of Narcotics in Detroit, Michigan, and Environs for the Period July 1, 1925, to June 30, 1926* (New York: Bureau of Social Hygiene, 1927), p. 18, notes that "patients suffering from chronic painful maladies and taking large doses of morphine or other opium equivalents were said by their physicians not to be addicted."

3. Isidor Chein, Donald L. Gerard, Robert S. Lee, and Eva Rosenfeld, *The Road to H: Narcotics, Delinquency and Social Policy* (New York: Basic Books, 1964), pp. 5–6.

ing, whether it be in the form in which it is manifested during regular use or as it exists in the abstaining addict impelling him to resume use. An unconscious patient or one who is given morphine regularly by attendant nurses without his knowing it could thus be described as habituated but obviously not as addicted.

Terminological confusion has been increased in the current literature by the introduction of a variety of new terms and redefinitions of old ones. "Habituation" is, for example, sometimes taken to refer to the regular use of a drug like marihuana which does not produce physical dependence as the opiates do. It has been suggested that, because there is ambiguity in the meaning of the terms "addict" and "addiction," the awkward and even more ambiguous terms, "drug abuse" and "drug abuser" be substituted for them. Some writers refer to "opiate-directed behavior" or to "sustained opiate-directed behavior," rather than to "drug use" and "drug addiction." A standardized terminology would be highly desirable, of course, but is not likely to be adopted. Confusion can be avoided only by paying attention to the substantive distinctions rather than to the terminology in which they are expressed.

## Characteristics of Addiction Behavior

In any inquiry the subject matter to be investigated must be defined and described as exactly as possible. This description is usually found at or near the beginning of the study even though the definition itself is to a large extent the result of the research. The distinction between habituation and addiction must be made by describing and enumerating those characteristics of the behavior of addicts which are unique and common and which do not occur among non-addicts. It is particularly necessary that a definition of addiction take into account the similarities and differences between habituation and addiction and sharply differentiate between them.

As already indicated, the most obvious characteristic of the addict's behavior is his intense desire and striving for the drug. This desire is not casual or vague but is a powerful conscious motive driving him to seek satisfaction in the face of almost insuperable obstacles and at the cost of unbelievable sacrifices. A

universal aspect of the behavior of addicts is that they permit little or nothing to stand between them and the drug. It would be
ridiculous to speak of an addict who wanted drugs but was unaware of the need around which virtually all of his behavior was
organized.

Another characteristic of the addict, and one that is as universal
as the first, is his tendency toward relapse. Once addiction is confirmed, the craving acquires an independent status; the desire
persists even after the original physiological conditions have disappeared. In other words, when the addict's supply is cut off and
he has been treated for withdrawal symptoms, he may be restored
to apparent health, but he still tends to relapse. Were it not for
this, addiction would obviously be no great social problem. It
would only be necessary to separate the addict from his source of
supply and then release him. Yet, in the vast majority of cases,
the cured addict apparently returns to his old habit.

There is a belief prevalent among addicts that it is a misnomer
to speak of a cure for addiction. They remark, "Once a junkie
always a junkie." They admit that now and then an addict may
refrain absolutely from using the drug for years, even though it
is available, and that others do not use it for long periods of time
simply because, either as a result of incarceration or for other
reasons, they cannot get it. These cases are not regarded as cures,
however, for the habitué knows only too well from bitter personal experience that the so-called cured case is merely one in
which the regular use of the drug has been temporarily discontinued. The number of cases accessible for study in which an
individual has voluntarily abstained from the narcotic for a period
of years is small.

Most of the addicts whom I interviewed said that they either
knew of no users who had voluntarily refrained from using drugs
for more than five years or that they knew of one, two, or a few
who had. All believed that the impulse to relapse was permanent
and ineradicable. Some argued that even those few addicts who
manage to abstain for long periods could probably be induced to
relapse by skillful propaganda over a day or two. Relapses have
been known to occur after more than ten years of abstinence.

These expressions of opinion by drug users must be discounted
to some extent to allow for the addict's rationalizations. The self-

help organization known as Synanon is made up of former users, and many of them have abstained from drugs for considerable periods. There is also some indication that with advancing age the user's periods of abstention become longer and that some may quit permanently. In a study of former residents of Kentucky who had been at the Lexington Hospital for addicts it was found that more than half were not using drugs when they were interviewed. This fact was determined by analysis of a urine specimen from each of them. Many of these abstainers succeeded in staying off by moving to small localities where there was no illicit traffic and where they knew of no other users.[4] Such abstainers obviously would not be known to active urban addicts. All the evidence suggests that the relapse rates for those addicts who go from institutions to the metropolitan centers where addiction is concentrated are much higher than those reported in the Kentucky study.

While there are undoubtedly some drug addicts who voluntarily and permanently renounce their habits, the matter of eradicating the impulse to relapse poses another and different issue. The same one arises with respect to alcoholics, of whom it is said that they cannot become casual or social drinkers no matter how long they abstain. Similarly, once an individual has been hooked on opiates his attitudes toward the drug are permanently changed and resumption of the habit after long periods of abstinence is easy.

The temporarily abstaining addict is a familiar figure to other addicts, who have themselves usually tried unsuccessfully to break their habits. The users are all too well aware of the boredom of non-use, and they know the rationalizations that the unhappy cured addict uses to seduce himself into a resumption of his habit. Such abstainers are not viewed as "squares" or non-addicts, but simply as addicts who happen at the moment to be off drugs. The abstainer himself, like the reformed alcoholic who joins Alcoholics Anonymous, thinks of himself, not as a "non-addict" but as an "ex-addict." Having joined the fraternity of those who have been hooked, he feels a continuing bond that unites him with others who have had the experience and a communication barrier between him and those who have not had it. It is in

4. John A. O'Donnell, "A Follow-up of Narcotic Addicts: Mortality, Relapse and Abstinence," *American Journal of Orthopsychiatry* (October, 1964), 34: 948–54.

this sense that addiction may be called incurable.

In contrast to the voluntary abstainer, the user whose habit is interrupted by a prison sentence is obviously in a very different category and is usually simply called an addict and regards himself as such. The imprisoned addict commonly connives and schemes to smuggle drugs into the prison and makes his keepers acutely aware that he is different from the other inmates. To a warden of a penitentiary it would seem absurd to argue that an addict ceases to be that whenever he is off drugs. Hence, in this discussion I shall simply use the term "addict" to refer to anyone who has been hooked.

## Relapse Rates

There are few reliable general statistics on relapse among American drug addicts, and estimates can be made only by indirect means. A careful study of about 800 German addicts led to the following findings: 81.6 per cent of the cures were followed by relapse within a year, 93.9 per cent within three years, and 96.7 per cent within five years. It seems probable that the relapse rate among American addicts may be even higher because of the predisposing circumstances in which "cured" American addicts usually find themselves. Moreover, relapse can take place after more than five years of abstention, so that even the remaining 3.3 per cent noted above could scarcely be regarded as cured, in the sense that the impulse to replapse had been permanently eradicated. On the other hand, it should be observed that some of the addicts who relapsed soon after being withdrawn may well have quit again before the end of the five years. Had the authors determined how many of the 800 were not using drugs at the end of the five-year interval the percentage would have been substantially higher than 3.3 per cent and the picture would have seemed more hopeful.[5] Because of the addict's propensity to resume his habit it is argued that progress in breaking the habit should be measured in terms of man-hours or days off drugs, rather than simply by whether relapse does or does not occur. The apparently higher rate of abstention among older addicts may

5. Dansauer and Rieth, *op. cit.,* p. 59.

mean that older users abstain more often or for longer periods than do the younger ones.

In a review of eleven studies of relapse among American addicts O'Donnell notes that the reported relapse rates varied from a low of 8 per cent over a five-year interval to a high of about 90 per cent over an interval of from one to 4.5 years. He notes that most of the studies focus on whether relapse occurred and do not provide information concerning the actual percentages of the time interval during which the addicts were not using drugs. When the problem is posed in this way, O'Donnell observes that the prospects appear more hopeful and that there appears to be a tendency for older addicts to abstain more on the average than is the case with younger ones. Relapse rates also are related to the addict's status during the period of study. For example, if he is on parole and threatened with reincarceration if he relapses, relapse is likely to be inhibited. The lowest relapse rate of only 8 per cent over a five-year period was secured with physicians who were assured of losing their licenses to practice medicine if they relapsed. Virtually all of the 8 per cent who did relapse under these circumstances committed suicide.[6]

Whatever the relapse rates may be for various categories of addicts, it is agreed by all who have studied them in any part of the world that relapse rates are high and that the impulse to relapse is probably permanent and ineradicable. Periodically in the past, special techniques of curing addicts have been announced with claims of an extraordinarily high percentage of cures. In no known instance have such cures turned out to be of any special significance. In some instances they were simply frauds; in others the apparent success hinged upon the brevity of the follow-up period or upon careless methods of determining whether the cured patient was actually off drugs. Clearly the word "cure" may be used in a variety of senses. It is sometimes used merely to indicate that the addict has been taken off drugs. It may also be used to indicate voluntary abstention for periods of time varying from a few weeks or months to five or more years, and it may be used to refer to the elimination of the desire or temptation to

6. John A. O'Donnell, "The Relapse Rate in Narcotic Addiction: A Critique of Follow-up Studies," in Daniel M. Wilner and Gene G. Kassebaum (Eds.), Narcotics (New York: McGraw-Hill, 1965), pp. 226–46.

relapse. If any addict who abstains voluntarily for a period of several weeks is said to be cured, then one can say of most long-term users that they have been cured many times. If, on the other hand, one reserves the term for those in whom the desire for drugs has been permanently eradicated, it is doubtful if there are any cured addicts.

The practical problem of controlling addiction, of course, is to promote abstention whenever this is possible. Theoretical interest is more focused on the nature and origin of the craving for drugs than on attempting to understand and explain the peculiar persistence of this craving when the drug has been removed. Similar problems exist with respect to smoking, alcohol addiction, and other habits which are periodically renounced and easily resumed.

## Habituation and Addiction Compared

Mere drug use without addiction, which we designate here as habituation, does not involve the tendency to relapse which is so characteristic of the addict. Patients who use or take morphine to the point of physical dependence do not, as has been indicated, necessarily become addicted. When they do not, the discontinuance of the drug does not predispose them to resume its use unless, of course, the pain or disease for which it was being used recurs. The contrast may best be brought out by the consideration of a number of cases of habituation, keeping in mind the behavior of the addict in similar circumstances. Dansauer and Rieth report the case, for example, of a patient who was given an opiate regularly from 1922 to 1927; when the drug was withdrawn the patient was weak and unable to work for seven months, after which he resumed his activities. These investigators do not classify this man as a genuine addict. Similar cases are reported elsewhere in the same treatise.[7] In all instances, the drug had been used daily for several years, yet the conclusion was that since these patients showed none of the craving typical of addicts they could not be considered addicts.

The outstanding characteristics of these cases are that the use

7. Dansauer and Rieth, *op. cit.*, case no. 588, p. 96; see also pp. 92, 94, and 97.

of the drug was related to painful and chronic disease and that upon withdrawal the patient had no desire for the drug, nor did he resort to it except when the disease recurred. Then, too, drug craving as expressed verbally and as manifested in the devices and chicanery employed by addicts to obtain narcotics was absent. These cases are no more distinctive or unusual than hospital patients to whom other types of medicine have been given with good results.[8]

The work of Dansauer and Rieth has been emphasized here because of the long period of time during which opiates were administered to their subjects (in some instances for more than ten years) without inducing a state of addiction. Although the time factor involved in similar cases known to me was less crucial, the situation on the whole was essentially the same. For example, a patient who had received the drug for two months suffered considerable distress when it was withdrawn, without knowing the reason until the nurse later explained it. When he heard that I was studying drug addiction, he expressed amazement that one could become addicted to morphine. He had felt absolutely no desire for it when the morphine treatment was suspended. All the cases of habituation interviewed in the present study conform to this pattern.

In summary, then, there are two principal aspects of addiction which distinguish it from non-addiction and from habituation. First, the addict desires the drug continuously, intensely, and consciously. Second, this craving, once established, becomes independent of the physiological conditions of tolerance and physical dependence, and predisposes the individual to return to the drug even after a lapse of years. The chronic user in prison, for example, often looks forward eagerly to his release and upon his discharge usually loses little time in securing an injection. He learns in advance exactly where to go to get his shot in the briefest possible time. The desire for the drug in such cases has become an independent psychological complex.[9]

8. See *ibid.*, p. 97, for authors' description of these cases.
9. Thus Charles Schultz in "Report of the Committee on Drug Addiction to Commissioner of Correction, New York City," *American Journal of Psychiatry,* (1930–31), 10: 492, as the result of careful experimentation on 318 patients with different kinds of cures, remarks: "As far as 'obliterating the craving for

There is still another difference between the addict and the individual who for a time is merely the passive recipient of the drug. The former, while under the influence of the drug, is constantly aware of his dependence on it, and attributes his state of mind to its effects.[10] The latter, on the other hand, receiving the drug unknowingly in connection with illness, cannot analyze its precise effects, even though he is under its influence and dependent upon it physiologically. In describing a cancer patient habituated to morphine, Bernhard Legewie reports that the drug obviously stimulated the sufferer and made him feel better. However, the patient failed to associate the beneficial effects with the injection, so that instead of desiring the drug he came to dislike it. According to Legewie, "the lack of desire for the drug in our patient was striking."[11] This attitude may be contrasted with that of the typical addict, whose point of view was well expressed by J. C. Layard, himself an addict. After a period of abstinence, he resumed taking the drug, and reported: "I now liked to work, the harder and the more of it, the better. The morphine has such a bracing and tonic effect! I felt when I walked as though I had a man on each side of me, supporting me."[12]

Dependence upon morphine or other opiates in the case of addicts is particularly emphasized when the drug is withdrawn. Craving for the drug and dependence upon it drive the user almost irresistibly to any lengths to obtain a supply. A writer, himself an addict, states that he knew of two suicides resulting from failure to secure drugs: "The awful mystery of death, which they

---

narcotics' by immediate medical treatment, we have found this 'craving' to be present after all treatments. The patients look forward to being discharged, in fact count the days, and if not discharged when they expect to be, some of them go into a state resembling frenzy, so great is their apparent eagerness to revert to drugs. Every imaginable excuse and pretext will be tried in order to be discharged sooner."

10. This preoccupation of the addict with the drug in his system is brought out in an amusing way by the fact that some of Schultz' patients, who volunteered for the cure, "refused to take hot showers for fear that the ensuing perspiration might cause a loss of some of their morphine."

11. Bernhard Legewie, "Delirium beim Morphinismus, Zugleich ein Beitrage zur Frage der Gewöhnung, Zeitschrift für die Gesamte Neurologie und Psychiatrie (1924), 89: 558–78, quoted by C. E. Terry and M. Pellens, The Opium Problem (New York: Committee on Drug Addictions and Bureau of Social Hygiene, 1928), p. 236.

12. James C. Layard, "Morphine," Atlantic Monthly (1874), 33: 705.

rashly solved, had no terrors for them equal to a life without opium, and the morning found them hanging in their cells glad to get 'anywhere, anywhere out of the world.'" The same writer describes a Chinese addict whom he saw "tear his hair, dig his nails into his flesh, and with a ghastly look of despair, and face from which all hope had fled and which looked like a bit of shriveled yellow parchment, implore for it [opium] as if for more than life."[13]

The addict, of necessity, organizes his entire life around his need for the drug. This preoccupation with the narcotic and slavish dependence upon it are incomprehensible both to the patient who is only habituated and to the neophyte. As Calkins observed, "Opium, an equivocal luxury in the beginning, daintily approached, becomes ere long under the demands of perverted appetite a dire alternative, a magisterially controlling power."[14] The hospital patient who every four hours is given an injection, the nature of which he does not know and concerning which he does not trouble himself, clearly cannot be compared with the addict who is eager to sacrifice anything to obtain the same substance.

The addict, if awake, is usually keenly aware of the fact that a shot buoys him up, and he knows precisely when he must have another. He proceeds to regulate his activities almost exclusively in terms of this drive. He takes a shot when he goes to bed. Upon awakening, his first thought is of the drug, and his first act, sometimes even before he gets out of bed, is to take his morning dose. Should he awaken during the night, the thought of a shot tempts him, and if he lies awake for any length of time he is likely to yield to the desire. In other words, the addict is dependent upon the drug during every conscious moment. The thought of the drug constantly sustains him.

By contrast, the patient who is only habituated reveals a different mode of behavior. A physician told the writer of the following incident:

> A woman went to a quack doctor with a stomach complaint. He gave her medicine which helped her, but in the course of time she noticed that whenever she stopped taking the medicine for a time

13. "Sigma," "Opium Eating," *Lippincott's Magazine* (April, 1868), 1: 409.
14. Alonzo Calkins, *Opium and the Opium Appetite* (Philadelphia: J. B. Lippincott, 1871), p. 188.

her stomach trouble came back. Wishing to be really cured of her disease, she decided to consult another doctor. She realized that the prescription was helping her, but was troubled by the fact that (as it seemed to her) the medicine had only repressed her ailment without eliminating it. The new doctor found that the medicine contained opiates and that there was nothing whatever wrong with her except that she had become habituated to the drug.

This case is a prototype of habituation associated with physical disease, the drug being used because of actual pain associated with the disease. The important factor is obviously the patient's belief. It will be shown later that as long as a patient believes he is using the drug solely to relieve pain, and regards it as a "medicine," he does not become an addict. When the pain or disease vanishes the drug may be removed without danger of relapse.

The patient's sense of dependence on drugs in the above case was clearly different from that of the addict; her preoccupation was with a disease rather than with the effects of opiates, which she recognized only vaguely. When she swallowed her medicine, the disease seemed to be abated. In the same way, a person who has a headache and takes an aspirin knows only that his headache is gone and that a hindrance to normality has been eliminated. He does not believe that normality is dependent upon the drug. This type of opiate use has frequently been termed "innocent" addiction, and—in contrast with the exceedingly pessimistic prognosis for genuine addiction—it is usually permanently cured following withdrawal of the drug, provided the disease does not recur. T. D. Crothers, a prominent American authority, distinguishes these two types in the following manner:

> Where morphine has been used ignorantly, or from a physician's prescription for the relief of some temporary pain, the permanent cure of the case may generally be expected to follow its withdrawal. . . . In cases where the patient has had a long preliminary occasional use of the drug, and then a period of protracted use until immunity to very large doses has been established, the withdrawal is always difficult, and the permanence of any cure is somewhat doubtful.[15]

15. T. D. Crothers, *Morphinism and Narcomanias from Other Drugs* (Philadelphia: W. B. Saunders, 1902), p. 138.

Discussing the possibility of a cure for addiction, Lawrence Kolb expresses the belief that there are thousands of cured addicts in the country (though the word "cure" evidently refers here to addicts who are merely off the drug). He says: "If we class as former addicts all those persons who after several weeks of opiate medication suffered for a few days with mild withdrawal such as restlessness, insomnia, and over-activity of certain glandular functions—the number of cured addicts must exceed those who remain uncured."[16]

¶ Another important respect in which habituation usually differs from genuine addiction is in the size of the dose and in its progressive increase. Physiological reasons for increasing the dosage are well established. For example, when morphine is administered over a period of months to a patient with incurable cancer, the dose is necessarily increased, but rarely, if ever, in the proportions that the addict finds necessary. The latter is so powerfully impelled to increase the dosage that he often regards an excess as essential and finds it virtually impossible to reduce it voluntarily. In therapeutic treatment, even in cases of protracted illness and pain, a daily dose of 3 or 4 grains is regarded as an extraordinary amount. The addict who has a large supply available to him regards 3 or 4 grains of morphine a day, taken in "skin shots" or orally, as a small allotment.

The difference between the addict's dosage and that of the patient in the condition of habituation is effectively demonstrated by data collected by Kurt Pohlisch in an attempt to determine the approximate number of drug addicts in Germany.[17] These data were taken largely from druggists' prescription blanks, and Pohlisch was therefore compelled to define addiction purely in terms of the size of the doses and the length of time during which they were taken. He was familiar with the distinctions made by Levinstein, Erlenmeyer, and others between "habituation" and "addiction," and he recognized the validity of this distinction; nevertheless, he was forced by the nature of his data to take these things into account only as they could be translated into amounts used

16. Quoted by Terry and Pellens, op. cit., p. 616.
17. Kurt Pohlisch, "Der Verbreitung des chronischen Opiatsmissbrauchs in Deutschland," Monatschrift für Psychiatrie und Neurologie (1931), 79: 1–32.

per day. Therefore, he established the minimum dosage as 1.5 grains per day but admitted that his figure classified too many as addicts.[18] If one were to use the concept of addiction (*Morphinismus*) generally employed in German clinics, the limit might have been placed, he said, at 4.5 grains per day. By using a very low limit he corrected unavoidable errors in the other direction.

When his cases are distributed according to dosage, they fall into a frequency pattern which does not at all correspond to expectations concerning addicts.[19]

TABLE 1[a]

| Size of Daily Dosage in Grains | Number of Cases |
| --- | --- |
| Under 1.5 | 2,856 |
| 1.5– 3.0 | 1,276 |
| 3.0– 4.5 | 650 |
| 4.5– 6.0 | 421 |
| 6.0– 7.5 | 309 |
| 7.5–15.0 | 607 |
| 15.0–30.0 | 212 |
| 30.0–45.0 | 16 |
| 45.0–60.0 | 9 |

[a] From Pohlisch, *op. cit.*, attached Table 1.

It will be noted that the number of patients using less than 3 grains per day is very large, about 65 per cent of the total, and that the number in each classification becomes progressively larger as one approaches the smaller doses. This, of course, contradicts general experience with addicts. Kolb found in a study of 119 cases of addiction that the average dose was 7.66 grains per day.[20] His subjects were medical cases, that is, persons who had become addicted in medical practice, and were not of the underworld. Since the majority obtained their supplies from legitimate sources, the average dosage reported by Kolb is therefore more

18. *Ibid.*, pp. 3–4.
19. *Ibid.*
20. Lawrence Kolb, "Drug Addiction: A Study of Some Medical Cases," *Archives of Neurology and Psychiatry* (1928), 20: 174.

reliable than figures derived from the testimony of underworld addicts, who use diluted drugs, generally do not know precisely how much they are taking, and cannot be counted upon to report it correctly if they do know. The only plausible explanation of Table 1, an explanation made by Pohlisch himself, is that a high percentage of the patients using very small amounts were not addicts, and that the percentage of those who were only habituated, but not addicted, decreases as the dosage increases. This conclusion is borne out if the physicians included in the Pohlisch study are listed separately, as follows:

TABLE 2[a]

| Size of Daily Dosage in Grains | Number of Doctors |
| --- | --- |
| Under 1.5 | 38 |
| 1.5– 3.0 | 99 |
| 3.0– 4.5 | 94 |
| 4.5– 6.0 | 64 |
| 6.0– 7.5 | 66 |
| 7.5–15.0 | 144 |
| 15.0–30.0 | 81 |
| 30.0–45.0 | 7 |
| 45.0–60.0 | 5 |

[a] From Pohlisch, *op. cit.*, attached Table 1.

The marked concentration around the lower figures is absent in this distribution; only 22 per cent of the doctors used less than 3 grains per day. One would expect that the percentage of addicts among doctors who are regularly taking morphine would be larger than among nonmedical persons. Thus Table 2 corroborates the distinction made here between habituation and addiction. Further support of my thesis, that addiction and habituation are radically different, may be obtained by listing separately those cases mentioned by Pohlisch in which cocaine was used in connection with morphine, heroin, or another opiate. One could also expect most of this group to be addicts because of the relative infrequency with which cocaine is prescribed and because the use of cocaine and an opiate in combination represents a degree of sophistication ordinarily encountered only among addicts. The users of cocaine and an opiate (usually morphine) took the following amounts per day:

| Size of Daily Dosage in Grains | Number of Cases |
|---|---|
| Under 1.5 | 9 |
| 1.5– 3.0 | 11 |
| 3.0– 4.5 | 15 |
| 4.5– 6.0 | 11 |
| 6.0– 7.5 | 14 |
| 7.5–15.0 | 35 |
| 15.0–30.0 | 23 |
| 30.0–45.0 | 2 |
| 45.0–60.0 | 4 |

ᵃ From Pohlisch, *op. cit.*, attached Table 1.

Only 16 per cent used less than 3 grains per day, as contrasted with 65 per cent of the total cases (including physicians and cocaine users). The distribution is again strikingly different from that of the ordinary run of cases and corresponds rather closely to general observation concerning the approximate size of the addict's dosage, as well as to the average of 7.66 grains per day reported by Kolb for his medical cases.

The impulse to increase the dosage is so powerful that most drug users with whom I discussed the matter regarded it as almost inevitable that an addict should use too much. They were skeptical of any addict who claimed to require only as little as 2 or 3 grains per day. It may be possible by resolute determination to stabilize drug consumption at a low level, but the trend toward a progressively larger dosage is probably a distinguishing characteristic of addict behavior. There is nothing in medical practice remotely corresponding to the insatiable appetite for large doses that characterizes most chronic users. It may safely be assumed that even those addicts who manage to stabilize their intake at a low level feel the desire to use more. Again in contrast to the addict, the habituated person not only uses a smaller amount on the average but does not feel the progressive need for more. Many German addicts studied by Dansauer and Rieth, for example, obtained their narcotics from two different doctors at the same time and tried similar deceptions, while nothing of the sort occurred among those who were using the drug without being addicted. I have known a number of cancer cases in which morphine was administered orally for more than a year without reaching a maximum of 2 grains a day, the equivalent of perhaps one grain hypodermically. Such moderation is practically unheard of among addicts, unless it is involuntary.

A final characteristic of addicts is that they know they are addicts and speak of themselves as such. American underworld addicts refer to themselves as "junkies" or "users," and are so regarded by others. Frequently, in a jocular sense, they use the more expressive term "dope fiend." Even the drug user in respectable society, who may have few or no addicted associates, secretly labels himself a "drug addict" or "dope fiend."

The most obvious way of defining addiction or of determining if a person is an addict is to ask him, provided, of course, that one has his confidence. Another simple procedure is to inquire among those of his associates who are in a position to know. While I was gathering the material for this study, I asked individuals who had once been "hooked" if they were addicts, and they always replied unhesitatingly in the affirmative, even though they were free of the drug or had voluntarily abstained for several years. In contrast to the addict, the hospitalized patient who has been receiving opiates to deaden pain does not regard himself as an addict. If he does not recognize withdrawal distress, he obviously cannot infer that his experience has any connection with drugs. The most striking demonstration of this point is to be found in Case 3, cited in Chapter 4. Further illustration is offered in the following case:

> While in his teens, Mr. D. fell from a telegraph pole and fractured his spinal column. He was taken to a hospital and, to relieve the pain, was given a number of white pills. His back was put into a cast, and the pills were discontinued, but the family doctor con-

tinued to give him a tonic. As he gradually recovered he continued to take this medicine, but derived absolutely no pleasure from it as far as he was able to recall, nor did he have the slightest notion that it contained an opiate. He had never seen a drug addict and had no conception of what addiction was. After ten months of this treatment, he suddenly decided to leave town and go to a distant city to seek work. He had noticed, in the meantime, that whenever he did not take his medicine he did not feel well, but attributed this to his accident. When he left home it did not occur to him to take any medicine along, so that when he became ill from withdrawal distress, he had no notion of what was wrong but assumed it was disease. He tried at first to treat himself, but, when he continued to feel worse and noticed that he was losing weight rapidly, he consulted a doctor, who diagnosed his condition correctly. It was then that he realized for the first time that he had been using an opiate. He then defined himself as a drug addict and began to read all the medical books on the subject that he could find. He also increased his dosage until he reached approximately 60 grains a day. This took place before the enactment of the Harrison Act, when narcotics were easily available and inexpensive.

It is noteworthy that during the initial period of habituation in this case the behavior symptomatic of addiction was entirely absent. Then, when the true situation was brought home to Mr. D., a pronounced change occurred in his attitude toward the drug, as evidenced by his interest in reading about it. It should also be observed that when this turning point was reached the dosage was rapidly increased.

## Summary

Addiction may be defined as that behavior which is distinguished primarily by an intense, conscious desire for the drug, and by a tendency to relapse, evidently caused by the persistence of attitudes established in the early stages of addiction. Other correlated aspects are the dependence upon the drug as a twenty-four-hour-a-day necessity, the impulse to increase the dosage far beyond bodily need, and the definition of one's self as an addict. This complex of behavior will hereafter be referred to as "addiction," and the organism which exhibits it will be called an "addict." The term "habituation," on the other hand, will be used to refer to the prolonged use of opiates and to the appearance of tolerance and withdrawal distress, when it is not accompanied by the behavior described above as addiction behavior.

It is evident from the above discussion that an animal cannot be called an "addict," regardless of how much opiate drug it is given. Johannes Biberfeld correctly expresses the relationship of animal experimentation to, and its bearing upon, the problem of drug addiction when he asserts that addiction involves two types of phenomena, tolerance for morphine and a craving for morphine, and that only the former has any connection with animal experimentation. The craving, he believes, is an exclusively human phenomenon and animal behavior cannot be compared with it.[21] While recent experimentation with lower animals has narrowed the gap between human and animal responses to opiates by inducing in lower animals some interesting parallels with the behavior of human addicts, the gap has by no means been closed and Biberfeld's conclusion is still essentially correct. The more cautious of the contemporary experimenters with lower animals recognize this and do not claim that their animal subjects exhibit the same behavior that a human subject does. This experimental work with lower animals will be considered in more detail in a later chapter.

The physiological conditions produced by the drug when it is habitually assimilated by the body are essential to addiction, but other factors are also present, for the physiological conditions are not always followed by addiction. The problem of the present study, then, narrows down to that of isolating the factors which account for the transition from a biological condition, induced by regular drug administration for a period of time, to a psychological state of addiction or craving. Undoubtedly the physiological concomitants play a role in addiction, for certainly no one becomes an addict without first experiencing them. Any explanation of addiction must, therefore, consider these phases, but it must

21. Johannes Biberfeld, "Zur Kenntnis der Morphingewöhnung. II, Ueber die Spezifizität der Morphingewöhnung," *Biochemische Zeitschrift* (1916), 77: 283. See also S. D. S. Spragg, "Morphine Addiction in Chimpanzees," *Comparative Psychology Monographs* (1940), 15: 120 ff. Spragg agrees with Biberfeld's statement concerning experiments other than his own. It is my opinion that Biberfeld's observations also apply to Spragg's work.

also take the psychic aspects into account. The theory proposed in this study must also account for the fact that some persons escape addiction while others, under essentially the same physiological condition, become incurable addicts. In other words, the physiological factors must be regarded as necessary concomitants of addiction but they are not causal in the sense that they "produce" such behavior. In subsequent chapters, the conditions which lead to the transformation of mere drug use or habituation into addiction will be specified and described. The theory that will be developed assigns an essential but not a determining role to the biological aspects of addiction.

Some students of addiction from the biological sciences insist that addiction ought to be defined in biological or biochemical terms and sometimes equate it with physical dependence. Such a definition is clearly unacceptable for one who studies the behavior of the addict since it would require that infants born of addicted mothers be called addicts while drug users locked up in jail could not be. As has been shown in this chapter, physical dependence may exist without addiction and addiction without physical dependence. If one is interested solely in the bodily effects of opiates it is certainly legitimate and necessary to study the phenomena of physical dependence and tolerance, but if one is concerned with the social psychology of addiction, that is, with behavior, the definition of addiction must be in behavioral terms.

If it is argued that the regular use of opiates produces permanent organic or biological changes which form the basis of the craving and of the relapse impulse, then it is necessary to assume that the same effects must be produced in countless hospital patients who unknowingly receive morphine and exhibit no craving whatever. To call such patients addicts is to do violence to the plain meaning of terms.

The definition of addiction that has been proposed here is one that focuses on what are believed to be essential, common, or universal aspects of the behavior of addicts. There are many other aspects of addiction behavior which occur in some addicts and not in others, and there are special forms of behavior associated with different ways of using the drug. All of these must be excluded from consideration because, being nonessential differences between the instances, they cannot form the basis of a sound definition and they are not of central theoretical relevance. A general theory of addiction must obviously be concerned with explaining the central core of common behavior, not the peripheral and idiosyncratic variations which sometimes occur and sometimes do not. Neither can a sound definition of addiction include any element of moral judgment such as an assertion that it involves the illegal use of drugs or that it is harmful to the individual or the society. Persons dying of cancer who are provided with liberal quantities of morphine by their physicians may be addicted in the same essential sense that any other person may be.

The definition proposed is one that is designed to apply to addicts anywhere, whether they use the drug intravenously, by inhalation, by smoking, by drinking it, or any other way. It distinguishes especially between those who are merely physically dependent on the drug and those who are psychologically dependent on it in the special sense implied by the word "addiction." One hypothetical qualification might perhaps be made. If one could imagine a society in which addiction carried absolutely no stigma and in which opiates were freely available to users, it is reasonable to suppose that the addict's preoccupation with maintaining his supply would not be as strong or as continuous as it has been described here. Much of the American user's anxiety and preoccupation stems from the scarcity of the supply and the difficulties in obtaining it and might be compared with attitudes toward food during a famine. In a hypothetical society made up entirely of addicts in which drugs were abundant and food scarce, no doubt the central preoccupation would be with food rather than with drugs.

CHAPTER

# 4

# THE NATURE OF ADDICTION

The nature of the process in which addiction is established may perhaps be most effectively presented by describing a few selected instances which exemplify it in an especially clear-cut manner. The first of these cases is quoted from an article by L. L. Stanley;[1] the second and third are based upon interviews that I conducted.

The assumption underlying the analysis of the nature of the addiction process presented in this chapter is that the special and extraordinary craving of the addict is derived in a learning process from the repetition of a certain kind of experience with the drug which all addicts have. The point of this discussion therefore is to isolate and describe this experience from which the "hook" in addiction is derived. The three accounts that follow should be considered, not as three unique historical accounts of how addiction was established several decades ago, but rather as especially critical instances from which it may be possible to infer what the universal features are in the acquisition of the pattern of behavior that addiction constitutes.

1. L. L. Stanley, "Drug Addictions," *Journal of Criminal Law and Criminology* (1919–20), 10: 65.

"*Case 1.* In 1899 I went to the Philippine Islands with the Third Infantry, landing in Manila in March. Along about the end of my service I developed dysentery and as a result became so weak that from 140 pounds I went down to 100 pounds. I would report at the sickline and the doctors would give me C and O (camphor and opium) pills. These pills I took for four months until the time of my discharge in 1900. Returning from Manila on the *Sherman,* I was so weak that I had to go to bed. I felt miserable, and the steward accused me of being an opium smoker. At this time I did not know anything about the habit, and did not know what made me so restless and nervous. After my discharge I could not sleep. I met an ex-soldier who said, 'I know what's the matter with you. You've been up against the pipe. You'd better start to shoot it.' Before this, though, he had given me laudanum and yenshee, which relieved my habit. I bought a gun and began to use two one-fourth grain tablets three times a day. I used more and more until I was using thirty grains a day.'"

*Case 2.* Before 1910, Mr. R. became acquainted with a number of persons who were using heroin nasally. At this time heroin was cheap and not regarded as habit-forming. He had once tried cocaine and found it unpleasant but observed that heroin seemed to have different effects, transforming a weak and miserable man into a normally alert one. He tried it once and liked it, and, inasmuch as it was cheap, he bought a dime's worth and kept it in his room. Every now and then, whenever it occurred to him or when he felt particularly downcast, he used a little. At first he used it only every few weeks or so, but gradually he began to take it more and more frequently, until, after five years of intermittent use, he had gone from once a month use to once a week, to once a day, and finally to serveral times a day. He did not realize that he was in any danger of acquiring a habit even when he used it every day. In the morning he took a sniff before he went to work, to arouse himself. Then, toward the latter part of the afternoon, when he noticed a let-down feeling, which he attributed to the blazing sun under which he was forced to work, he found that a sniff of heroin, which he now carried about with him, enabled him to finish out the day's work in a satisfactory state of mind and body. He had no idea that he was hooked.

Somewhat later, while Mr. R. was on his way to Chicago, he made plans to be picked up by a friend in Joliet, but when his friend failed to appear be became worried, since he did not have sufficient funds to pay his fare. Having exhausted his heroin supply, he threw away the empty box and did not think of buying another. Gradually he noticed that he did not feel well; his eyes and nose were running and he yawned incessantly. He began to wonder if he was getting the flu. He walked into a restaurant, for he suddenly realized that he had not eaten for a long time, but the sight of food repelled him and he left without eating.

At the corner drug store he might have purchased all the heroin he needed for only a dime, but it did not occur to him to do so. Instead, he attempted to obtain money from a stranger whom he accosted and to whom he explained his condition, but he was turned down. This affected him so much that he could not accost another prospect.

By catching a ride on a train, he finally got into Chicago that night, and early the next morning, feeling more miserable than ever, he visited a friend, who was still in bed. As he sat talking, he noticed a box of heroin tablets on the dresser. Quite naturally, without altering the tone of his voice or interrupting the conversation, he reached for the familiar box and mechanically broke up a tablet of heroin and sniffed it. In a few minutes the entire aspect of the world changed, and in a flash he realized that this was what "dope fiends" experienced and that he was addicted. All his distress and misery vanished and then, feeling hungry, he went out and ate heartily. Mr. R. attributed great importance to this critical experience, saying that if, instead of coming to Chicago and meeting a heroin user, he had been taken to a farm, he might have suffered a few days and then recovered rapidly and never have been the worse for it. He believes that he would never have become a "dope fiend" under such circumstances.

*Case 3.* Dr. H., a physician, was given morphine liberally and regularly for months, when he was undergoing an appendectomy and two subsequent operations resulting from complications. For a time he was not expected to live, but as he recovered the dosage of morphine was gradually reduced and finally withdrawn. He knew that he had received morphine, but during the gradual withdrawal he attributed those symptoms of distress which he noted to the after-effects of the operations and to the processes of convalescence. During the next five years he went on with his practice, without craving the drug, and nothing whatever was amiss with his mental state. He had seen drug addicts in the course of his medical practice and felt a horror of them. He believed that he would certainly shoot himself in preference to being one. This attitude remained absolutely unaltered by the hospital experience just described. Several years later Dr. H. contracted gallstone trouble and was advised that an operation would probably be necessary. With his previous operations still fresh in his mind, he wished to avoid another, if at all possible, and was told that it might conceivably not be required; in this case it would be necessary for him to take opiates for his attacks. He did not like the idea of using narcotics, but was more afraid of an operation, so he resorted to them to ease his pain. He now required them more and more frequently, both because the attacks came oftener and because he gradually used the drug for less severe pains. Being permitted to administer the opiates himself, he finally "caught himself" taking injections every day, even when he had no pain. During the process his horror of drug addiction disappeared, and he began to read all the books he could find on the subject. He still believed he was an exception to the rule and would be able to quit easily. He realized *in retrospect* that he had experienced withdrawal symptoms several years before and had failed to recognize them. His efforts to cure himself soon ended, and a year later he acceded to his wife's request to enter a sanitarium. Upon discharge, after three years, he did not feel right without the drug. He is still an addict; he has lost his practice, money, and family, and uses the drug whenever he is out of jail.

In all three of these instances it is striking that there is no evidence of craving for the drug and of the other changes in attitude that characterize addiction appearing solely as a consequence of physical dependence. It is also evident that mere knowledge of the drug is not a critical factor since the third case involved a doctor who became physically dependent upon morphine on two separate occasions, knowing in each instance that he was receiving morphine, but not becoming addicted until the second. Neither can it be said that the transition from merely taking drugs to becoming addicted occurs when the individual ceases having the drugs given to him and begins to administer them to himself. Case 2 contradicts this idea, since the person involved administered the drug to himself for a substantial period without developing the craving. It will be pointed out later that addiction is sometimes established in persons who never administer the drug to themselves.

What these three cases do suggest is that a critical and universal feature of addiction is the recognition and proper identification of the withdrawal distress, given the fact of physical dependence. It was inferred that the experience from which the addict learns to crave the drug is that of the relief or avoidance of withdrawal distress when the latter is understood for what it is. The "hook" in opiates is thus conceived, not as something inherent in the pharmacological action of the drug or as the consequence of the sheer biological facts of physical dependence and relief of withdrawal, but as a product of learning in a situation involving biological events as they appear to or are interpreted by the subject. Addiction is not established in an instant of time, as these three cases might suggest, but is acquired over a period of time from the repetition of the relief of withdrawal. Recognition of the nature and significance of the withdrawal symptoms does sometimes occur as a flash of sudden insight, but in other instances it dawns upon the beginner gradually. In any case, the cognitive experience alone is not sufficient by itself to generate addiction and does not do so, for example, if use of the drug is discontinued at once or if recognition comes long after the withdrawal distress has vanished. Both the cognitive and the biological elements in the situation are indispensable features of the total experience, and both must be present as the repetition of the experience establishes the behavioral and attitudinal patterns of opiate addiction.

The above paragraph states the core of the theoretical conclusion of this study. According to it, the hook in addiction arises, not from the euphoria which the drug initially produces, but from the beginner's realization that the discomfort and misery of withdrawal is caused by the absence of the drug and can be dispelled almost magically by another dose of it. The repetition of this experience functions as a conditioning process of the type known to psychologists as "negative reinforcement," which quickly establishes in the beginner the fatal craving for the drug. The beginning phase of the process involves an *escape* experience, but as addiction progresses and the addict learns to anticipate withdrawal it becomes, to a large extent, an *avoidance* experience as the user tries to space his shots so as to prevent withdrawal distress rather than to relieve it. The cognitive feature of the experience which is the source of addiction is an essential aspect of it, since addiction evidently does not occur when a person who is physically dependent on opiates fails to understand the withdrawal symptoms.

At first glance, it may seem incomprehensible that the novice who deliberately experiments with drugs, and who knows and associates with addicts, should fail to realize the cause of the distress that accompanies sudden abstention. But the withdrawal symptoms are poorly understood by the layman, and even by doctors and students of the problem, and are often regarded as "imaginary" or purely mental, without any organic or physiological basis. There is, moreover, nothing about the initial use of the drug for very short periods of time that forecasts future developments. The confirmed user ordinarily cannot explain his craving for the drug to the satisfaction of the non-addict; nor can he ordinarily explain it to his own satisfaction, since it is a basically irrational impulse which he himself does not understand. The non-addict finds it hard to imagine himself as an addict. Being inclined to regard addicts as weaklings or abnormal types, he discounts their tales of suffering and regards the withdrawal distress either as insignificant or as nonexistent, a product of the user's imagination. A trial or two of the drug further convinces him that he is right and increases his confidence that *he* cannot become addicted. This very self-confidence is likely to lead to carelessness in the further use of the drug, until too many injections are taken too close together, and the person, as the addict says, "wakes up some morning with a yen."

The following cases illustrate both the effects that the withdrawal symptoms have on the beginner and the inability of the non-addict experimenter to appreciate the nature of the danger he is courting.

*Case 4.* Mr. H. became addicted to opium smoking in about 1909, when he was living in California. Acting as a messenger and in other capacities, he was in a racket that brought him into associations with underworld characters. He also attended parties with pimps and prostitutes at which opium was smoked. He smoked along with the rest and liked it. The pimps told him that he would get hooked and warned him against it. He laughed and told them to mind their own business.

When asked how he finally got hooked, he said, "Well, just the way most of 'em do. I kept using the pipe and one day I woke up gasping and feelin' like hell. My bones ached all over. Naturally, I didn't know what was the matter, and like they all do I told somebody how I felt, and naturally I told an addict. He said, 'Jesus, boy, you've got a habit,' and then I took a pill and smoked it and was all right."

*Case 5.*[2] I told you that I first got acquainted with narcotics through a woman I was living with on Wabash. She used to go to the Chink joints to fix her yen. She smoked the pipe. She asked me to go with her and I went. . . . I first learned that I was hooked when I could not satisfy the girl with whom I was living, and she told me that I was just like the rest of the birds. This did not mean much until I got under the weather and could not get the usual dose that I needed. Some of the boys in the honky-tonks told me I was weak under the gills. I went to see a Negro doctor and told him that I was sick. He asked me how I was sick and I told him that the pain I had began in my stomach and went out through my toes. He laughed and told me, "It's got you, kid. What is the usual dose you take?" I went from that doctor feeling that this could not have happened to me. I couldn't be affected the same as the rest of the muff divers that were hanging around the corners, but I soon grew to know that the dinge [Negro] was right. From that time on I knew that the whole world would be against

2. Interview by Steven Orskey.

me the same as I had been when I had seen the condition of the
other dopes around the South Side. . . . It is not a pleasant feeling
to be told that you are a dope. It is something like the doctor telling you that you are suffering from an incurable disease, although
at the time I did not think so.

Dr. Schultz observed that the drug user does not intend to become an addict and that he is surprised the first time he notices
the withdrawal symptoms. He writes:

> A drug user does not expect at first to become addicted, but addic-
> tion is impressed upon the individual as soon as the abstinence symp-
> toms are severe enough to frighten him. He then awakens to the
> fatal knowledge that he is "hooked," which information other addicts
> are only too glad to give him. When more of the drug is taken and
> the symptoms are relieved, this idea of the necessity of continuing
> its use is indelibly impressed on his mind and accepted without
> much resistance, as there is, besides the pain of withdrawal, con-
> siderable pleasure and relief also.[3]

C. E. Sandoz comments upon the same point as follows:

> People who have acquired the morphine habit and do not know
> about withdrawal symptoms sometimes do not realize that the latter
> are due to the want of the drug when they try to stop its use, but
> will attribute them to some other cause, and perhaps consult a
> physician. Occasionally in these cases, the physician himself does
> not suspect or recognize morphinism, and interprets the symptoms
> as due to some other diseased condition.[4]

Most or many of the persons who experiment with opiates for
the sake of kicks do not know the nature of the danger involved
and pay attention to the wrong things. They think that the power
of the habit must come from seductive or even uncanny pleasures
produced by the drug. From a few injections they discover that
these pleasures are overrated, but in their preoccupation with

3. Charles Schultz in "Report of Committee on Drug Addiction to Commissioner of Correction, New York City, *American Journal of Psychiatry*
(1930–31), 10: 469–70.
4. C. Edouard Sandoz, "Report on Morphinism to the Municipal Court of
Boston," *Journal of Criminal Law and Criminology* (1922), 13: 16.

them they are not prepared for the abstinence symptoms which steal upon them and force them to continue the habit. More sophisticated experimenters who know of the significance of withdrawal distress take care never to use heroin or any opiate on two consecutive days. Such a schedule permits the individual to enjoy the euphoric effects of the drug and, if rigidly followed, avoids the possibility of addiction. I have met persons who have adhered to such a program for from ten to twenty years.

The way in which a person may have addiction thrust upon him and be caught in the trap without knowing it, and without ever giving himself a single injection, is illustrated in the following instance:

*Case 6.* Mr. G. was severely lacerated and internally injured in an accident. He spent thirteen weeks in a hospital, in the course of which he received opiates frequently both by mouth and hypodermically. He was unconscious part of the time and suffered considerable pain during convalescence despite the intake of opiates. He did not know what he was getting and noticed no effects except that his pain was relieved by the shots. He was discharged from the hospital, but in several hours he began to feel restless and uncomfortable, without recognizing his condition. That night he became nauseated and vomited blood. Fearing that he was going to die, he summoned his family doctor. The physician did not realize what was the matter and administered a mild sedative. During the next day Mr. G.'s condition became steadily worse, and by the second night he was in such misery that, as he said, he began to wish that he would die. He again summoned his family doctor. This time the doctor began to suspect that Mr. G. was suffering from opiate withdrawal and prepared an injection of morphine. Mr. G. remembers nothing after the injection except that the doctor sat down by his bed and asked him how he felt. He replied that he noticed no effect, but the doctor said, "You will in a few minutes." Soon the patient fell asleep and continued in perfect comfort for many hours. When he awoke, he was informed of the true nature of the relieving dose by his wife and by the physician's comment: "Now we're going to have a hell of a time getting you off." The patient remained free of the drug for a few days and then purchased a syringe and began to use it himself.

It will be observed that in most of the descriptions of the onset of the habit presented in this chapter, the drug user was first enlightened concerning his withdrawal symptoms by some other person—usually an addict or a doctor. This, of course, is not always the case and is probably less often true now than it was several decades ago when the general public was not as well informed. The individual who makes his own correct interpretation of the withdrawal symptoms does so by drawing upon information and beliefs that have been transmitted to him as part of the social heritage. If he is a physician or if for any other reason has special advance knowledge of opiates, it is more likely that he will understand his symptoms by himself without the help of others.

A considerable theoretical advantage is obtained if one can show that the power of the opiate habit rests upon the person's reaction to withdrawal distress rather than upon his reaction to a fleeting and often nonexistent euphoria. The reversal of effects and the apparent paradox that the drug user continues his habit only to feel "normal" become intelligible; indeed, they become integral aspects of the habit. In terms of the euphoria theory they are inexplicable paradoxes and contradictions. A similar view was held by Erlenmeyer, who wrote:

> Precisely in the difference between the effect produced by a dose of morphine just once to a healthy person and that produced by morphine when habitually incorporated, lies the fatal development of the morphine craving. . . . If the withdrawal is made *after* this reversal, there comes into existence a "vacuum" as Legewie says, i.e., the abstinence symptoms; that host of painful sensations, intolerable feelings, oppressive organic disturbances of every sort, combined with an extreme psychic excitement, intense restlessness, and persistent insomnia. In such moments the *craving for morphine* is born and rapidly becomes insatiable, because the patient has learned during the period of habituation, when abstinence symptoms set in after the effect of the last morphine dose has passed off, that those terrible symptoms are banished as if by magic by a sufficiently large dose of morphine.[5]

5. Charles E. Terry and Mildred Pellens, *The Opium Problem* (New York: Committee on Drug Addictions and Bureau of Social Hygiene, 1928), pp. 601–602.

Dr. L. Guy Brown[6] also corroborates this view, although he does not elaborate upon it.

There is still another sense in which drug addiction is acquired. If a person is given morphine or some other drug in the hospital without his knowledge of the fact, or without any previous information concerning the habit, he will not become an addict even though he suffers all the bodily 'aches' when its administration has been discontinued. Unless his suffering has been defined to him as being caused by a narcotic drug, he will not have a desire for the drug.

The viewpoint stated above also accords with the addict's typical comparison between the opiate habit and the use of cocaine. He says that "there is no habit in cocaine," and that it is a "luxury," whereas morphine is a "necessity." Cocaine does not create a state of bodily tolerance during the early period of use, and there is no reversal of effects as in opiate addiction. Moreover, nobody under the influence of cocaine can be said to be normal, nor is the discontinuance of this drug accompanied by organic or physiological withdrawal symptoms.[7] One addict emphasized the contrast between the two drugs by characterizing the use of cocaine as a matter of "desire," and that of opiates as a "habit." Marihuana, of course, like cocaine is not an addicting drug and provides the same contrast with the opiates. It may be suggested that the essential difference between the habitual use of non-addicting drugs such as cocaine, marihuana, and LSD in comparison to opiate addiction is that while the latter is established by negative reinforcement the former is motivated by the positive reinforcement involved. Cocaine, marihuana, and LSD are, in other words, used for the sake of their positive effects and in order to obtain a feeling that is extraordinary or other than normal; they are not used to relieve or avoid withdrawal distress, since these drugs do not involve withdrawal symptoms. It is of interest to observe that, probably because of the built-in condi-

6. "The Sociological Implications of Drug Addiction," *Journal of Educational Sociology* (February, 1931), 4: 359.

7. For a further comparison of the effects of cocaine and morphine in these respects, see Ernst Jöel and Fritz Fränkel, "Zur Pathologie der Gewöhnung. II, Ueber Gewöhnheit und psychische Gewöhnung," *Therapie der Gegenwart* (1926), 67: 60–63.

tioning mechanism provided by the withdrawal symptoms in the case of the so-called addicting drugs, addiction to them seems more automatic and less influenced by personality factors than is the case with the non-addicting drugs. There are, of course, some persons who are strongly attached to such drugs as marihuana, LSD, and cocaine and who use them regularly. In general, however, these habits seem to be much less powerful or compulsive than the genuine addictions, and they seem to depend upon special personality attributes which cause some people to obtain extraordinary satisfactions from these drugs. As the terms "addicting" and "non-addicting" themselves suggest, the use of non-addicting drugs is usually not strongly compulsive or regular. The average marihuana smoker, for example, smokes when the drug is at hand and when it is not available simply waits for it to show up again.

Since it is being argued that addiction to opiates is learned or acquired in the process of consciously and knowingly using the drug to alleviate and prevent withdrawal distress, there are a number of questions which may be raised. What happens, for example, if a person who has become physically dependent on an opiate recognizes the withdrawal symptoms at once when they appear but never thereafter uses the drug to relieve them? The desire to escape from pain and discomfort is, of course, easily understood, but why does not the person who discovers that he has become physically dependent at once resolutely stop taking the drug, endure the withdrawal, and free himself from the trap? Two answers may be suggested. In the first place, the individual is not likely to appreciate the significance of the choice that faces him; secondly, even if he does realize it, the persistence and intensity of withdrawal distress may be sufficient to wear down the firmest resolution. Furthermore, the temptation to use the drug to seek relief is strengthened by its availability and the individual's failure to see that any moral issue is involved. He persuades himself that it is logical to take a shot, that there is no danger, and that he will not be trapped thereby. This rationalization becomes still easier since all that is involved is the repetition of an act to which he is already accustomed. He may intend to quit at the first opportune moment, tomorrow, the next day, or next week, but not immediately. I have never heard of a user who, having experienced the full intensity of the withdrawal symptoms in full knowledge of their relation to the absence of opiates, did not become an addict. This fact is easy to understand when one considers the severity of the symptoms and the impression they make on the uninitiated. Note Case 6, in which Mr. G., on the second night of withdrawal, was in such misery that he wished to die.

There still remains the problem of explaining those cases in which the person knows exactly what to expect from the very beginning and therefore is aware of the withdrawal symptoms before they become severe. The most illuminating instance of this kind which has come to my attention is that of Louis Faucher, who, as already mentioned, deliberately experimented upon himself, taking one injection every evening for six days in succession, then stopping for fifteen days, and finally repeating the experiment. He describes his experience as follows:

> My first series of injections was finished. Well and good, but night was still ahead of me. I took advantage of every opportunity so as to be able to resist more effectively. I dined out; I drank with friends; I amused myself; and I returned home very late. All of this entertainment seemed dull to me, the wine and the food seemed bad. Nevertheless, I had had the necessary diversion, and after coming home early in the morning I went to bed fatigued and slept a little. The following night I was enabled to sleep by a small dose of veronal which took immediate effect. During the following days I invariably thought of and desired the injection, when the time came, but I was able to resist.[8]

In the second series he increased the dose greatly. The euphoria was thus increased, but it lasted a shorter time after each injection:

> Needless to say, these seductive hours left behind them a certain regret which caused me to stimulate myself artificially in order to combat the darkness that invaded me. It made it necessary for me to exert myself deliberately for several days in activity so as not to find life stale as an ordinary alcoholic does. In the intellectual sphere I noticed for several days an intense apathy, a remarkable disinclination to work, and a noticeable lack of decision.[9]

8. Louis Faucher, *Contribution à l'étude du rêve morphinique et de la morphinomanie* (thesis, University of Montpellier, no. 8, 1910–11), p. 18.
9. *Ibid.*, p. 23.

From Faucher's conclusions it is obvious that, in his own case, six days' injection was sufficient to produce a condition bordering on addiction. This suggests that the use of the drug to avoid the abstinence symptoms, even during their incipient stages, quickly leads to attitudes that characterize addiction. Faucher, of course, had advance knowledge and therefore noticed and understood the symptoms at once. He first became aware of them after the third or fourth dose; when the fifth dose was due he began to look forward to it eagerly. This case may be contrasted with that of the patient in a hospital who unknowingly receives the drug for weeks, months, or even years, and is none the worse when it is successfully withdrawn. I described Faucher's experience to an addict, whose comment was that the former was "halfway hooked."

Another borderline case, showing how early and rapidly the symptoms of psychological dependence upon the drug are established, is the following:

*Case 7.* While in his teens, Mr. W. had an affair with the wife of a doctor who was much younger than her husband. She was a drug addict, and gave W. an injection at his own request. He liked the effects, returned for more, and used it regularly for a few weeks until the doctor sent his wife away, presumably for a cure. The doctor then discovered that the boy also had been using the drug, for the usual withdrawal symptoms set in. The doctor took him in hand and reduced the dose gradually. The entire experience, from the first injection of the drug to its complete elimination, lasted six weeks, and the maximum dosage attained was about one grain a day. The boy was not in a position to know how to renew his supply or to make the money necessary to continue his habit. When interviewed, he affirmed that he had not used the drug for nine years. He was using marihuana, however, and said that he felt an attraction to drugs which he compared to the fascination that dizzy heights exercises upon some people: mingled fear and desire. The fact that this man was using marihuana regularly and associated with a drug addict suggests the strong probability of his returning to opiates. Having had only one opportunity of talking to him, I do not place unqualified confidence in his story.

Unfortunately, borderline cases are exceedingly difficult to find, so that definite conclusions cannot be made regarding the length of time it takes to establish addiction. Further research may bring more instances to light and permit a closer examination of the initial stages of addiction. For example, it would be interesting to know what the effects would be if the person who suffers intense withdrawal distress were to be informed of his condition but prevented from obtaining any drug. Two possibilities are sugggested by this hypothetical situation: either the experience would serve as a warning and a deterrent, or it would create something like the usual desire, resulting in a tendency to resume the drug at a later time. One might also reason that the individual could not truly be said to know that an opiate would relieve his suffering until he had actually tried it. In the absence of cases illustrating these borderline problems, no definite conclusions are justified.

There still remains for consideration the adequacy of the proposed theory as an explanation of the essential characteristics of addiction. As noted earlier, these characteristics are: a desire for the drug and dependence upon it; a powerful impulse to increase the dosage beyond the point of bodily need; an awareness of addiction and the definition of oneself as a "junkie" or addict; and the tendency to relapse into the habit when the drug has been withdrawn. The first three aspects will be discussed here, the fourth in a later chapter.

## Craving and Psychological Dependence

In the early stages of drug use before the withdrawal symptoms become a dominant element in the user's motivations, the reasons for using the drug are extremely varied and quite different from what they become when addiction is established. Initial use may be for the purpose of alleviating pain, experiencing kicks, or simply to conform with what others in a specific group are doing. In their long history, opiate drugs have been used for the alleviation or treatment of most of the physical and mental ailments known to mankind and have been recommended by folk cultures as well as by the medical profession. Addiction may follow regardless of the specific nature of the original motivations for use and, as has been indicated, even when the first experience of the drug's effects occur in connection with their being administered by a physician. With continued regular use, initial motivations or their absence become irrelevant.

An addict I interviewed told me that before he himself started to use drugs he regarded addicts with disgust and thought of opium smokers as creatures from another world. The account of how he became addicted was as follows:

*Case 8.* Mr. A. R. began to mingle with criminals, prostitutes, and gamblers before he was twenty. He was in poor health and had been sporadically spitting blood for more than a year when an older man who smoked opium noticed it and made inquiries. "You'd better smoke hop," was his advice. Mr. R. soon acquiesced and accompanied the man to an opium smoking joint. He liked his first trial very much. "I kept myself so full of hop for the next eight months that I didn't have a chance to find out about being sick. I just liked it and used it. I didn't think about whether it was habit-forming or not." On one occasion, when he accidentally happened to omit smoking, he began to yawn and to manifest the usual symptoms; without any great difficulty he realized that opium was the cause, yet he continued its use for about four years without thinking of quitting. He stopped spitting blood shortly after beginning to use the drug but does not pretend that that is why he continued to use it. He says that he liked opium so much at first that he used far too much and got himself into a state of drowsiness and sluggishness which he found unpleasant.

The casual way in which A. R. began using drugs without considering possible consequences might be compared with the way in which a child may eat candy simply because he likes its taste and without regard for unpleasant consequences. The euphoric effects during early use, of course, tend to encourage the user to continue. They may be thought of as the bait on the hook. With continued regular use these effects vanish and the withdrawal symptoms provide a new and different reason for continuing to use the drug. As this happens, the element of compulsion makes its appearance and the drug becomes a matter of necessity rather than of desire. This characteristic feature of addiction behavior is characteristically absent during the initial period.

The above points are further illustrated in the following case:

*Case 9.* Mr. X, at about the age of eighteen, began to live with a prostitute who smoked opium. After spending his first night with her, he describes his subsequent experiences as follows: "We slept most of the day until late afternoon, and when I woke up she got up and got a tray out of the dresser drawer and brought it over and placed it on the bed. I had seen opium pipes two or three different times since I had been working on the messenger force, so I recognized the contents of the tray as an opium layout. She told me she was a smoker and asked me if I had ever smoked hop. I told her I never had and she said that I ought to try it once, as she was sure I would like it." He then smoked. "I suddenly became very nauseated and had to leave to vomit. I vomited till there was nothing left on my stomach and I was still sick so I went to bed. She wet some towels with cold water and put them on my forehead and after an hour or so I fell asleep. I slept two hours and when I woke up I felt all right again. I went to work that evening as usual, and every time I would sit down in the messenger office I would feel drowsy and fall asleep and my body would itch all over and when I scratched it would feel awfully good."

The next night the girl again offered him a smoke. "It made me so sick the night before that when she started cooking the opium this morning it seemed to kind of nauseate me again. So I declined, and told her that I didn't feel very well, and I wanted to get some sleep. . . . As soon as we were awake she again got the tray and lit the lamp and got back into bed and started to cook her opium again. She cooked and smoked six or eight pills as I lay there watching her and then she again offered me some. I told her that I was afraid to smoke again for fear that it would make me as sick as I was the night before. She told me that it wouldn't make me sick this time, and she coaxed and coaxed until I finally gave in and said all right, that I would smoke a couple of pills with her just to be sociable.

After I had lived with her for six or seven months she told me that she had a letter from a sister who was very sick, so she asked me if it would be all right if she went to Helena to see her. I told her to go if she wanted, so I gave her enough money to go with and took her to the train. We had smoked just before she left and

she had packed the layout in a small handbag and took it with her.
I worked that night as usual and everything went along fine, until
I went home in the morning, and then I started to get sick. I went
to bed, but I couldn't sleep. I felt very restless and I rolled and I
tossed all day. Towards evening I began getting awful cramps in
my stomach and was also nauseated and started vomiting. I had
not eaten any food all that day, so there was nothing on my stomach but a little water, and when I started vomiting nothing came
up but green bile and the more I vomited the sicker I got. I finally
rang the bell and sent for a messenger, and when he came I told
him to tell the boss that I was sick and wouldn't be able to come
to work that night. The messenger asked me what was wrong and
I told him I didn't know. I told him that I had awful cramps and
was vomiting all the time. He asked me if I had been smoking
every day with my girl and I told him I had. Then he asked me if
I had any opium since she had gone to Helena, and I told him
that I hadn't. He told me that was the reason why I was so sick.
. . . He looked in the drawer and found a jar of opium, so he
cooked some and gave me three pills. He went to the restaurant
and got me a pitcher of black coffee and told me to swallow the
pills and drink some of the coffee. I did as he told me, and laid
down on the bed again, and in about ten minutes I began to feel
all right again. This was the first time that I had missed smoking
in the six months that I lived with this girl.

It is evident that Mr. X was not preoccupied with opium during
these six months. His chief interest, naturally, was his first major
sex experience. His apparent unconcern about his future supply
of the drug is striking and contrasts sharply with the behavior of
the confirmed addict. Keeping in mind the casual or episodic character of initial use before withdrawal symptoms have achieved
dominance, it is instructive by contrast to observe the addict when
his supply is threatened or actually cut off. Light, Torrance, and
their colleagues describe the behavior of addicts who *voluntarily*
took the cure under their care:

> After a person has become firmly addicted to the use of opium or
> one of its derivatives, we have reason to believe that the problem of
> securing and maintaining an adequate supply of the drug comes to

mean the major purpose of his existence. To an extraordinary degree he comes to develop a sagacity and persistence in this direction which may outmatch the abilities of those conducting the investigation. The ingenuity that is displayed in maintaining channels of supply is amazing. He will plead with or threaten those about him who are in a position to supply him with the drug. Whatever method he may use has been previously determined by careful consideration on his part as to which may be the more successful. . . . When the addict is admitted to the ward and understands that the drug is available and will be given for a time, he is amenable. He is cooperative in anything which does not interfere with his daily dosage. . . . But when the effect of the drug passes off, all the sagacity and ingenuity on his part are brought into play, as only those who have been associated with this type of person can appreciate.

Not only must the observer forestall the schemes which the addict is devising to obtain the drug, but he must defeat plans, made before the admission, for the restoration of his supply should his craving become unbearable. He may have attempted to bring the drug into the ward concealed in his clothing, jewelry, or in any orifice of the body large enough to hold it. . . . Should his attempts to bring a certain quantity into the ward have failed, he resorts to plans devised to obtain it from friends outside of the hospital, or he schemes with fellow addicts who are about to be discharged, and who have signified their intentions to him of immediately returning to the drug. He will attempt to bribe anyone who appears open to temptation. Letters will come addressed to him which have been written on paper previously saturated with the drug, dried, ironed out, and then inscribed with some harmless message. . . . Sometimes the drug is concealed under the stamp of an envelope. The wooden stem of a match changed into a cylinder has been found to contain a drug. He will accuse or betray his best friend in order that he may obtain favor from those in charge. Telegrams and telephone messages will arrive, bringing the news of the death of a member of the family, asking his immediate return home. These are but a few of the methods employed to obtain drugs, and unless forestalled, they will ruin any studies made during the withdrawal period. In addition, there is always danger that the patient may be aided by a fellow addict who may have drugs in his possession, or by a drug peddler who will furnish drugs without charge when it insures him the return of the addict with funds in the near future.

The scopolamine treatment that we have employed has always been stated by the patient, who has been previously treated and who wishes to enter the ward, to be "the best he has undergone, all others being torture." When he is just recovering from the effects of the scopolamine, it is the "worst," all others being excellent. When the time approaches for his discharge, and he is anxious to obtain his liberty, the treatment again becomes the most successful he has ever had; he appears to have fully recovered his normal strength, when he may still be so weak that he may not be able to walk several blocks without collapsing.[10]

The fact that the patients here described volunteered to have the drug gradually eliminated, and then behaved in this manner, suggests the desperate preoccupation of the addict with the maintenance of his supply. This preoccupation arises from the addict's apprehension of the consequences of deprivation; it depends, in other words, upon his anticipation of the withdrawal symptoms. Before realizing that there are withdrawal symptoms, or understanding their true nature, the addict is naturally not interested in the problem of supply. Not comprehending that the drug has become a daily necessity, he supposes that he can stop taking it any time he wishes. The following sentiments of a true addict remain essentially unintelligible to anyone who has not himself been tortured by withdrawal:

> To the opium consumer, when deprived of this stimulant, there is nothing that life can bestow, not a blessing that man can receive, which would not come to him unheeded, undesired, and be a curse to him. There is but one all-absorbing want, one engrossing desire, his whole being has but one tongue—that tongue syllables but one word—morphine.
>
> Place before him all that ever dazzled the sons of Adam since the fall, lay sceptres at his feet and all the prizes that vaulting ambition ever sighed and bled for, unfold the treasures of the earth and call them his; wearily, wearily will he turn aside and barter them all for a little white powder.[11]

From his experience in avoiding the withdrawal symptoms which recur after each injection, the addict comes to regard him-

10. A. B. Light, E. G. Torrance, W. G. Karr, Edith G. Fry, and W. A. Wolff, *Opium Addiction* (Chicago: American Medical Association, 1929), pp. 7–12. Reprinted by permission.
11. "Sigma," "Opium Eating," *Lippincott's Magazine* (April, 1868), p. 406.

self as being supported, or as he says, "carried" or "held up"[12] by the drug at all times. Whenever he omits a regular dose, he feels himself slipping into a state of mental and physical depression which seems to him unbearable. This realization of being constantly supported by the drug makes apparent the fact that the addict's normality is self-conscious and introspective and inextricably related to the presence in his body of a sufficient quantity of opiates. If he has had his supply, the addict, when asked how he feels, may answer, "Fine!" and perhaps add, "The shot I had this morning is holding me up well." It is as though an ordinary person, when asked the same question, were to reply, "I am feeling fine. The lunch I had this noon is holding me up well."[13]

The desire for opiates, which begins after the initial period of its use as a relief from physical suffering caused indirectly by the opiate itself, grows rapidly with the continued use of the drug. Every additional dose makes it more difficult and painful to quit. Every fruitless struggle to free himself from the habit only impresses upon the addict his imperious need for the drug. The beginner does not usually have the information that would enable him to fight the habit intelligently and effectively. The expenses and discomforts associated with the habit in its early stages are not sufficiently pronounced to furnish him with a powerful enough motive for combating the desire to be relieved of withdrawal distress. Consequently, by the time the beginner has fully awakened to the seriousness of the situation, the habit is likely to be irrevocably fastened upon him.

The most substantial pleasures associated with addiction are probably actual relief and exaggerated anticipation of this relief. To a considerable extent, the addict's life is one of anticipation: of withdrawal, of a loss of supply, and of the relief which is sometimes glorified as pleasurable in itself. When he does suffer, he exaggerates his distress.[14] During the initial stages of withdrawal,

12. See Glossary.

13. See also Chapter 6 for a discussion of the differences between the "normality" of the addict and that of the non-addict. Scarcity of food results in preoccupation with the means of obtaining it, and one might perhaps argue that there is a parallel between addiction to drugs and addiction to food.

14. T. D. Crothers states, "The addict's conceptions of pain are very largely anticipatory and imaginative, and associated with mimicry." The implication

every slight stomach cramp, which De Quincey described as "the gnawing of some imprisoned reptile," is endowed with some of the significance and painful attributes of all the stomach cramps the user knows there are to follow. The suffering becomes all the more unendurable because the means of relief are so simple.

## The Increase of the Dosage

Although not every addict increases his dosage greatly beyond the point of bodily need, the vast majority of them probably have the impulse to do so, and success in controlling this tendency comes only through resolute and calculated self-control. Dosage may be divided into two parts: first, the daily quantity necessary for comfort, and second, the additional amount which the user uses and believes to be necessary. This "deluxe" dose,[15] as the latter has been called, represents for the most part just so much more expense and trouble. Its physical effects are detrimental, yet it is usually regarded as a necessity, and the addict will often move heaven and earth to maintain a daily consumption far exceeding that which would result in maximum physical efficiency. The deluxe dose may thus be said to represent a psychological rather than a physiological need. Its psychological character is evident from the fact that an addict using large quantities daily may have the amount cut to a fraction of its former level and be none the wiser, providing he is unaware of the reduction. His condition tends to improve when that is done, but when he attempts to reduce his own dosage, even though he is fully aware of the resulting benefits, he finds it difficult or impossible.

This irrational tendency to increase the dosage may be interpreted, according to the theory, as the result of an increased sensitivity to the withdrawal symptoms.[16] As the user becomes famil-

that the withdrawal distress is unreal or slight is incorrect, but the author evidently perceived the importance of the imaginative and anticipatory aspects of the habit. It is only fair to repeat that the withdrawal distress is not trivial. Its severity accounts for and enhances its influence on the imagination of the addict. (*Morphinism and Narcomanias from Other Drugs* [Philadelphia: W. B. Saunders, 1902], p. 222).

15. Terry and Pellens, *op. cit.*, p. 553. Roger Dupouy, following Joffrey, called this part of the daily dose "the proportion of luxury."

16. See Case 164 in Friedrich Dansauer and Adolph Rieth, Ueber Morphinismus bei Kriegsbeshädigten, *Arbeit und Gesundheit: Schriftenreihe zum Reichsarbeitsblatt* (1931), 18: 109–110.

iar with these symptoms, he learns to detect the very first signs; these warn him of future distress, and as a result he is inclined to magnify their extent and importance. He feels sicker than he really is, and, since he regulates the time of each injection by the way he feels, he is impelled to use the drug sooner than otherwise. Then, having taken the dose prematurely, he finds that he does not "feel the shot" as he did the last time. The effects of an injection are noticed in proportion to the contrast between the states *before* and *after* the dose takes effect; it follows, then, that in order to "feel his shot" the addict must now increase the size of the dose. The impact of the drug has become a symbol of security from withdrawal; if, however, he takes his injections a little sooner than before, the symbol is blurred, and in order to restore it he must use a greater quantity. The process is further promoted by the tendency of the organism to adapt itself to doses of any size. Caught in this vicious circle, the addict's consumption often is limited only by the tremendous expense involved.

A further incentive for increasing dosage is often found in the addict's realization that he is trapped. Since he must, in any case, continue the shots, he throws caution to the winds and seeks the greatest possible satisfaction. Having learned to value the physical impact of the drug for its symbolic significance, he may strive to enhance this symbol quantitatively. As a result, he creates the illusion that he feels well even at the expense of greater financial outlay and actual physical discomfort.

The addict's intense preoccupation with and craving for the drug, and his tendency to increase the dosage, are probably connected with scarcity of supply and the difficulties and dangers of obtaining it. The insecurity created by these factors intensifies the addict's psychological attachment to the drug much as the scarcity of food intensifies the desire for it and leads persons who are chronically undernourished to overeat when the opportunity presents itself. In situations in which the drug user feels assured of adequate supply his concern with the drug would probably be much more comparable to the average American's concern with food than it now is. Reports from an experiment in New York City in which Drs. Vincent Dole and Marie Nyswander provided addicts with regular maintenance doses of methadone, a synthetic equivalent of the opiates, support this idea. Drs. Dole and Nyswander have told me that the addicts in their experiment reported that they quickly stopped thinking and talking about drugs, exclusively at least, shortly after they entered the program. There was also no difficulty in stabilizing the dosage of these users.

## Awareness of Addiction

The user of a drug does not think of himself as addicted to it as long as he is convinced that he can stop taking it any time he wishes to. In the case of the opiate addict, this confidence begins to dissolve when he first realizes that the withdrawal distress bars the way to prompt and easy abstinence. Repeated experiences further reduce confidence in the ability to quit. A relatively full realization is reached when the user who has succeeded in staying off drugs voluntarily for a time relapses and resumes his habit. The first experience with withdrawal may suggest to the beginner that it may be difficult to break the habit, but he is likely to underestimate the difficulties and to think that he will succeed. The withdrawal symptoms provide the user with his first inkling that he may have fallen into a trap, and this realization frequently leads to voluntary attempts to break the habit. When these fail, the user becomes relatively fully aware that he is an addict, and he is then ready for assimilation into the addict subculture. From other addicts he learns what to do to obtain supplies and to avoid arrest. In the course of time, under the pressure of the habit, more and more of his daily associations and activities become focused on matters connected with his habit.

The beginning of this process of assimilation and the motives for it are illustrated in the following case:

*Case 10.* Mr. Q., a professional criminal, began to use drugs about 1925, when his wife died. He drowned his sorrows in liquor, and one night, as he was coming home after considerable indulgence, he was accosted by an addict who had often begged money from him before. Knowing that the man was an addict because he had been pointed out as such, Mr. Q. decided to play a joke on the beggar by pretending to arrest him. Then, dropping this pose, he decided on the spur of the moment to try some morphine. They went to the beggar's regular agent, and the purchase was made.

Mr. Q. took a very small injection and gave the rest to the addict. He greatly enjoyed the sensation produced by the drug. Several weeks later, the addict looked up Mr. Q. in order to get help in obtaining a supply, offering to share the returns fifty-fifty. Mr. Q. had had no intention of using the drug, but agreed to help, so the addict insisted that Mr. Q. accept his share. He first refused, then accepted the drug and took it home, forgetting about it for quite a while. He had no means of administering it at this time. One day a friend who ran a small business establishment moved into new quarters where he found an all-metal syringe concealed behind the molding. Mr. Q. took it home and, finding that it worked, began to use his little supply of morphine. When it was exhausted, he noticed that he wasn't feeling entirely right, and, remembering that morphine had helped him before when he felt depressed, he decided to buy some more. He went to the place where he and the beggar had first purchased some, and there, by sheer accident, met a man who had a large bottle of the stuff which he was willing to sell cheap. Mr. Q. commented, "Well, I took it home and really got hooked on that stuff. Before it ran out I knew that I would have to have more, so I went out and made connections."

When asked how he knew that he was addicted, he explained, "I used to take a couple of shots a day of the stuff, and then I noticed that I was beginning to depend on it, so I thought I'd do without it one day and didn't take my morning shot. Well, along in the afternoon I was with some of the fellows in a saloon somewhere, and I was feeling rotten and yawning all the time. One of the fellows was an addict and asked me if I had a yen.

" 'What the hell's a yen?' I asked, and he said it came from having the drug habit. He asked me if I was taking morphine at home, and I said I was, about two times a day.

" 'When did you have your last shot?'

" 'Yesterday afternoon.'

" 'And you didn't have anything this morning?'

" 'No.' He asked me if my legs hurt, and they did.

" 'Why, Jesus Christ!' the man said, 'You've got a habit and don't know it.'

"I went home and on the way I thought I could hardly make it because my legs were so wobbly. Well, when I got home, naturally I was feeling bad and wanted to feel better, so I fixed up a shot and thought I would see if the fellow was right. In a few minutes I was all right, feeling as lively as a spring chicken. Naturally, I began to find out what I could do about this habit by talking to addicts and by reading."

The following case, by way of contrast, offers an instance in which physical dependence on drugs existed, in which mild withdrawal distress occurred and was understood, but in which the drug was *not* subsequently used. As would be expected from the proposed theory, this person continued to have the feeling of confidence with regard to becoming addicted which is characteristic of most non-addicts and there were no changes of attitude or behavior which could have motivated her to join the addict subculture:

*Case 11.* Mrs. D. received morphine for about a month because of an illness. A relative, who was a doctor, was free and easy with morphine, leaving it at her bedside. She does not recall how much she used or how often and noticed only that after a dose she would feel stimulated and would want to talk and play cards. She noticed no letdown when the effects of the tablets wore off, and, after approximately a month, her condition was improved and use of the drug was to be discontinued. Withdrawal symptoms appeared and were reasonably severe though they were not accompanied by nausea or vomiting. She realized fully that these were due to not using the drug, noting chiefly restlessness, nervousness, and aching joints. A number of times it occurred to her to try morphine, but inasmuch as it was no longer called for, and because she recalled that it was not supposed to be good practice to go on using it when the illness was gone, she did not do so. In two days the symptoms disappeared.

She asserts that if the distress had been severe, or if her original ailment had returned, she would unhesitatingly have taken more of the drug, yet she is quite sure that she could not have become an addict.

According to the viewpoint outlined above, addiction to opiates is determined by the individual's reaction to the withdrawal symptoms which occur when the drug's effects are beginning to wear off, rather than upon positive euphoric effects often erroneously attributed to its continued use. More specifically, the complex of attitudes which constitute addiction is built up in the process of conscious use of the drug to alleviate or avoid withdrawal distress.

This theory may be stated in another form. If we suppose that an individual uses drugs regularly at four-hour intervals, it proposes that the experience from which the patterns of thought and behavior that constitute addiction are learned is encompassed in the approximately ten-minute time interval immediately following injection, not in the other 230 minutes between injections. The craving for drugs, it is argued, is fixed by negative rather than by positive reinforcement, by relief and avoidance of discomfort and pain rather than by positive pleasure. Response at the voluntary level to events and situations generally depends upon how these events are perceived and interpreted. It is therefore not surprising that the behavioral consequences of the withdrawal experience do not produce addiction except when the experience is cognitively grasped in a particular way; that is, when it is understood by the subject.

This theory seems to provide simple and plausible lines of explanation for varied and seemingly paradoxical aspects of addiction such as the addict's claim that he merely feels normal under the drug's influence, the fact that addicts can be deceived about whether they are under the drug's influence, and of the common tendency of users to increase the dosage. The theory also makes the addict's constant preoccupation with the drug intelligible and indicates how he is compelled by his experiences to recognize and admit to himself that he is a drug addict, junkie, or "dope fiend."

According to the hypothesis that has been developed here, the sheer physiological or biological effects of drugs are not sufficient to produce addiction although they are indispensable preconditions. The effect which the biological events associated with using drugs has on human behavior is seen as one that is mediated by the manner in which such events are perceived or conceptualized by the person who experiences them. Persons who interpret withdrawal distress as evidence of the onset of an unknown disease act accordingly, and, if they are not enlightened, do not become addicted. Persons who interpret the symptoms of opiate withdrawal as evidence of a need for the drug also act accordingly and, from using the drug after they have understood, become addicted. As the user applies to his own experiences and behavior the attitudes, symbols, and sentiments current in his society, he is faced with a problem of adjusting himself to the unpleasant implications of being an addict in a society that defines him as an outcast, pariah, and virtual outlaw. In his efforts to rationalize his own conduct, which he cannot really understand or justify, and to make it more tolerable to himself, he is drawn to others like himself.

The process of becoming addicted, as it has been described, presupposes membership in social groups and linguistic intercommunication. Understanding withdrawal distress means to conceptualize it, to name and categorize it, to describe and grasp it intellectually through the use of linguistic symbols. Addiction is therefore a uniquely human form of behavior which differs from the superficially comparable responses of lower animals much as human cognitive capacities differ from those of lower forms.

# 5

# PROCESSES IN ADDICTION

The confirmation of a theory, such as that which has been outlined in brief form in the preceding chapter, requires more than mere assertion of a relationship between two kinds of events or processes and the presentation of confirming instances. I assume that the proper meaning of "verifiability" is better expressed by the term "falsifiability." In other words, a genuine theory that proposes to explain a given phenomenon by relating it to another phenomenon must, in the first place, have clear empirical implications which, if not fulfilled, negate the theory. In the absence of such negative evidence a theory may be accepted as valid, but only in a provisional sense, because further evidence accumulated at some future time may require that the theory be rejected or revised. The characteristic of a good scientific theory is that, if it is false, it can readily be shown to be so. It can rarely or never be shown to be absolutely and unconditionally true. The verification of the theory that has been proposed will therefore consist primarily of the description of the search for evidence to negate it.

Another central aspect of scientific explanation that has already been alluded to is that besides identifying the two types of phenomena that are allegedly interrelated, there must be a description of the processes or events that link them. In other words, besides affirming that something causes something else, it is necessary to indicate how the cause operates to produce the alleged effect. This requires a description of a sequence of inter-related events in which the characteristic attributes of the phenomenon being explained emerge in the later phases as necessary or understandable consequences of earlier phases. To be specific, if it is assumed to be true that the craving for drugs is generated in the experience of using them to alleviate and prevent withdrawal distress which is understood as such by the subject, what are the implications of this and are those implications empirically confirmed?

## The Usual Case

While in previous chapters specially selected instances of the addiction process were presented for illustrative purposes, none of the addicts I have interviewed gave any reason for discrediting the theory. Obviously, all drug addicts experience and understand withdrawal symptoms, and, despite occasional claims that addicts sometimes experience no withdrawal distress when their addiction is interrupted, no authenticated case of an addict who never experienced withdrawal has ever been described. It also seems fairly obvious that addicts would not continue using drugs in increasing amounts at great cost and risk if there were no threat of withdrawal and if it were as easy to quit as it is, for example, to quit eating ice cream.

The addicts whom I interviewed can be grouped in two classes with respect to their first experiences with withdrawal symptoms. The first group became acquainted with them gradually, sometimes as a result of repeated experiences with relatively mild symptoms. Others, because they knew in advance what to expect, noticed and recognized the symptoms at once. As users of this type gradually develop an appreciation of these symptoms, they tend to become apprehensive and, without realizing or admitting that they may already be hooked, attempt to stop using the drug to see what will happen. Ordinarily a relatively brief delay of the next injection is sufficient to persuade the user to resume the drug, and as he does so he develops a fuller realization of the insidious nature of the habit. Through repeated brief experiences with the abstinence syndrome users of this type may become thoroughly addicted and fully aware of their dependence on the regular use of the drug without ever passing through the critical type of acute withdrawal.

The second way in which addicts become acquainted with withdrawal symptoms is by having them explained or by realizing their nature suddenly in a flash of insight. Several such instances are cited in the preceding chapter. In this case, the experience often comes to the beginner as a shock and a surprise. The subsequent adaptations evidently proceed relatively rapidly when this point is reached, and addiction is quickly established, although the user may continue for some time to resist the idea that he has become an addict and to nourish the delusion that he will be able to break his habit without too much difficulty when he puts his mind to it.

One addict told me that, in his first experience with narcotics, he was quite confident of his capacity to resist. Later he "began to be afraid of himself" and, in a gradual process of transition, came to a point where he "had to have it." He confided, "Whenever I was full of it, I would wish that I wasn't using it, but when the effects began to wear off, I'd go out for more." In this process, no sudden realization of addiction occurred, and even when encouraged to give a detailed account, he continued to describe his experience as a gradual and continuous transition. This case is at the opposite pole, with all degrees of variation between, from that in which the realization of addiction comes as a sudden fatal flash of insight in connection with severe and prolonged withdrawal.

Addicts of the class to which this case belongs may fail spontaneously to emphasize the role of withdrawal symptoms simply because the whole experience seemed self-evident and was so gradual and unspectacular.

Terry and Pellens observe: "It is self-evident that there can be but one direct cause of addiction, namely, the continued taking of the drug over a sufficiently long period to produce upon withdrawal distress of some kind to the patient."[1] Formal attempts at defining addiction invariably include withdrawal distress. In this connection, Emil Kraepelin's statement is pertinent. He writes:

> The severity of the symptoms of withdrawal varies to an extraordinary degree. It depends upon the size of the dose, the duration of the addiction, the general condition of the patient, and the individual tendency. Sometimes the disturbances are limited to a little diarrhea, sweating, excitability and insomnia, while in other patients the condition becomes exceedingly severe, threatening life. My experience, however, does not include an instance of withdrawal wholly without discomfort. When the manifestations are very mild or the health altogether undisturbed, morphine is unquestionably being supplied clandestinely.[2]

As a matter of fact, addicts regard withdrawal symptoms as a perfectly obvious and essential aspect of addiction and cannot conceive of addiction without them. This is why they describe drugs such as cocaine and marihuana as non-habit-forming and differentiate them sharply from the opiates. In order to qualify as addicting, a drug must produce physical dependence and withdrawal symptoms. The addict, admittedly, is not an authority in the field of psychopharmacology, but this particular conclusion of his is solidly grounded in his direct experience of the marked qualitative differences between the drugs that produce physical dependence and those that do not.

### Linguistic Evidence

Since the experience of addicts are in a sense crystallized and summarized in their special language or argot, it is significant to note some of the features of this language which are relevant to the ideas being considered. Of particular interest is the use of

1. Charles E. Terry and Mildred Pellens, *The Opium Problem* (New York: Committee on Drug Addictions and the Bureau of Social Hygiene, 1928), p. 134.
2. Quoted in Terry and Pellens, *op. cit.*, p. 197.

the term "hooked" to designate addiction. The reference to with-drawal symptoms is obvious, and the analogy embodied in the word could scarcely be more appropriate. The addict sometimes speaks of persons who were hooked without knowing it. When he does, he means simply that the individual was physically de-pendent on the drug without knowing about or recognizing the withdrawal symptoms. Since the addict associates primarily with persons who are hooked and know it, there is no particular need or occasion for him to make a sharp analytical distinction between knowing and not knowing that one is hooked. Should a novice fail to recognize the cause of his misery during his first experience of withdrawal, the more experienced addict attaches little signifi-cance to enlightening him. This is especially true because of the addict's tendency to identify addiction with physical dependence and withdrawal distress; the person who experiences these al-ready has the habit as far as he is concerned. The fact that some beginners at first do not recognize withdrawal experiences is regarded as something that is merely odd or interesting.

The possibility of receiving the drug without knowing it, suffer-ing withdrawal symptoms when it is removed without realizing it, and not becoming addicted, is admitted by the addict. Such persons, however, are not regarded as being "really hooked"—implying that the process of being "really hooked" involves not only withdrawal symptoms but also realization that they are due to the absence of the opiate. Furthermore, when an addict in-quires of someone he meets for the first time, "Have you been hooked?" an affirmative answer not only implies a withdrawal experience, but also a recognition of it. On the other hand, an individual who had been "hooked without knowing it" would not be likely to comprehend the question, and if it were explained he would answer in the negative.

Anyone who has ever been "hooked" is regarded by other ad-dicts as one of the "in-group." Whether or not he is using opiates at the moment, he is considered "one of the boys," a "junkie," a "user," or as an "ex-junkie"—never a "square," or non-addict. The addict who is temporarily not using drugs is familiar to other addicts and is regarded with tolerance and often encouraged in his effort to stay "off the drug." He is never viewed as an outsider. Since other addicts remember only too well their own helpless efforts to quit, they fully appreciate the position of the former user. Consequently, they wish the abstainer good luck by such remarks as "I hope you make it; I can't." Between the addict who is using drugs and the one who is not there is never the social barrier that separates the addict from the non-addict.

In the present study, drug users were asked in their own vernacular whether they had ever known or heard of anyone who had experienced and understood withdrawal and used the drug to avoid these symptoms without becoming addicted. This involved asking the self-contradictory questions, "Have you ever heard of a person who got hooked without becoming an addict?" or "Did you ever hear of an addict who was never hooked?" Both questions were meaningless to addicts, and I was compelled to explain myself. To the drug user, to be "hooked" is to be addicted and to be addicted is to be "hooked."

Another term, "yen," is used popularly as a synonym for "desire"; for example, "I have a yen for a piece of pie." In the addicts' argot, this word signifies the desire for narcotics incidental to abstinence distress. In this sense, the drug user who is full of narcotics cannot feel a "yen," nor can he feel it after he has been in prison a few months and the withdrawal symptoms subsequent to the removal of the drug have vanished. The desire for narcotics that persists after abstinence symptoms have vanished is not called a "yen" by addicts.[3] On the other hand, the term is actually applied to the withdrawal symptoms as such, whether they are understood or not by the individual experiencing them. Thus, it will be recalled that in Case 10 (Chapter 4) Mr. O., who was yawning and feeling bad, was asked if he had a "yen." This question was evidently asked, not because Mr. O. had verbally expressed any desire for narcotics, but because he yawned constantly and showed other physical symptoms of opiate withdrawal. The identification of withdrawal symptoms with the desire for narcotics is evident in the warning frequently given to those who

3. See Chapter 4.

experiment with the drug: "You'll put too many shots too close together sometime and wake up some morning with a yen." In other words, the "yen" or "desire," which is basic to addiction, is so inextricably bound up with withdrawal distress that the two are designated by the same term. I once jokingly remarked that I was talking so much about drug addiction, withdrawal, etc., that I was beginning to wonder about the possibilities of developing a "yen." The addict's reply was, "It can't be done by proxy."

As further evidence it may be mentioned that when a drug user declares that he "feels his habit," he means that the distress of withdrawal is being felt. On the other hand, the addict who has all the drug he wants does not "feel his habit." Another significant usage distinguishes between the "pleasure user," or "joy popper," and the addict. A "joy popper" is simply an individual who uses the drug intermittently and *who has never been "hooked."* It is probably true that most of the so-called pleasure users eventually become addicted, but as long as they space their shots so as to avoid withdrawal symptoms, they are sharply distinguished from those who have been "hooked" and they do not regard themselves as addicts. Those who use drugs irregularly, for example, once a week, are called "pleasure users," or they may be said to have "week-end" or "ice cream" habits. The distinction between the joy popper and the junkie is almost exactly paralleled by that between the "social drinker" and the alcoholic. Just as the alcoholic cannot again become a social drinker, the junkie cannot revert to the status of a joy popper. The addict's standard remark, "Once a junkie, always a junkie," possibly refers to this fact. An addict elaborated on this idea by remarking, "Any man who has ever been hooked who says he doesn't want to use morphine again is either a damn fool or a liar."

## Immunity to Morphine Effects

The wide range of differences commonly observed with respect to withdrawal effects suggests that certain individuals may use the drug with impunity, or at least without suffering much distress. It is well known that in certain rare cases the drug may

have other than the usual pleasant effects during the initial period
of use. In such cases, continued injection does not produce tolerance but simply results in progressively aggravated distress. Such
persons obviously cannot become addicted. Are there, on the other
hand, persons who obtain the usual pleasureable effects from opiates without experiencing the customary withdrawal symptoms?
In this connection, I was very interested in the report of an unusually reliable addict concerning a user who was ostensibly immune
to the withdrawal symptoms. Since no other pertinent information
is available on this case, it is reported with a frank acknowledg-
ment of its hearsay source.

*Case 12.* Mr. Y. was a rather heavy drinker who sometimes used
morphine in association with friends of his who were drug addicts.
According to the informant, who was a professional thief, Mr. Y.
used morphine regularly for at least two weeks and probably
longer. At the end of this time he stopped it abruptly, gave away
whatever morphine he had left, and went about his affairs. The
addicts with whom he had associated were dumfounded at his
casual attitude toward the drug and his ability to withstand addiction. He himself was astonished and discussed the situation with
his friends. With the exception of a pain in his back lasting only
a few hours, he noted nothing unusual after he stopped and had
neither an inclination to use the drug steadily nor a craving for
it. In fact, he considered the behavior of addicts with as great
surprise as they did his. Their constant conniving and sacrifices
to keep themselves supplied with the drug were absolutely unintelligible to him, and he told them so. In his entire association
with these men he never succeeded in acquiring an understanding of them nor did he become addicted. One occasion particularly impressed the informant. Setting out to attend the funeral
of a mutual friend who had died from an overdose of morphine,
the group stopped their automobile in front of the public library
to administer shots of morphine in the library washrooms. Mr. Y.
was amazed and remarked upon the utter absurdity of a group of
apparently sane individuals attending the funeral of a user who
died from the effects of morphine and finding it necessary to con-
sume the same poison before going to the funeral!

Since there was no way for me to communicate with Mr. Y., I questioned the informant closely. No motive for exaggeration or distortion of the facts was found.

## The First Shot

At first glance it may seem that those cases of addiction in which the results of the first injection were tremendously impressive and led at once to continuous use are apparent exceptions to the theory in that addiction may have preceded the experience of withdrawal symptoms. A very intelligent addict, asked to explain the drug habit, cited his own case to support his contention that the very first injection was decisive.[4]

*Case 13.* Mr. F. was wounded in World War I and, during his convalescence in an English hospital, was employed by the hospital authorities. He had hoped the work would be easy, because of his condition, but found instead that he had to spend fifteen to sixteen hours a day at it. Consequently, he became exhausted and, in an effort to overcome his chronic fatigue, drank whiskey in small quantities in company with other members of the staff. As he said, "For months I wasn't either entirely sober or entirely drunk." The drug supplies of the hospital were under his care, and one day he determined to try a little heroin to see if it would help overcome his chronic fatigue. He sniffed a little and found the effects marvelous. It not only enabled him to work long hours, but gave him energy for recreation and entertainment. He used the drug a little each day for two months.

At this point in his story he stopped, feeling that he had sufficiently explained the crucial importance of his first experience. Encouraged to go on, he continued his story.

After two months of using the drug regularly, he went on a short vacation without taking a supply, for it did not occur to him that there was any need for it. Gradually he became more and more affected by withdrawal distress. At first he was unable

4. See Chapter 2.

to diagnose his trouble, but eventually he realized what it was. The symptoms became so severe that he was forced to take the train back to the city where he worked in order to replenish his supply. It was then he realized, though in an incomplete way, that he was "hooked." After about six months he returned to Canada, using the voyage as an opportunity to quit his habit. He threw his supplies overboard. Persons on board attributed his withdrawal symptoms to seasickness. After surviving the abstinence distress, he was certain that he could stay off the drug, but he relapsed after about six months, stating that he was then convinced that "this thing was stronger than I was."

In spite of Mr. F's own theory, it should be noted that in his case, as in others, the drug was continued for reasons intimately associated with the very use of the drug itself and not because of the original drive. The fact that Mr. F. abandoned his source of supply without providing for future needs demonstrates that his attitude toward the drug did not at that time qualify him as an addict. What really impressed addiction upon him was his experience with the acute withdrawal distress during the sea voyage. Evidently during the first four months of use the withdrawal symptoms were an unconscious and unrecognized factor which favored the continuance of the drug, although Mr. F. himself thought that he used it solely to avoid fatigue and to increase efficiency. After his experience with withdrawal, however, these symptoms became conscious factors in his conduct.

Mr. F.'s account is representative of those instances in which the initial effects of the drug are so pleasurable and impressive to the beginner, that, provided he has no strong inhibitions against it, regular use is likely to be continued. In such instances one may say that there is a desire for the drug and even a habit of using it prior to addiction. This habit and desire, however, were obviously very different qualitatively from the subsequent addiction and the craving that it entailed. The fact that Mr. F. went on a vacation in England without thinking of taking a supply with him is sufficient evidence of this. Clearly also, while Mr. F. thought that he used heroin for the first two months because of its positive effects in reducing fatigue and stimulating him, it was not for such reasons that he resumed its use after he had tried to quit. It should also be remembered that, however marvelous the initial effects of morphine or heroin may seem during the beginning or honeymoon period of use, they are considerably less than marvelous when addiction is fully established. The determined effort made by Mr. F. to break his habit on his return to Canada suggests that he had discovered this.

In a discussion of cases of this sort in which the authors speak of a primary or pre-existing desire for euphoric drugs in what might be called addiction-prone personalities, Ernest Jöel and Fritz Fränkel remark:

> The unusual and complicating aspect of this second phenomenon is that the continued use of morphine with the gradual development of tolerance and the appearance of withdrawal distress upon the removal of the drug, leads to a morphine-hunger which has not the slightest connection with the original desire for euphoric drugs. . . . It is possible to make a drug addict out of anyone, regardless of his constitutional make-up.[5]

In the same connection, Kolb comments: "The original impulse [toward narcotics] may have subsided long ago, but this new craving grows stronger and is more difficult to throw off the longer the drug is used. Normal people, who never had an intoxication or narcotic impulse, are as much subject to it as the inebriate."[6] In another article, the same author asserts: "It thus happens that the drug taken in the beginning because of its power to raise an inferior individual above his normal level, must be taken in the end to keep him from sinking slowly below it and to relieve conditions that the drug itself has produced."[7]

## Self-Experimentation

A consideration of cases of self-experimentation by technical workers with advance theoretical knowledge of the habit presents interesting problems. If one assumes, for example, that a

5. Ernst Jöel and Fritz Fränkel, "Zur Verhütung und Behandlung der Giftsüchten," Klinische Wochenschrift (1925), 4: 1716.
6. Lawrence Kolb, "Types and Characteristics of Drug Addicts," Mental Hygiene (1925), 9: 307.
7. "Pleasure and Deterioration from Narcotic Addiction," Mental Hygiene (1925), 9: 700.

thorough-going acquaintance with the phenomenon of addiction confers upon the investigator the ability to control his reaction, it follows that opiates could be systematically used for relatively long periods without inducing addiction. Louis Faucher, as noted above, may be placed in such a category. He used the drug only once a day for six days and affirmed that knowing what to expect enabled him to take precautions to discontinue its use after that time. What would have happened had he extended the experiment for six weeks? Faucher declares that further use of the drug even a short time would have made him an addict. How may one account for the difference between this case and that of the patient mentioned by Dansauer and Rieth who received opiates steadily for six years without showing any desire for the drug?[8]

The implications of the theory advanced here with respect to such cases is quite clear. The deliberate self-experimenter, who knows what to expect, will note and understand the withdrawal distress sooner and more certainly than an ignorant layman, and he is, therefore, more susceptible to addiction under these conditions. Morphine addiction seems to be a case in which foreknowledge is a dangerous thing, in the sense, that, if the drug is administered regularly, this very knowledge aggravates susceptibility to addiction rather than providing immunity. In the light of this interpretation, it should, therefore, be expected that cases of habituation which did not lead to addiction would be relatively more numerous among non-medically trained individuals than among members of the medical profession.

This is precisely the situation found among German medical men; here addiction, defined by Pohlisch as the use of more than 1.5 grains of morphine or its equivalent per day for at least six months, was over 100 times more prevalent in the medical profession than in the general population.[9] The percentage of drug-using doctors estimated to be not addicted was only 6.6 per cent, in comparison with 48.9 per cent of the non-doctors.[10] Pohlisch's distinction between addiction and habituation, based solely on

8. Friedrich Dansauer and Adolph Rieth, "Ueber Morphinismus bei Kriegsbeshädigten," *Arbeit und Gesundheit: Schriftenreihe zum Reichsarbeitsblatt* (1931), p. 96, Case 58.

9. Kurt Pohlisch, Die Verbreitung des chronischen Opiatsmissbrauchs in Deutschland, *Monatschrift für Psychiatrie und Neurologie* (1931), 79 (1): 27.

10. *Ibid.*, Table 1.

the size of the dosage, is, of course, arbitrary and subject to error, as has already been indicated.

The literature on the subject records numerous instances of personal excursions into addiction by curious individuals who have been lured into smoking opium once or twice or trying a few injections of morphine. During part of the nineteenth century and earlier, when the drug habit was little understood and its dangers inadequately realized, such experiments were more common than they are today. Nevertheless, so far as I have been able to ascertain, not a single instance has come to light of a self-experiment, carried out beyond the several weeks' trial admittedly necessary to establish full-fledged withdrawal symptoms, which did not end in the addiction of the experimenter.

This is all the more significant in view of the frequent accounts of supposedly "cured" addicts, and the interest in "cures." One would suppose that a user demonstrating his immunity to the habit-forming tendencies of the drug would be widely advertised and pointed out as proof that persons with "strong will power" or a certain type of character might escape addiction despite steady and prolonged use. Apparently, such experiments have always ended in grief, for while it is easy to find accounts of addicts who began out of "curiosity" or a desire to experiment, accounts of individuals who have knowingly *experimented with severe withdrawal symptoms and escaped addiction* are entirely absent.

William Willcox describes a patient who believed that regular use of heroin or morphine would not be dangerous:

> This patient, who is a man of very strong will and brilliant attainments, took morphine some years ago in order to relieve the pain of sciatic neuralgia. He said, "I have a strong will, and there is no risk in my taking morphine, though others should not do so." He has been an addict for fifteen years.[11]

In another article, Willcox declares:

> It has been said with truth, I think, that the administration of morphine or heroin hypodermically daily for a month is likely to give rise to addiction in a person of normal temperament. We know

---

11. William H. Willcox, "The Prevention and Arrest of Drug Addiction," *British Journal of Inebriety* (1926–27), 24: 4–5.

people who say: "I am a man, and one having a strong will. Morphine or heroin will not affect me; I can take it as long as I like without becoming an addict." I have known people—sometimes medical men—who have made that boast, and without exception they have come to grief.[12]

Dr. J. B. Mattison records instances resulting from too frequent self-experimentation; commenting on the causes of the frequent addiction among medical men, he states: "Still another genetic factor, and in my opinion the one which outranks all others relative to the frequency of this disease in medical men, is their ignorance or unbelief as to the subtle, seductive, snareful power of morphia."[13] He adds that physicians do not usually use the drug for pleasure:

"Rather, they are impelled thereto by force of physical conditions that, with the largely prevailing failure to realize the risk incident to incautious morphia using, are practically beyond control. . . . The subtly ensnaring power of morphia is simply incredible to one who has not had personal observation or experience. . . . I make bold to say that the man does not live who, under certain conditions, can bear up against it. . . . Let him not be blinded by an underestimate of the poppy's power to ensnare. Let him not be deluded by an over-confidence in his own strength to resist, for along this line history has repeated itself with sorrowful frequency and, as my experience will well attest, on these two treacherous rocks hundreds of promising lives have gone awreck."[14]

12. "Medico-legal Aspects of Alcohol and Drug Addiction," *British Journal of Inebriety* (1933), 31: 132.
13. Jansen B. Mattison, "Morphinism in Medical Men," *Journal of the American Medical Association* (1894), 23: 187–88.
14. *Ibid.* Writers on drug addiction who experimented upon themselves through motives of "scientific curiosity" are Louis Faucher, *Contribution à l'étude du rêve morphinique et de la morphinomanie* (thesis, University of Montpellier, No. 8, 1910–11); F. S. Queré, *Contribution a l'étude comparée de l'opium et de l'alcool au point de vue physiologique et thérapeutique* (thesis, University of Bordeaux, 1883); H. Libermann as described in Roger Dupouy, *Les Opiomanes* (Paris: Alcan, 1912), p. 83. For authors who have commented upon the fatal results of experimentation and have cited cases, particularly of medical men, see Daniel Jouet, *Étude sur le morphinisme chronique* (thesis, University of Paris, 1883); Alonzo Calkins, *Opium and the Opium Appetite* (Philadelphia: J. B. Lippincott, 1871). "Curiosity" and "experimentation" are often cited as "causes" of addiction.

Thus, though the theory advanced in this study makes the reaction to withdrawal symptoms the decisive factor in the establishment of addiction, and although this theory could be destroyed by the self-experimentation of a single person, if he demonstrated his immunity, no such negative evidence has appeared in the literature of the last century. Those who have been bold or foolhardy enough knowingly to risk the prolonged experimental use of morphine on themselves apparently either have stopped before it was too late, as did Faucher, or have fallen into the ranks of the addicted. New recruits are being enlisted in this manner today. I have often been told by non-addicts with perfect assurance that *they* would never become addicts, even though they might take morphine or heroin regularly for a long time. Most addicts believed this before they became addicted.

Alexander Lambert, an outstanding authority on addiction, makes the following assertion:

> Morphine given daily for three weeks or longer, in small doses, almost invariably produces that peculiar narcotic necessity which we designate as the narcotic habit. Some patients may resist longer than others; but the average power of resistance is slight.[15]

Charles E. Sceleth, another well-known student of the subject, states that three weeks of regular use of opiates can form the habit in anyone, no matter how strong his will, and that three months will make it impossible to break the habit unaided.[16] C. C. Wholey likewise affirms:

> Unlike the poet, the morphinist may be made, not born such; there need be neither special neuropathologic constitution, nor hereditary taint. . . . The average individual can take alcohol in ordinary doses for long periods and still retain his independence; no individual can do this with morphine. It is not a rare occurrence for some alcoholic of some length of habit to take a brace and the pledge, and remain sober ever after. But after a corresponding period with morphine—a period much less in point of duration—it is

15. Quoted in Terry and Pellens, *op. cit.*, p. 149.
16. Charles E. Sceleth, "A Rational Treatment of the Morphine Habit," *Journal of the American Medical Association* (1916), 66: 862.

almost unheard of that an habitué is able voluntarily to break away from his habit.[17]

Similar statements, common in the literature, would seem to conflict with another well-established finding, namely, that many persons who receive narcotics regularly for long periods of time do not become addicts. These statements apparently imply that addiction is simply the invariable and necessary consequence of the development of tolerance, but the assumption is obviously implicit in them that tolerance and physiological dependence are accompanied by *awareness*. Otherwise they would be contradicted by an immense body of evidence which proves beyond question that the development of tolerance for morphine in medical practice is, in fact, rarely followed by addiction.[18] If it may be said that statements such as those quoted assume that the prolonged and regular use of morphine inevitably leads to addiction, when accompanied by the addict's full recognition and understanding of his dependence upon the drug, then they clearly accord with the theory that has been advanced.

## Marginal Cases

There are, of course, many instances reported of persons who have become mildly physically dependent upon opiates and who have experienced and understood the milder manifestations of withdrawal, as Faucher did, without continuing the use of the drug or perhaps continuing for only a brief period. Since the theory proposes that the constellation of behavior patterns and attitudes that constitute addiction are learned over a period of time from a substantial number of repetitions of the experience that generates these changes, it follows that one or a very small number of repetitions would not be expected to be sufficient to complete the process of establishing addiction. It appears, however, that a very few repetitions or even a single such experience does *start* the process. Persons who have had brief encounters

17. C. C. Wholey, "Morphinism in Some of Its Less Commonly Noted Aspects, *Journal of the American Medical Association* (1912), 58: 1855.
18. See Terry and Pellens, *op. cit.*, chapter 5, on this point.

with morphine withdrawal in medical practice, for example, develop attitudes toward the drug and toward addiction which are characteristically different from those of persons who have not had such experiences. Common effects of limited exposure to the addicting experience are that the individual loses some of his self-confidence about his capacity to resist the drug, that he becomes apprehensive about possibly becoming addicted, that he reports some degree of understanding of what it is like to be addicted, and that he exercises caution with respect to the regular consumption of a drug.

The above points have been clearly documented by a study,[19] made in Los Angeles by Robert Schasre, of young persons who used heroin for a time but stopped before the full pattern of addiction was established. In nine of the forty instances examined use of heroin had been discontinued, according to the individuals' own statements in interviews, because of fears and apprehensions associated with the fact that they had used heroin long enough to become physically dependent and had become somewhat aware of this. The author remarks:

All nine of these cases hastened to point out the fact that they had only had "little habits," they were not "strung out." They emphasized strongly the fact that they had only felt a "little sick." These people had used for at least six months, three of them had used for nine months to a year; all related that they had experienced fear as well as surprise at the realization they were "hooked."

In each of these cases the decision was made to "quit using before it got out of control." In none of these nine cases, apparently, was there immediately recourse to narcotics of any kind to ward off the relatively mild withdrawal distress which ensued. Six of the cases reported getting advice from personally known users or addicts to "quit now." Three of these admonitions had involved the same addicts who were present at the interviews. [All of these persons were interviewed with an addict present.] Interestingly, in three of the other interviews where the ex-users cited physical addiction as the reason for quitting heroin usage, rather heated exchanges were touched off between the non-user and the addict being interviewed.

19. Robert Schasre, "Cessation Patterns among Neophyte Heroin Users," *International Journal of the Addictions* (June, 1966), 1 (2): 23–32.

The addict interviewees in these three cases found it difficult to conceive of. In their opinion, "Once you get a habit—even a little one—
you've had it!"[20]

In medical practice the patient's comprehension of withdrawal
distress is frequently blurred by the tendency to confuse it with
the symptoms of the disease for which the drug is administered or
prescribed. The patient may complain vigorously to his physician
about pains which are in part those of withdrawal but neither he
nor his doctor may be able to distinguish those connected with
the disease from those connected with the drug. In this situation
of cognitive confusion the patient often only dimly realizes or
suspects that he may be physically dependent on the drug and
he may deny it utterly. There has been deplorably little systematic research on such marginal cases, but it appears that many
or most of them probably do not end in full fledged addiction—
a result which is again implied by the theory.

A representative of a drug company told me of a technique
used by his company to assist doctors in withdrawing drugs from
such marginal patients. It consisted of selling the doctor bottles
apparently containing capsules of a drug, with a certain variable
percentage of the capsules being placebos, that is, containing
none of the drug. Since the placebos could not be externally identified, neither the doctor nor his patient could be sure whether a
given administration was of a drug or of a placebo. The doctors,
without telling the patient, might, for example, begin the withdrawal process by administering injections from a container in
which 10 per cent of the capsules were placebos and progress to
others in which the placebos constituted 50 per cent or more.
At some point in this process the patient would have matters
explained to him and would discover to his surprise that he had
been getting along quite well and would usually be convinced
that he did not need the drug and could get along without it. My
informant stated that his company had received many grateful
letters from physicians concerning this device.

As has been noted, the realization of addiction is traumatic for
most persons, and it can readily be understood that it will be

20. *Ibid.*, pp. 27–28.

avoided or resisted when this is possible. In most of the previously cited instances of the origin of the habit, the situation of the user was relatively unambiguous and the correct cognitive conclusions concerning it could hardly be escaped. However, when opiates are used in medical practice to relieve pain, the patient sometimes faces an ambiguous situation in which it is possible for him, even though physically dependent on the drug, to cling to his former identity as a non-addict and to reject identification or self-definition as an addict. This may be accomplished by insisting that the drug is required for medical reasons to relieve pain associated with organic disease, in short, by self-identification as a medical patient rather than as a junkie.

F. B. Glaser, in a study at Lexington, compared 25 cases of this type with 30 ordinary addicts as controls. The findings indicated concerning those claiming the "medical patient" identity: (1) they had first used narcotics to relieve pain, obtained their supplies primarily from physicians, and had never obtained them from an illicit dealer; (2) none had ever used heroin or marihuana, none preferred the hypodermic method of injection, and it had not occurred to most of them; (3) all supported themselves by legal means, and none had ever been arrested for a narcotics offense or ever sold narcotics; and (4) they did not identify themselves with the addict subculture.

Despite the fact that these persons had come to or been sent to the Lexington hospital to have the drug withdrawn, Glaser observes:

> Our patients do not, by their acts, identify themselves as addicts. . . . The patient's frequent remark that 'I'm not like the other patients here' is borne out by the study. But clinical experience indicates that the pain-prone patients do not see themselves as persons with psychological problems either. In their view, their presence in a psychiatric hospital is purely fortuitous. The taking of narcotics was a medical necessity, sanctioned by the authority and wisdom of their physician, and had nothing whatever to do with any emotional difficulties.
>
> Thus, the patient is self-defined neither as a narcotic addict nor as a psychiatric patient. Rather, her identity is that of a medical patient. . . .

To attempt to challenge the patient's identity as a medical patient . . . is invariably to provoke the patient's bitter hostility, something most physicians prefer to avoid.[21]

Other marginal or ambiguous patterns of drug use which range from persons who have tried narcotics and pretend to be addicted when they in fact are not, to true or ordinary addiction, have been identified and described.[22] In all or most of such instances the marginality or ambiguity involved arises from the manner in which the patient interprets or perceives his behavior, the drug, and withdrawal distress. In some instances, it is possible that a physiological eccentricity may cause withdrawal distress to be absent or too slight to be of importance. In others, the marginality clearly seems to be related to the fact that the person does not experience the withdrawal symptoms often enough or in a sufficiently severe form. Medical techniques of withdrawing the drug from a physically dependent patient understandably include the attempt to manage the process in such a way as to minimize distress so that it does not intrude itself on the patient's attention. If such an attempt does not succeed the first time it is attempted, the difficulties increase in subsequent attempts and the probabilities of addiction increase. Repeated unsuccessful cures create an unfavorable prognosis because each of them repeats the conditioning experience with withdrawal distress that impresses the craving for the drug on the user.

### Habituation and Addiction during the Nineteenth Century

This point leads to the interesting problem of habituation so prevalent during the nineteenth century and the beginning of the twentieth when opiate-containing patent medicines abounded on the open market. Preparations such as laudanum, McMunn's Elixir of Opium, Godfrey's Cordial, Mother Bailey's Quieting Syrup, Winslow's Soothing Syrup, and Black Drop were widely

21. Frederick B. Glaser, "Narcotic Addiction in the Pain-Prone Female Patient. I. A Comparison with Addict Controls," *The International Journal of Addictions* (June, 1966), 1 (2): 57.

22. Norman E. Zinberg and David C. Lewis, "Narcotic Usage: A Spectrum of a Difficult Medical Problem," *New England Journal of Medicine* (May 7, 1964), 270: 989–93.

used. Also, in those days physicians gave opiates liberally, believing that morphine taken hypodermically was not habit forming.[23] As already observed, when heroin was first introduced at the beginning of the twentieth century it was widely hailed as a non-habit-forming substitute for morphine.[24]

In 1888, Virgil G. Eaton examined 10,000 prescriptions from Boston drugstores and found that 1,481 of them contained opiates.[25] Of the prescriptions renewed once, 23 per cent contained opiates; of those renewed twice, 61 per cent; and of those renewed three times, 78 per cent contained opiates. Raising the question as to what percentage of patients progressed to addiction through the initial consumption of opiate-containing medicines, Eaton says:

> It is hard to learn just what proportion of those who began by taking medicine containing opiates became addicted to the habit. I should say, from what I learned, that the number was fully 25 per cent—perhaps more. . . . When a person once becomes an opium slave, the habit usually holds for life.[26]

How and why does the change from opiate-containing medicines to morphine, or from innocent habituation to confirmed self-conscious addiction, take place? This transition should have occurred when the user who had become physiologically dependent upon the drug was told, or himself realized, the nature and significance of this dependence; namely, that it was created by withdrawal symptoms induced by consumption of that very same drug.

Fortunately, Eaton gives an excellent illustration of how the transition occurs in the story of an old woman who took opiate-containing "cough balsam" in order to "quiet her nerves."

> One apothecary told me of an old lady who formerly came to him as often as four times a week and purchased a 50 cent bottle of "cough balsam." . . . He told her one day that he had sold out of the

23. Terry and Pellens, *op. cit.*, p. 66.
24. *Ibid.*, chapter 2.
25. Virgil G. Eaton, "How the Opium Habit Is Acquired," *Popular Science Monthly* (1888), 33: 666.
26. *Ibid.*, pp. 665–66.

medicine required, and suggested a substitute which was a preparation containing about the same amount of morphine. On trial, the woman found the new mixture answered every purpose of the old. The druggist then told the woman she had acquired the morphine habit, and from that time on she was a constant morphine user.[27]

In 1881, D. W. Nolan observed:

The careless manner in which physicians prescribe opiates, and the prevailing custom among druggists of duplicating prescriptions, are prolific sources of the evil. The physician prescribes morphia for a patient suffering from some painful disease, and relief is obtained. Moreover, the sensations experienced under the influence of the medicine are peculiarly pleasurable. He goes back to the drug store and has the medicine renewed without the physician's advice or direction. He finally learns that it is morphia he has been taking, purchases a quantity, and finds that by its use he can relieve his pain or waft himself into Elysium at pleasure. Finally, he ascertains that his health is being injured, or is otherwise warned of the danger, and attempts to give up its use. Suddenly his eyes are opened to his folly and he realizes the startling fact that he is in the toils of a serpent as merciless as the boa-constrictor and as relentless as fate. With a firm determination to free himself he discontinues its use. Now his sufferings begin and steadily increase until they become unbearable. The tortures of Dives are his; but unlike the miser, he has only to stretch forth his hand to find oceans with which to satisfy his thirst. That human nature is not often equal to so extraordinary a self-denial affords little cause for astonishment. At length he surrenders, but with bad grace, determined to renew the contest at no distant day under more favorable circumstances; returns to the drug and is again happy—happier than ever in contrast with the misery lately endured—but far from satisfied. He realizes that he is being enslaved and suddenly resolves that it shall not be. Little he reckons that he is enslaved already, or that his late submission has shortened his chain a link. He waits for the favorable opportunity, meantime increasing the quantity imperceptibly but steadily, and, when the effort is repeated, finds himself more firmly bound than before. Again and again he essays release from a bondage so humiliating, but meets with failure only, and at last submits to his fate—a confirmed opium-eater. The effort made and the misery endured

27. *Ibid.*, p. 665.

before finally submitting can never be realized by the self-righteous man who arrogantly inquires: Why doesn't he stop it? Is it strange that opium-eating is styled by the people of the East the "Sorcery of Majoon" or that superstition attributed the power of the poppy to the influence of an evil spirit?[28]

Old accounts such as this indicate that, although the methods of consumption were oral rather than hypodermic and the manner of exposure was different than at present, the same essential steps were involved. The startled surprise of the beginner at his first experience of withdrawal distress and his realization of its significance are the same; so also is the struggle against the withdrawal symptoms which fixes the habit. The theory that addiction begins with perception of the significance of withdrawal symptoms, and the subsequent use of the drug to relieve or to forestall suffering, explains why some users of opiate-containing patent medicines became addicts and others did not. It also permits an acceptable explanation of the consequences of the Harrison Act. After passage of this and other restrictive laws, opiate users were eliminated from the legitimate market. Many who were habituated to laudanum and opiate-containing patent medicines undoubtedly discontinued their use, experienced varying degrees of discomfort, and were none the wiser. On the other hand, it is equally certain that some who had the misfortune to know the nature of their ailment continued to use the drug illegally.[29]

## Addiction in India

As would be expected, the basic features of drug addiction in India are the same as they are in the United States and in other countries of the world. Sociologists sometimes argue that generalizations about human behavior are necessarily culture-bound, that is, that they can be valid only in a given culture because of the

28. "The Opium Habit," *Catholic World* (September, 1881), 33: 829–30.
29. The significance of the knowledge of the name of the drug administered is brought out by the *British Medical Journal*, June 4, 1932 (1: 1044), commenting editorially upon the 25th annual report of branches of the Norwood Sanitarium, Ltd., which handled 580 drug cases: "In some instances the patient had only learned the nature of the drug used by seeing the label on an empty tube left at the house by the doctor."

enormous cultural differences that exist in the world. Admittedly and obviously, addiction in India differs in many respects from the contemporary American pattern just as the latter differs from that of nineteenth-century America. If a theory of addiction that applies to twentieth-century America cannot apply to India or to nineteenth-century America, then it seems evident that no genuinely general theory of addiction is possible. The assumption that is made here is the contrary one; namely, that while addiction, like malaria, manifests itself in a variety of superficially different forms in various parts of the world and at different times in the same part of the world, the basic processes that produce it are always the same the world over, as they are in the case of malaria.

Even a superficial reading of the available literature on addiction in other countries creates an overwhelming impression that this is the case. Everywhere, the addict shows the same characteristic craving for his drug, and everywhere he does what he must to obtain a supply of it. The power of the habit and the difficulties in breaking it are apparently much the same everywhere. The extensive publications of Chopra and his associates in India demonstrate that this is certainly true in that country. Chopra and Gremal tell of a "curious" case in which an individual regularly drank opiate-containing tea with a friend. When the friend left, this person became miserable even though he continued to drink tea.[30] Chopra and Gremal do not say how he discovered that the tea contained opiates, but this was evidently the case, for he became addicted. This report and others indicate that the role of withdrawal symptoms in causing addiction among Indian users is the same as in the United States.[31]

## Modern Medical Precautions

While there can be little question that physicians and druggists were to a great extent responsible for opiate addiction during the

30. R. N. Chopra and K. S. Gremal, "The Opium Habit in India," *Indian Journal of Medical Research* (1927), 15: 61.

31. See the work of Chopra and his associates: *Indian Journal of Medical Research*, vols. 15, 16, and 20, and in the *Indian Medical Gazette*, vols. 66, 68, 69, and 70.

nineteenth century, it is agreed that medical practice is responsible for only a few addicts developed today. What are the reasons for this change?

A report of the British Ministry of Health in 1926 furnishes a clue to the answer. It points out that, although psychoneurotics may experience greater initial pleasure from opiates than most normal persons, they can be saved from addiction if the proper precautions are taken in opiate administration.[32] The report emphasizes that when these precautions are not taken, anyone may become an addict. Therefore, two of its chief recommendations are: that the patient be kept in absolute ignorance of the drug being used and that the utilization of the hypodermic needle be avoided. Both precautions have been stressed for a long time, for it was soon appreciated that a patient who was ignorant of the dose, or who had been deceived about its true contents, could not become an addict. Pertinent is the statement of a physician in 1896:

The danger of physicians creating morphine fiends, it needs hardly be said, is greatly overestimated. Intelligently used, there is little danger of such results. With our highly neurotic temperaments we must, however, exercise more than usual tact, so as not to be deceived into its unnecessary use. It is the general and erroneous impression of the laity that all hypodermic injections are necessarily composed of morphia—it is the only drug that they can associate with them. When one has a patient wherein the protracted and regular hypodermic use of morphia may be required for a length of time, it would be well if an occasional hypodermic of strychnia were given, with particular care that some of the family, or the patient, should pick up *that* vial and read the label . . . It is a mistake to tell the patient that you are using morphia . . . Diminish the dose, or substitute something else with the dosage as you gradually diminish the morphia. Do not make a consultant of your patient in these matters.[33]

32. Ministry of Health of Great Britain, *Report of the Departmental Committee on Morphine and Heroin Addiction* (London: His Majesty's Stationery Office, 1926).

33. P. C. Remondino, "The Hypodermic Syringe and Our Morphine Habitués," *Medical Sentinel* (1896), 4: 5.

Dr. Paul Wolff, an eminent German student of addiction, comments appropriately:

> In my opinion a further great advance would be made if morphine, etc., were replaced as far as possible by the use of suppositories. Not only do these produce the same qualitative and quantitative effects, but also the patient is not immediately aware that he has received morphine. In many cases where medical treatment is the origin of addiction, numerous mental associations would be avoided in the absence of the symbol of the syringe.[34]

It can be seen that the "mental associations" referred to are connected with the patient's previous knowledge of stereotypes concerning drug addiction. When these associations are made he becomes attentive to certain effects and expects them. The same effects under different conditions might have elicited no response, but when understood they place him in the dangerous position of understanding the reasons for whatever distress he may experience when the drug is removed.

These two devices—avoiding the syringe and keeping the patient in ignorance—as well as other precautions such as mixing the opiate with less pleasant drugs, changing methods of administration, using sterile hypodermics, disguising the opiate in medicine, misinforming the patient, and gradually reducing the dosage when it is desirable to eliminate further use, all serve the same end. By preventing the patient from gaining a clear conception of the significance of his sensations and keeping him from associating what he knows or thinks he knows about drug addiction with his post-injection feelings, addiction is avoided. When a patient has been completely and successfully deceived and is completely in the dark concerning his withdrawal distress and the drug that produces it, he cannot, in the nature of the case, consciously desire opiates as a means of relief. What he ordinarily does instead of this is to attribute his discomfort to the disease from which he is suffering, or in some instances, to the after-effects of surgery.

34. Paul Wolff, "Alcohol and Drug Addiction in Germany," *British Journal of Inebriety* (1933), 31: 164.

## Experimental-Type Evidence

The methodological assumptions of the present study are those that form the logical foundations of the experimental method, and the theory proposed clearly suggests experimental operations, which, if they could be performed with human subjects, would directly verify or falsify it. This fact has been observed by experimental psychologists who have reformulated the theory in terms of positive and negative reinforcement and subjected it to experimental test with lower animals. I shall describe this experimentation in the following section and shall be concerned here with occurrences which, although they happen spontaneously without experimental intervention, are of precisely the same type and seem to carry the same weight as if they were actual experiments.

When the fundamental theoretical propositions of this study had been developed to an appropriate point, it occurred to me that it should be possible to find instances in which persons who had become physically dependent on opiates and escaped addiction had, in a later and separate episode again become physically dependent and also addicted. It was inferred in advance of the examination of any such instances that, after the second episode in which addiction was established, the person would retrospectively report that he had not recognized withdrawal distress during the first episode. Such instances seemed to provide the possibility of something very like a crucial test of the proposed theory. Since the same individual would be involved in both episodes, it would be logically unsound to attribute the addiction following the second to defects of personality structure which are often cited as explanations of addiction. It was also anticipated that any single instance of this type which clearly contradicted the deductive implications of the theory would carry sufficient weight to invalidate or cast serious doubt on the whole theory. However, this contingency did not arise, because all of the instances of this type which I was later able to find were in striking conformity with the deductive predictions implicit in the theory.

One instance of this type, Case 3 in Chapter 4, has already been described. It involved a physician who became physically dependent upon morphine during a serious illness that involved repeated surgery and a fairly long period of hospitalization. The drug was successfully withdrawn, and the doctor resumed his normal life for a period of several years. A subsequent attack of gallstones again led to the regular use of morphine, and this time resulted in addiction. During this second episode, this physician reported that he realized in retrospect that he had also suffered withdrawal symptoms during the first episode but without recognizing them. He had been hooked, he said, without knowing it. Four other instances of same kind were uncovered, three of them in the literature. The fourth was an addict whom I interviewed and whose story followed the pattern of the case of the doctor cited above.

Erwin Straus tells of a German woman who was given a morphine injection twice daily for six months (February–July, 1907) because of gallstones.[35] In July she was operated upon, and during her ensuing convalescence the drug was successfully removed. Nine years later, at the age of 49, she lost her only son in World War I and was prostrated by grief. After weeks of anguish and thoughts of suicide, she happened to recall that she had once benefited from morphine. She then purchased some in a drugstore and began to use it. In a short time she became addicted. When asked by the physician if she had experienced withdrawal symptoms in 1907, when the drug had been withdrawn, she replied *that she did not recall any.* I had not anticipated this particular response but I should have. It corroborates the theoretical position even more strikingly than the others by indicating that the memory of withdrawal distress, and of events in general, is strongly affected by the manner in which they are perceived and by the significance attached to them. The addict, for example, generally has a clear, even vivid recollection of his first experiences with the abstinence syndrome, which he realizes marks a dramatic turning point in his life.

Another instance of the same general type is briefly summarized by Dansauer and Rieth,[36] and another was found in docu-

35. "Zur Pathogenese des chronischen Morphinismus," *Monatschrift für Psychiatrie und Neurologie* (1920), 47: 90–97. The fact that the patient purchased the drug herself demonstrates that she was not ignorant of its name, and corroborates the view that although this knowledge is important, it is not the crux of the matter.

36. Dansauer and Rieth, *op. cit.,* case 115, p. 103.

ments collected by Dr. Bingham Dai which I was permitted to examine. While instances of this kind are understandably rare, the fact that all that could be found conformed closely to theoretical expectations gives considerable additional weight to the theory. There is, moreover, no other current theory that is applicable to such instances.

### Recent Experiments with Lower Animals

When I first published a fully developed account of my theoretical position on opiate addiction in 1947, very little experimental work of any direct relevance to the analysis and interpretation of human responses to opiates as manifested by the addict had been done with lower animals. I noted at that time in the process of defining the basic characteristics of addiction behavior that this behavior was not found in the lower animals and could not be induced in them because it presupposes the higher cortical functions associated with language behavior and found only in man. While this conclusion still seems generally valid, some qualification of it is now necessary in order to take account of subsequent experimental work with animal subjects.

The work of J. R. Nichols is of special relevance in this connection. He began his work by taking my theory as his point of departure and reformulating it in the terms of reinforcement theory and concepts as developed in B. F. Skinner's theories of operant conditioning. He then developed ingenious experimental techniques designed to test the idea that the hook in morphine, for animals as well as men, comes from using the drug to alleviate withdrawal distress rather than from positive euphoric effects.

In one of Nichols' experiments rats were first given morphine injections over a considerable period of time so as to establish physical dependence. Using some of these rats as his experimental group and the others as controls, Nichols then subjected the experimental group to "training sessions" which involved depriving them of morphine and all fluids for 24 hours. For the next 24 hours they were given nothing to drink but a bitter morphine solution which rats ordinarily dislike and reject. Since the rats during the second day of the training period were suffering both from thirst and from drug withdrawal, drinking the bitter morphine solution simultaneously relieved both the thirst and the withdrawal. After a number of repetitions of such training periods the morphine was withdrawn and, after 14 and 49 days when the withdrawal symptoms were largely gone, the rats were offered the alternatives of drinking either plain water or the morphine solution in any quantity. Nichols found that the rats that had learned to drink the morphine solution in connection with withdrawal now spontaneously drank much more of the bitter morphine solution and that some of them drank enough to reestablish physical dependence. The control animals, on the other hand, in this and other similar experiments, showed no similar interest in the drug, even though they had in some instances received much more of it than had the experimental animals.[37] The controls were not subjected to the two-day training periods but received the drug continuously.

While the control devices used by Nichols and others who have made similar experiments cannot be adequately described here, it is relevant to note that Nichols' conclusion that the attachment to morphine which he succeeded in inducing in rats (which he called "sustained opiate directed behavior") depended upon negative reinforcement involved in the relief of withdrawal distress and not upon the positive effects of the drug has been accepted and corroborated by a number of other investigators who have performed similar experiments on the same issue. Among the latter are Abraham Wikler, J. R. Weeks, and H. D. Beach.[38] Other aspects of Nichols' conclusions, such as those connected with his attempt to interpret his findings and the phenomena of addiction generally in terms of operant conditioning, are more dubious and debatable and will be considered in a subsequent chapter. While my statement of 1947 that relapse behavior

37. John R. Nichols, "How Opiates Change Behavior," *Scientific American* (February, 1965), 212: 80–88.

38. Abraham Wikler, "Conditioning Factors in Opiate Addiction and Relapse," in Daniel M. Wilner and Gene G. Kassebaum (Eds.), *Narcotics* (New York: McGraw-Hill, 1965), pp. 85–100; James R. Weeks, "Experimental Narcotic Addiction," *Scientific American* (March, 1964), 210: 46–52; H. D. Beach, "Morphine Addiction in Rats," and "Some Effects of Morphine on Habit Function," *Canadian Journal of Psychology* (1957), 11: 104–112, 193–98.

had never been induced in lower animals and probably could not be, has been shown to be incorrect, and while the gap between animal and human responses to opiates has been narrowed by experimental work of the type described, it still appears unwarranted to argue that the behavior of rats and monkeys in response to opiates in these experimental situations is essentially identical with the behavior of human addicts or that it is justifiable to call these animals addicts. A conclusion of this sort appears untenable both because it is inconsistent with existing knowledge of the differences between men and animals and also because the necessary point-by-point empirical comparison between the behavior of human addicts and their animal counterparts has not yet been made.

## Summary

In this chapter, the theory outlined in earlier chapters has been further elaborated and evidence that tests its consistency, validity, and applicability to the data of addiction behavior has been presented. It was noted that the theory is indirectly confirmed in the addict's argot and directly supported by evidence which indicates that persons who knowingly experiment with severe withdrawal distress invariably become addicts while those who experience it without understanding it do not. Persons who have only very brief encounters with this distress of withdrawal or whose understanding of it is incomplete or blurred, although they may not become addicted, manifest some of the initial changes in behavior and attitude which characterize the beginning of the fixation of the habit. The practice of preventing addiction in patients, even when they appear to be addiction-prone, by keeping them in ignorance of the drug and its effects, fits neatly into the proposed analytical scheme. Finally, the theory is directly and strikingly confirmed by the instances in which persons become physically dependent on the drug on one occasion without becoming addicted and subsequently become addicted. It is also confirmed somewhat indirectly by a considerable number of experiments with lower animals which suggest that whatever hook opiates have for animals is derived from the alleviation of withdrawal distress and not from the positive effects of the drug.

# 6

# CURE AND RELAPSE

In the preceding chapters the theory has been proposed and elaborated that addiction is generated in a specific type of experience with withdrawal distress. From this experience the beginner acquires the behavior, attitudes, and impulses that make him an addict and compel him to recognize himself as such. The tendency to relapse is obviously an integral aspect of addiction, for if it did not exist addiction would not constitute a social problem and breaking the habit would be a simple matter readily accomplished in a few weeks. Implied in the suggested explanatory scheme is the idea that this pervasive and persistent impulse to relapse is a consequence of the persistence of impulses, cognitive patterns, and attitudes originally learned from experiences with the withdrawal distress. Since addicts are tempted to resume the use of drugs long after all withdrawal symptoms have vanished, it is not suggested that relapse occurs because of these symptoms in any direct sense. The argument is rather that the craving for drugs originally established in connection with these symptoms becomes functionally independent of them and of any and all chemical or physiological properties of the drug and its effects. As an independent cortical function the behavioral tendencies designated as a craving for drugs persist in a modified form in the abstaining addict and predispose him to resume his habit.

The addict's impulse to relapse is qualitatively very different from his desire for the drug when he is physically dependent on it. In the latter situation the user's need is urgent, immediate, and continuous, since he knows that he is constantly threatened by withdrawal if he omits a regular injection. The impulse to relapse depends for its efficacy on more subtle long-range influences and is not urgent and immediate. The addict who is taken off drugs sometimes resumes his habit at the first opportunity, but frequently he does not. Under certain circumstances and provided he has adequate motives, he may deliberately postpone his relapse for weeks, months, and sometimes for years. An addict who was on parole when I began my interviews with him in the fall told me repeatedly during the winter that he intended to start using drugs again in the spring before his parole expired. He was living at the time in a kind of half-way house which afforded little privacy, and he did not relish the idea of traveling during the winter months. He planned when he resumed his habit to go to the southwest part of the country. Late in March he did just what he had planned to do and tried very hard to get himself a shot before he left town.

Another addict who served in the army in France during World War I said that he did not use morphine while he was there, even though it was readily procurable, because of the notorious lack of privacy of army life: "There were too many people around and not enough privacy." When he returned to the United States he at once resumed his habit.

The statistics of relapse are further indications that the relapse impulse is not an overpowering compulsion requiring instant gratification. It is more in the nature of a persistent, intermittent, but unrelenting and subtle pressure. Cocteau exclaimed, "The patience of the poppy! He who has smoked will smoke again. Opium can afford to wait."

Some idea of the nature of the relapse impulse may perhaps be obtained by considering the difficulties experienced by tobacco smokers in quitting a habit which is far less powerful than opiate addiction. Like the urge to take another shot of morphine, the urge of the abstaining cigarette smoker to have a cigarette is usually not constant or overwhelming and can be resisted. Nevertheless, over a period of time, it tends to win the battle. The opiate addict's craving and his tendency to relapse, it should be emphasized, are not rational impulses any more than are those of the cigarette smoker. The cigarette smoker does not smoke and does not resume smoking after a period of abstinence for the purpose of exposing himself to the risks of lung cancer and emphysema, although he knows this is the effect of what he does. Neither can he be said to weigh the risks against the satisfactions and to conclude logically that the risks constitute a fair price to pay. The same reasoning applies to the drug habit, for the addict does not relapse because he enjoys the prospects of again undergoing the ordeal of withdrawal. What he does is to give way to an irrational impulse or desire, permitting it to seduce him by means of a variety of stratagems which have the effect of neutralizing the negative import of withdrawal as well as the many other burdensome and unpleasant features of addiction.

An important feature of the mechanics of addiction is that the positive satisfactions involved in taking a shot are assured and immediate; in contrast, the negative effects of the habit are remote and indirect and can sometimes be avoided or postponed. It is a commonplace to observe that even a small immediate and certain gratification may counterbalance the effect of a dire but remote and contingent threat.

There are two separate and somewhat different theoretical problems involved in dealing with relapse. The first is to determine the source of the tendency; the second and more difficult problem is to try to describe the mechanisms which lead to relapse. The first of these theoretical problems has already been dealt with in preceding chapters; the second is the concern of this one.

It may be observed in passing that the linkage between withdrawal distress and the craving for drugs which prompts resumption of the habit is strongly suggested by a curious phenomenon that has been noted frequently in the literature. This is that addicts who have been off drugs for long periods of time frequently experience what may be called pseudo-withdrawal symptoms on occasions when they are strongly tempted to resume use. At a conference on drugs in California, for example, an addict in the audience approached me and said that in the course of the afternoon's programs he had been gripped by a powerful "yen" to have a shot of the drug that was being talked about so much. I asked him what he felt. He reported that he broke into a cold sweat and felt a peculiar sensation in the pit of his stomach. As he himself pointed out, these are also among the initial symptoms of withdrawal. This phenomenon seems to fit neatly with the idea that the relapse tendency is a residual aspect of the craving that is established in a conditioning process in which the withdrawal symptoms play an indispensable role. Having become functionally linked with each other in the initial conditioning process, each subsequently tends to elicit the other; withdrawal elicits desire, and desire withdrawal.

## The Desire To Be Cured

Certain paradoxical features of the opiate habit should be indicated here, and the reader's attention should be focused again upon the ambivalence of the user who not only bends all his efforts toward maintaining his supply but also hopes to be extricated from the trap into which he has fallen. The original effectiveness of the drug diminishes and eventually disappears with continued use, and at the same time its consumption must be constantly increased. Before long the user consumes large quantities merely to keep himself normal, and when this point is reached, as it usually is within a few months, the addict is trapped. As H. H. Kane said of opium smokers, "Then the good spirit of the pipe disappears, giving place to a demon who binds his victims hand and foot. Smoking no longer gives the pleasure of the first few months, and the victim of the habit continues not for the pleasure obtained from it, but is driven to it by the terrible suffering that surely comes if the pipe is not smoked at the accustomed time."[1] The drug user then sees the folly of the habit and, realizing the transitory character of its pleasures, he desires to escape. Sandoz said of drug users that "most of them realize their bondage and its consequences. If their lives were not all they should have been

1. H. H. Kane, *Opium Smoking in America and China* (New York: G. P. Putnam, 1882), p. 59.

before their addiction, they know now how much worse they have become since."[2]

This desire to be cured is best demonstrated by the large number of cures attempted by the chronic user. Charles Schultz[3] found that the average number of cures taken by each of the 318 addicts who came under his care was four. If one were to include those attempts to quit which were given up after a day or so, or after several hours, there is no question that this average number would have been much larger. I once asked an addict if drug users often tried to go off the drug and his reply was, "Every time they take a good jolt." The same idea was expressed by another user: "A junkie always quits on a full ounce. He never quits when he is out." Kane has described this tendency as follows:

> A very odd conceit obtains among many smokers. When you ask them, "Can you stop this?" they will answer with the instant assurance, especially if they have been smoking opium for an hour or two and are well primed with opium, "Stop it? Certainly. For instance, this will be my last smoke for a month." Nevertheless you will find him there smoking as usual the next day, and for many days thereafter. Some men will bid their companions good-night and good-bye night after night, sometimes for months, about as follows: "Well, boys, good-bye. I've had my last smoke with you. It has given me a world of pleasure and served to while away many a tedious hour, and I forgive it whatever it has done to me. I wish you joy. Goodbye." The next night he will be found smoking again as hard as ever, and at the finish go through the same performance.[4]

I have never met a chronic user addicted for several years or more who had not tried to free himself of the habit. Moreover, contrary to the frequently expressed notion that so-called criminal addicts do not desire to be cured,[5] I have encountered profes-

2. C. Edouard Sandoz, "Report on Morphinism to the Municipal Court of Boston," *Journal of Criminal Law and Criminology* (1922) 53: 38.
3. "Report of Committee on Drug Addiction to Commissioner of Correction, New York City," *American Journal of Psychiatry* (1930–31), 10: 471.
4. H. H. Kane, *op. cit.*, pp. 73–74.
5. Dr. Wilder D. Bancroft, for example, declares, "Nothing will keep a man from taking morphine again if he wishes to. . . . I doubt whether much can be done in the way of permanent cure for the criminal addict. I am interested in the man who really wants to be cured" (unpublished paper,

sional thieves who voluntarily abstained from opiates for as long as five to eight years in grim determination to throw off the habit. Recognition of the evil effects of addiction, however, bears little relationship to the probability of permanent cure. Otherwise there would be few addicts, for they are keenly aware of, and often bitterly resentful of, the stigma and misfortune attached to being a "dope fiend." Addicts relapse again and again after the drug has been removed at their earnest request. It is sometimes said, therefore, that the user's desire to be cured cannot be sincere and that he is motivated by ulterior purposes, such as reducing the size of his dosage, recreating the initial pleasure, obtaining admission to an institution during the cold winter months, avoiding the law, or complying with the demands of relatives. This skeptical view is discussed by Schultz:

> They do not think their habit is a vice, or that it degrades or injures them. To them it is a pleasure, which they see no reason for giving up, and as a result they are often amused at others' attempts to "reform" them.
> If a patient of this type openly declares he is going to revert to drugs (and many do) and boasts about it, enlarging upon the pleasures of his first shot upon discharge, others are apt to do likewise.
> This attitude is detrimental to the exercise of self-control and will power on the part of the more sincere patients, as sometimes they will ridicule such a patient's statements that he is going to try to stay off drugs; e.g., one patient declared on discharge that he was "through with drugs." Another patient then told him, "For God's sake, be a man. Get shot up!"[6]

While this account is correct, as far as it goes, it does not imply that the hardened addict has no desire to be rid of his habit. The addict who is least motivated to quit is probably the young user with a recently acquired habit. As the habit is continued there is

---

"The Chemical Treatment of Drug Addicts," presented at the fifth annual conference of the committees of the World Narcotics Defense Association and the International Narcotic Education Association, in New York, 1932). See also the writings of Lawrence Kolb. This invidious distinction between so-called criminal and noncriminal addicts simply discriminates against the impoverished addict. In this country, he is *ipso facto* a criminal.

6. "Report of the Committee on Drug Addiction to Commissioner of Correction, New York City," *op. cit.,* pp. 532–33.

increasing disenchantment. The long-term addict often more or less gives up the struggle after a series of attempts to quit have failed. Some of them reach a point of disillusionment and despair which leads them to consider or attempt suicide. Users who comment cynically on the impurity of the motives of others who take cures usually insist that their own efforts are sincere. What often happens is that the user begins to quit with sincere but inadequate motives and promptly changes his mind and postpones the attempt. In this respect, opiate addiction is not very different from a great many other bad habits.

While there may be some addicts who never fight the habit but simply accept it and allow themselves to be swept along by it, I have never met such a person. An apparent attitude of unconcern is frequently a pose, an adaptation to a hopeless situation. In group association with each other, addicts commonly assume an attitude of bravado and defiance, and they ridicule users who want to quit. Such association often creates shared misconceptions in the mind of each addict about the others. Each privately admits that he wishes he could quit and that he has tried to do so, but each assumes that the others accept their addiction and have no real desire to break it. The group attitude gives the individual user relief from the frustration, guilt and sense of helplessness that come from fighting a long, losing battle and provides supporting rationalizations for continuing the habit.

The hope of cure is not easily extinguished, even in the confirmed and experienced addict; he wants to die as a "square," not as a dope fiend, and he may permit himself to be deceived into believing that his next attempt will succeed. He tries once more and adds to his own disillusionment. If the addict's desire to be cured were not genuine and persistent, it would not have been commercially exploited for so many decades of the nineteenth century. The addict steadfastly maintains that he wants to quit and that he would if he could only feel right off the drug.[7]

7. T. D. Crothers states: "Not infrequently the question comes up as to the advisability of treating elderly morphinists and opium users who seem not to be greatly injured by the use of the drug. Often such persons who have long been addicted . . . become very anxious to break away from its influence. The prognosis is usually unfavorable and the treatment unsatisfactory" (*Morphinism and Narcomanias from Other Drugs* [Philadelphia: W. B. Saunders, 1902], p. 149).

The following case from my notes lists the major attempts of one addict to break his habit:

*Case 14.* Mr. T. became addicted to morphine in 1909 after using the drug occasionally for several years. He was a periodic drunkard and first took morphine to recover from inebriety. An only child, his parents, reasonably well-to-do, left him an adequate income. The following list of cures shows how often he attempted to get rid of his habit.

1. 1910: took a home cure without any real determination to quit. He spent $40 and reduced the dosage without getting off the drug.

2. 1912: took a cure lasting five weeks which cost him $175. The drug was completely removed for a time. He resumed using it immediately upon release.

3. 1916: took another home cure without serious intentions of quitting.

4. 1916: took a free cure lasting twelve weeks. He managed to get off the drug, but drank paregoric a number of times and relapsed at once when released.

5. 1917: took another free cure lasting six months. He resumed using the drug at once when released.

6. 1917: took a free cure in an asylum for three weeks. He was off the drug one week and drank paregoric the other two.

7. 1919: He was jailed for fifty days. This was his only involuntary cure. He resumed using the drug at once when released.

8. 1920: took a cure in private sanitarium at a cost of $200. He resumed use of the drug as before.

9. 1922: six months' free cure in a state asylum. He resumed use of the drug at once.

10. 1922: took the "Keeley cure" at a cost of $250. He relapsed at once.

11. 1925: cure lasting six months. Relapsed.

12. 1927: cure lasting three months. Relapsed.

13. 1930: cure lasting six months. Relapsed.

14. 1932: cure lasting three months. Relapsed.

15. 1933: six months' voluntary cure in the Chicago Bridewell. Relapsed.

16. 1934: quit voluntarily while living in the Chicago shelters

for unemployed men because of the extreme difficulty of begging sufficient money during the winter months. This was the first time in his life that he ever succeeded in quitting by himself, outside of an institution. He resumed using the drug as soon as warm weather began in the spring of 1935 and was killed by a speeding automobile.

This man was repeatedly interviewed for a period of several months prior to his death, and the cures are described as he recalled them. He said he was not quite sure he had included all.

It will be noted that this addict distinguished carefully between those cures he took with the serious intention of quitting and those he took for other reasons. He told the story with an air of shame and bewilderment. When asked to explain why he had taken so many cures, he was at a loss for an answer, except to remark that he had hoped each time to remain free. He confessed that his life had been ruined by the drug and all that remained for him was to wait for old age and death. In the meantime, he thought he might as well go on using the drug, since he no longer had anything to lose.

The addict's desire to be cured is readily understood as a consequence both of the social stigma attached to addiction and of the fact that the habit becomes a burden when the beginning euphoria vanishes and physical dependence is fully established. Prior to addiction, the addict generally shares the negative attitudes of the society toward junkies or dope fiends. When he himself becomes addicted he necessarily applies these attitudes to himself and his conduct. The realization that one has become an addict is not pleasant; it is a self-conception that is impressed upon the user when he is trapped by the drug. The desire to quit is so much an integral part of being addicted that it should perhaps be included in the definition of addiction.[8]

The addict's wish to be cured indicates his membership and

---

8. It is significant that Dansauer and Rieth cite this desire to quit as evidence that in a number of their cases of habituation the subject had begun to develop a "craving" for the drug, that is, was becoming an addict ("Ueber Morphinismus bei Kriegsbeshädigten," *Arbeit und Gesundheit: Schriftenreihe zum Reichsarbeitsblatt* (1931), 18: 92–93, case 28; p. 95, case 459; and pp. 96–97, case 616).

participation in the wider social order that condemns his behavior. When he is under the influence of the drug and is functioning normally, these collective ideals exercise their greatest influence, for he is then in relatively full contact with society and responsive to its demands. Moreover, with the drug in his body, he does not at the moment crave more of it and the social pressure which creates the desire to quit operates without opposition. As the effects of the drug wear off, persistent and increasing organic distress separates him from the wider social order. In this situation he changes his mind about quitting. Physical need eclipses all other considerations, as Jean Cocteau has graphically explained:

> Let me profit by insomnia to attempt the impossible: to describe the craving for opium. Byron said: "Love cannot survive seasickness." Like love, like seasickness, the need penetrates everywhere. Resistance is useless. First there is discomfort. Then things get worse. Imagine a silence which corresponds to the cries of thousands of children whose nurses have not come home to give them their milk. An amorous uneasiness translated into the physical world. An absence which reigns, a negative despotism. The phenomenon becomes more clear. Electric moire, champagne in the veins, frozen syphons, cramps, sweat at the roots of the hair, a sticky mouth, mucous, tears. Do not insist. Your courage is a pure waste of time. If you delay too long, you will not be able to take your material and stuff your pipe. Smoke.[9]

The desire to quit represents an integral aspect of the drug habit, for obviously a person who is merely habituated and unaware of his dependence upon the drug cannot wish to be cured.

### How Relapse Occurs

Addicts occasionally relapse deliberately, but more often they yield without meaning to; that is, they try "just one more shot," but plan not to take the drug often enough to get hooked again. This type of reversion is known as "playing around," and it is proverbial that an addict cannot "play around" without being

9. Jean Cocteau, *Opium: the Diary of an Addict,* translated by Ernest Boyd (New York: Longmans, Green, 1932), pp. 55–56.

caught eventually. Nevertheless, the user just released from prison or from a cure often decides to take a shot only now and then, for old times' sake. When he is told, "If you keep putting that thing in your arm, you know damn well you will get hooked," he may protest that while it is dangerous for other addicts with less will power to play around, he will not succumb. At that remark, "You laugh right in his kisser," one addict said, for "you know that in a week or so he will be right back on the drug."

The following incident illustrates the unintentional type of relapse:

*Case 15.* I was talking one day with Mr. K., who had just been released from the penitentiary on parole. He said that he was certainly not going to get hooked until he was off parole. Mr. K. was an intelligent person of a serious and inquiring frame of mind. Another addict, whom Mr. K. did not know, appeared and was introduced. The addict's first inquiry was whether Mr. K. was "hooked." He explained why he was not yet using the drug and said he would not use it until he was off parole in a few months. The other addict laughed and said, "I'll give you two weeks. By that time I bet you'll be hooked." Mr. K. protested and, after the other had gone, remarked on the tendency of persons to judge others by themselves.

I saw Mr. K. often during the next several weeks and each time suspected, from the appearance of his eyes, that he was under the influence of the drug. He did not deny it but said he had only taken a "little shot" now and then so that his addict associates would not regard him as peculiar and that he would certainly never permit himself to be a fool and get caught. After a number of repetitions of this incident, he finally said, "Well, I'm hooked again, and hooked good and strong." Then he elaborated on how "next time" he would not make the mistake of assuming that he could "play around" with impunity. He reproached himself for violating parole and began to talk about taking a cure somewhere and getting off the drug before he was caught and sent back to prison. He felt that there was no possibility of avoiding detection. He was caught and sent back to prison for parole violation.

A similar example is the case of a user who related that he had relapsed several times because of liquor.[10] He had taken to drinking during an abstinence period and finally, becoming disgusted with himself, decided to have a shot of morphine to try to get over his drinking. After obtaining the necessary dose from a doctor, he returned the next day for just one more, still believing that he wanted it only to relieve his hangover. After three or four injections, he realized that he wanted the injections for their own sake. Remarking, "Aw, hell, what's the use? I'm hooked now anyway," he bought a full supply and used it regularly. After several experiences of this kind, he stopped "kidding himself," as he put it, and said that he would never quit in the future unless forced to.

Another addict confided that the longest time he had ever voluntarily abstained was thirteen months. The first several weeks and months involved a struggle because of the debility and other after-effects of the habit. Later his condition improved, and he felt that he had freed himself entirely. He began to feel jubilant and triumphant. During the thirteenth month he took a shot to celebrate and demonstrate his mastery of the drug and was soon readdicted. It is notorious that the drug user's statements of his intentions are very poor indicators of what he is likely to do. This is perhaps because of the conflict between what reason tells him he ought to do and what the irrational compulsion of the habit impels him to do.

I once discussed relapse with Broadway Jones, the thief who helped Sutherland write *The Professional Thief.*[11] At the time of the conversation he had been off drugs for more than ten years. He denied that he felt tempted to use it again, even when he was with addicted friends who were using it in his presence. He was engaged in legitimate employment at the time and to the outside observer would surely have seemed to be a prize example of a permanently cured addict. I wrote of him at that time as follows in the original edition of this book:

> A casual observer might conclude that this was a case in which twenty-five years of addiction in connection with a "life of crime"

10. This is a fairly frequent cause of relapse. After he has been drunk for a while, the addict usually decides that "it's better to be a junkie than a drunkard," or he decides to have a shot to "get straightened out."

11. Chicago: University of Chicago Press, 1937.

had left few traces; in other words, one might ask if this man were not a cured addict. In reply, it may be pointed out that he refers to himself as an "ex-user," not a "square John," or non-addict, and looks upon himself as "one of the boys." Two other aspects of his behavior indicate that there is justification for this definition. One is his belief that morphine is a marvelous cure for most of the afflictions of mankind. Secondly, he frequently sees friends who are addicts and talks with them about narcotics and associated subjects. I do not maintain that this man must of necessity revert to the habit, but only that certain conditions distinguish him from the non-addict and function as predisposing factors toward relapse. The factor of association *per se* cannot be regarded as the crucial condition in his case because he is and has constantly been in close association with drug users for more than ten years without relapsing.

Some years later, after close to eighteen years of abstinence, he wrote to Professor Sutherland at Indiana University to ask for money. Surmising that he was readdicted, Sutherland, without sending any money, advised him to commit himself to Lexington for a cure. The next letter from Jones was mailed from the hospital for addicts in Lexington, Kentucky, where he was successfully withdrawn from the drug. He did not relapse again.

## Attitudes That Facilitate Relapse

An individual suffering from a chronic illness notes chiefly, if not solely, the alleviation of pain which the drug brings, and therefore uses it for that purpose. On the other hand, the addict soon learns that, no matter what his difficulty, it is aggravated by his need for the drug and at the same time is relieved by its use. The contrast between the misery caused by the absence of the drug and the well-being which follows the injection gives the user an exaggerated notion of the effects of the shot. He begins by taking the drug for a limited purpose and finds that its usefulness constantly increases. Besides relieving withdrawal distress, the addict quickly learns that morphine also relieves almost all other kinds of distress. If he has a job, he says he cannot work well without it; if he feels anxious, ill, or uncomfortable, he feels that he needs more of it. When he has to appear in court he takes an extra quantity to bolster his morale. The significance of the drug is, in short, generalized as a symbol and guarantee of security, not only against withdrawal but against most of the disturbing and unpleasant aspects of life. By the same token, the significance of withdrawal distress is also expanded so that the addict eventually responds to many or most of the troubles that beset him *as if* they were withdrawal distress to be remedied by another fix.

The addict's exalted notion of the virtues of opiates is suggested by the fact that they sometimes refer to it as "G. O. M." or "God's Own Medicine." However, since I have also heard members of the medical profession use the same expression with regard to morphine, which is still evidently the best known analgesic, it may be argued that there is at least some truth in the addict's view of the efficacy of opiates.

The addict may, of course, realize that his personal difficulties are not associated with withdrawal distress. Thus an addict, earning $90 a month on a WPA project, bought an ounce of heroin and remarked to me that it would last him about a month. He actually consumed it in half the time. Part of his explanation was that he had a foot complaint and simply had to use more. Other users to whom I mentioned the incident accepted this as a perfectly legitimate and satisfactory explanation. The point is even more directly illustrated by the user who made hypodermic injections into a painful knee in order to alleviate the discomfort. Virtually every addict I interviewed had high regard for opiates as a curative or ameliorative agent. The more intelligent insisted that the potency of opiates was a fact and not a figment of the imagination. On one occasion in conversation with an intelligent addict, I ridiculed the unfounded belief that morphine is good for anything. The addict joined in the laughter, agreeing that the drug was so regarded, then added seriously, "But, you know, morphine *is* good for anything."

When the addict is taken off drugs, he does not lose his belief in their efficacy, nor does he cease to respond to discomfort and distress as though it were withdrawal distress calling for a shot. Untoward or unpleasant experiences of almost any sort therefore constantly remind the abstainer of the potency of the drug and subtly impel him to take it again. The addict's tendency to interpret all discomfort as withdrawal distress is strengthened by the fact that the initial manifestations of withdrawal, such as nervousness, irritability, depression, and lethargy, cannot be distinguished out of context from the same feelings when they are not connected with the drug or when they occur in a non-addict. Not only does the addict use drugs to alleviate withdrawal and virtually all other ordinary forms of distress but he may also use them to alleviate discomforts which the habit itself produces, such as those connected with chronic constipation or with excessive dosage.

From considerations of this sort it is easy to understand that the abstaining addict often appears to be a hypochondriac, complaining of a variety of illnesses, pains, and discomforts which he argues did not bother him when he was on the drug because he could banish them at once with a shot. Having reached this point, the abstaining addict may rationalize his relapse by saying that he really does not crave the drug but that he hates to go on suffering unnecessarily from a host of complaints. He may contend that his condition is so bad that he is unable to work unless he resumes use of the drug. This frame of mind is illustrated by an addicted woman who wished to send an expensive Christmas present to her child, who was being cared for by others. Her dilemma was that she would be unable to work unless she were on drugs, but that if she were on drugs she would be unable to save any money.

Much relapse is, of course, directly produced by the withdrawal symptoms themselves. When an active addict is locked up in jail for a day or two or even for a couple of weeks and then released, he is still often in a weakened condition or still undergoing withdrawal. Severe and abrupt withdrawal is sometimes advocated on the grounds that it will serve as a deterrent to relapse but the actual effect may well be the opposite. A prolonged, gradual withdrawal, on the other hand, although it is more humane and less dangerous than the cold turkey method, prolongs suspense and anxiety and probably enhances the addict's feeling that he needs the drug. Schultz has commented on this point:

> There is no feeling of sudden relief from intense suffering as in the abrupt withdrawal treatment; on the contrary they feel that an injustice is being done them when they are taken "off shots" as opposed to the feeling or relief and gratitude when taken off with the abrupt treatment. They resent being taken off treatment and

psychologically this suspicious, resentful frame of mind and the sug-
gestion which is impressed upon them by each injection that the
narcotics are essential to relieve their symptoms, is not one conducive to the patient's abstaining from narcotics when discharged.[12]

"Cured" addicts often relapse when they are in the best of
health, much better than they were when using the drug. I have
been told by addicts discharged from Leavenworth that poverty-
stricken addicts enter prison in an extremely emaciated and
starved condition, as a result of the bitter financial struggle to
maintain their habits. In fact, some are so bony that they find
it difficult to make injections into their shrunken veins. Under the
regular prison routine, they put on weight and gradually achieve
sound, normal health. Often one of these ex-addicts will rub the
veins of his well-rounded arm and exclaim with satisfaction, "Boy,
will I be able to hit that when I get out!"

Another influence that lures the cured addict back to his drug
may be called a cognitive factor. It consists of the knowledge the
addict acquires about the effects of opiates from his personal experiences. When he is on drugs he knows that he can regulate
how he feels at will. From direct experience he knows what the
drug can do. It is useless for the non-addict to argue with the
user about such matters of direct experience, since the addict has
had the experiences and the non-addict has not. The addict's
"knowledge" is sometimes merely an erroneous belief or a rationalization, but if it appears as knowledge to him it tends to function as if it were. Such knowledge contributes to relapse, and
since people cannot be cured of the knowledge they have, this
intellectual or cognitive element is probably close to the heart of
whatever there is in addiction that is permanent and incurable.

A nineteenth-century addict, S. T. Morton, who had not used
opiates for two years wrote the following:

There is one thing which the habitué wishing to be cured would
perhaps anticipate with dread: that is an insatiable craving for the
old stimulant, and a consequent prolonged and weary resistance of
temptation. I can only say that, greatly to my surprise, I have felt

12. Charles Schultz in "Report of Committee on Drug Addiction to Commissioner of Correction, New York City," *American Journal of Psychiatry*
(1930–31), 10: 519.

no craving for it at any time since the beginning of the treatment. This may seem a strange statement to any one under the sorcery of the drug, and conscious of its fearful grip. There is of course the knowledge from experience of the marvelous potency of opium in annulling all discomfort and distress of body or mind, but this is all. The sense of profound satisfaction, ever present at the release from its slavery, as well as a lively appreciation of the great danger of again tampering with it, is sufficient to leave the temptation—whatever it may be—from such knowledge, powerless.[13]

This remarkable statement brings out clearly one of the common experiences of addicts prior to relapse. They seem to have no desire whatever for the drug. Yet the impulse to relapse in the above case was present, but in a different form, as revealed in the words, "knowledge from experience of the marvelous potency of opium in annulling all discomfort and distress of body or mind." The anonymous author underestimates the significance of this factor, for, when the "sense of profound satisfaction" at having quit has worn off, this knowledge is still present, subtly attracting the user to his favorite drug. Given a certain situation, certain misfortunes, or a certain mood, and the ex-user may decide to throw caution to the winds and have "just one pop."

For those who are disposed to regard the praise bestowed on opiates by this anonymous addict as sheer exaggeration, a reminder of the traditional view of medicine may be pertinent. Alonzo Calkins has this to say:

Opium has been denominated, and in no extravagance of hyperbole, the grand catholicon for human ills. Laudation here has scarcely been exhausted, even in the excess. In the "Opiologia" of Wedelius, opium is the "medicamentum coelitus demissum,"—the heaven-born gift. Tillingius styles it the "anchora salutis sacra,"— the bower-anchor of health. Sydenham says that "medicine without it would go at a limping gait"; and John Hunter, in an exuberance of enthusiasm, exclaims, "Thank God for opium!" Van Swieten in his estimate does not fall behind: "Opium le plus efficace de tous les medicaments et sans quoi l'art de guérir cesserait d'exister, est le remède de quoi le Tout-Puissant a fait présent pour le bonheur et la consolation de l'humanité souffrante."[14]

13. "An Experience with Opium," Popular Science Monthly (1885), 27: 339.
14. Alonzo Calkins, Opium and the Opium Appetite (Philadelphia: J. B. Lippincott, 1871), pp. 135–36.

## Boredom and Disgust in the Cured Addict

One addict whom I interviewed a number of times was imprisoned for a few weeks in the Chicago Bridewell Prison on a charge of theft. When he came out, he returned to precisely the same locality in which he had been living. I expected him to relapse at once and was amazed that he did not do so. A number of weeks passed. He denied that he felt any great temptation or craving but admitted that he did not intend to practice abstinence permanently. His state of mind when off the drug appeared markedly worse than during addiction. He was inordinately bored and extremely inert, spending most of his time sleeping. He was no longer interested in reading magazines, and his conversation was unanimated and dull in comparison to the sparkle which had characterized it before. Later he obtained a temporary job distributing hand bills and, becoming fatigued by the walking he had to do, felt the need of a shot after work. Sometime later, when he had developed minor, though irritating, complaints, he took nembutal hypodermically. Seeing the fresh drops of blood on his bed, I had assumed that he was re-addicted. It was a week or so before he admitted having had a few little shots, and still another week before he announced that he was "hooked" again. He now resumed his alert, active attitude; his indifference, apathy, and dullness were gone. He had found a motive for living and was himself again, conniving and stealing as before.

It cannot be assumed in the case of this addict, who abstained for only a few weeks, that he had recovered from the withdrawal of the drug. Erich David, for example, remarks concerning the time element in the treatment of addiction:

> As we have seen, after six weeks the patient is generally physically well, but he still feels the lack of stimulation furnished him thus far by morphine. The days seem endless, but he has not yet the energy to busy himself with work. He has not yet regained completely the capacity and desire for work, and just because of that, he will inevitably be seduced to a relapse by the recollection of his former greater capacity and the oppression of his complete lack of energy. That he is not yet mentally fully recovered, we can easily prove by giving him some easy scientific book to read and asking him to give a report

on it after a few days. The patient will not yet be capable of doing that. If it is at all possible for him to read the book through intelligently, it will take him weeks and weeks to finish his task.

This lack of stimulation, however, passes after several months, and I am willing to say that after four or five months every withdrawn individual has completely recovered capacity and desire for work. If then assigned the task just mentioned, he will perform it very quickly with utmost satisfaction. This test seems to me the most infallible indication as to whether the time for discharging him has arrived. To retain him any longer in an institution, just because it is true that physical alterations with reference to morphine still exist, would be absolutely senseless, since we have seen that the same phenomena are present even after a year. The prognosis is unfortunately very inauspicious.[15]

An addict who read this manuscript expressed the opinion that it was the boredom of abstinence that was hardest to endure. He told of going to baseball games, in which he was normally very interested, and leaving after a few innings. He walked out of movies before they were finished. He could not enjoy life without the drug, so he eventually resumed using it. Another user, who had once abstained for more than ten years, confessed that he had never felt altogether right throughout the period. He used alcohol as a poor substitute for opiates and finally returned to the drug in disgust.

The word "disgust" is one that recurs in the addict's explanations both of why he decides to quit and of why he relapses. When he is on drugs he becomes disgusted with himself, the habit, other users, informers, the police, the public, and so on; when he is voluntarily off drugs he discovers that people are slow to accept him in his new role as an abstainer. This tends to disgust him, as do a great many other aspects of his tentative new identity as a cured addict. These include boredom, lack of motivation, the suspicious attitudes of others, job discrimination, the effects of whiskey and other inferior substitutes for the drug, and lack of communication with former friends.

15. Quoted by Charles E. Terry and Mildred Pellens, *The Opium Problem* (New York: Committee on Drug Addictions and Bureau of Social Hygiene, 1928), p. 594. David's conclusion concerning the length of time necessary for all traces of withdrawal distress to disappear are substantially the same as those reached by researchers at the Public Health Service Hospital in Lexington, Kentucky.

In a study of relapse and abstinence, Marsh B. Ray quotes an addict's description of how he resumed use:

> When I got home I stayed off for two months but my mother was hollering at me all the time and there was this one family in the neighborhood that was always "chopping me up." I wanted to tell this woman off because she talked all right to my face but behind my back she said things like she was afraid I would turn her son on because I was hanging around with him. She would tell these things to my mother. I never turned anybody on! She didn't know that but I wanted to tell her. Finally, I just got disgusted because nobody wanted to believe me and I went back on.[16]
>
> [Another user commented pungently]: My relatives were always saying things to me like 'Have you really quit using that drug now?' and things like that. And I knew that they were doing a lot of talking behind my back because when I came around they would stop talking but I overheard them. It used to burn my ass.[17]

The boredom and disgust of the abstainer may be said to spring from the inability of the ex-user to resume his pre-addiction social identity and role. His experiences as an addict have spoiled his other identity and set up communication blocks between him and those from whom he hopes for support and confirmation of his new role. He recalls, perhaps with some nostalgia, the feverish whirl of activity and excitement that engulfed him when he was on drugs, and he recalls the intimate associations with other addicts and the frank, unfettered talk, especially about everything connected with drugs. By contrast, his life off drugs seems empty and dull, and his personal associations seem unsatisfactory, inhibited, and hypocritical. There is no good easy resolution of this dilemma. The addict is not happy with either of his two possible identities and tends to move from one to the other and back again.

## The Influence of Availability and Associations

Because the addict is generally stigmatized and is often a criminal, he finds it difficult to secure and hold a legitimate job whether

16. Marsh B. Ray, "The Cycle of Abstinence and Relapse among Heroin Addicts," in Howard Becker (Ed.), *The Other Side: Perspectives on Deviance* (New York: Free Press, 1964), p. 172.
17. *Ibid.*, p. 173.

he is using drugs or not. If, as in the United States, the user leaves respectable society to join the addict subculture, his associations tend to be heavily or exclusively concentrated within it. It is within this subculture—which includes addicts, drug peddlers, narcotics policemen and informers—that the user learns the folk-lore of addiction. It is this subculture that makes the drug available to him. His closest associations are naturally with other users with whom he shares his preoccupation with drugs. Most of his activity and most of his conversations center on the drug habit, which is the organizational basis of the subculture.

When an addict who is part of such a subculture attempts to quit his habit voluntarily, or when he is sent to jail or prison, any attempt that he may make to remain free of the drug is obviously jeopardized if he returns to his old environment and old associates. This, however, is usually what he does because he has no other friends and no other place that he wants to go. Returning to his old haunts, he has no difficulty in finding a supply, and in the process of resuming old associations he strongly tends also to resume his habit. If he has been in prison it is probable that his range of acquaintanceship with addicts, peddlers, and criminals has been broadened, and the probability of his encountering prison acquaintances is increased. Such encounters tempt him to relapse, make the drug available to him, and provide opportunities to make money by illegal means to support his habit.

It is a mistake, however, to think of relapse exclusively in terms of the external cultural environment. Both the impulse to quit and the impulse to relapse first manifest themselves in the private thoughts of the addict, and both impulses may be translated into action without any direct influence or pressure from others. Thus, an addict whom I interviewed, a former physician, became addicted through medical treatment and for several years was unacquainted with any other addict. During this period he made five attempts to quit and remained free for a year on one occasion. Such instances are fairly common among addicts within the medical profession where the availability of the drug makes it quite possible for a person to use it or stop using it in secrecy and privacy.

The abstainer who wants to relapse often goes out of his way to seek the environment favorable for this project, just as the determined abstainer may deliberately move out of such an environment. This point is illustrated by an addict who was discharged from prison in the spring of 1937 and went to Chicago with more than a hundred dollars in his pocket. Fearing re-addiction and yet desiring just one shot, he walked the streets for about two weeks looking for some old friend who might help him make the necessary contact. Frustrated on every side, he finally met another addict just released from the same penitentiary. The latter reported the meeting in these words: "He just fell on my neck and asked me for a shot of anything. He said he was sick of booze and blondes  and just wanted a shot." From cases such as these it is evident that relapse cannot be explained in terms of the external situation.

## An Addict's Rationalizations

The following account of his own experiences by a nineteenth-century American drug user is particularly interesting and significant because of the manner in which it exemplifies the addict's rationalization of his addiction and of his relapses, presented in this case with amazing naiveté but with obvious sincerity.

Finding then, that a grain of morphine was just the quantity required in my case, I took that amount every day in the evening, while the neuralgia continued, which was for three or four weeks; when this disease left me. Being now free from pain, I ceased taking morphine, as the necessity for it had ceased. This was my first experience with morphine; would to God it had been my last! And this experience was pleasant, leaving no sting behind. Is it then to be wondered at, that upon my next attack of my hereditary enemy, and in all subsequent attacks, I employed a remedy which had worked so well before, in fact the only remedy I knew for this painful affliction. . . .

But there came a time when matters took a different turn, when my relations with morphine were not of so friendly a nature, and when my reflections became of a more somber hue. . . . [He tells of becoming ill.] Before I had fully recovered from the effects of the fever, the neuralgia set in, in the chronic form; and I was never free from pain a single day for four months, except when under the influence of morphine. In the meantime I had become an inmate of a water-cure, but had not as yet received any benefit from the treatment. At the end of four months the neuralgia suddenly ceased, and I immediately laid aside the morphine, as I had done always before on the subsidence of the pain. Although I had been using the drug in moderation, never exceeding a grain to a grain and a half daily, yet having taken it continuously for four months, I found a difficulty in thus suddenly leaving it off which I had never experienced before. I felt as weak as a child, and as though I was falling to pieces. All the secretions of my system, which under the influence of morphine had been locked up, were now poured forth abundantly. Perspiration was profuse. Yet it was a cold and clammy sweat, and I was compelled to go to bed and cover up with blankets in order to keep warm in the middle of a July day. I had a gnawing sensation in my stomach which demanded for its satisfaction mustard, pepper, and other hot and stimulating condiments. And for eight days and nights I never closed an eye in sleep. But in a little over a week the system had fully reacted, and I began to feel pretty comfortable. I had not yet become a confirmed opium-eater, but I had made a narrow escape. I had been standing on dangerous ground. . . . The neuralgia returned before I had been free from it a month. Being still at the water-cure, I brought to my aid all the resources of hydropathy. I tried cold baths and warm baths, and a most rigid diet, all to no purpose; and after suffering as none but a neuralgic invalid can suffer, I again resorted to the old remedy, and the only remedy for this protean malady. It may be that I resumed the use of the drug without proper reflection; but when does a man in severe and agonizing pain ever reflect? Although I suffered, suffered severely, when last I abandoned the use of morphine, still I did not suffer as much from that cause as I was now suffering from neuralgic pain. I thought I was choosing the lesser of two evils. . . .

I now struggled both against the disease and against the remedy. I tried hard not to become an opium-eater. I tried hard to sever the links of the chain rapidly forging about me, links which were every day becoming more adamantine. And at one time, and that within four months of the date of my last resumption, taking advantage of a temporary cessation of pain, I almost succeeded. Yet I did not succeed. After this period my pains increased, calling for increased doses of morphine.

I had now become a conformed opium-eater. I had been taking morphine every day continuously for several months.[18]

18. James C. Layard, "Morphine," *Atlantic Monthly* (1874), 33: 698–99.

He then goes on to describe his relapses after temporary abstinence:

My health had now become pretty well established. But it was for a brief period indeed. About the beginning of July of this year symptoms of my old malady began to make themselves felt. I took every precaution to ward off the attack. I tried all the resources of allopathy, homeopathy, and hydropathy, together with a most rigid regimen; for above all things I did not wish again to become an opium-eater. But what was to be done? Although my condition before when taking morphine habitually was a truly deplorable one, still it was more tolerable than my condition was now, without it. While using it moderately I could give some attention to business; I had still some enjoyment to life, especially intellectual pursuits, for it seemed to stimulate the intellectual faculties to increased activity. And barring all considerations of this kind, I was free from pain while under its influence. Now I was wholly incapacitated for business of any kind, and enjoyment was out of the question. I had no pleasure in existence, life was a burden. I fought the enemy long and desperately; I fought him with the energy of despair, until, overcome with suffering, I finally succumbed. Then I took morphine for a single day, making a truce with the enemy, as it were, for that short period, only to renew the battle the day following. Then on the third day I took morphine again. In this way I kept the enemy at bay for several weeks, making it a rule never to take morphine two days in succession, thus giving the system time fully to recover from the effects of one dose before taking another. I thought that in this way I incurred less danger of falling back again into my old habits. But the time came when this rule could no longer be observed, and I took morphine every day, but once a day for a while, and, by the time winter had set in, twice a day, or oftener, as required. Thus in about a year from the time I had gone through the tremendous crisis described a little further back, I was again in the gall of bitterness. Indeed, I had come to that condition in which I cared but little whether I lived or died. I had become, in short, perfectly reckless of consequences. . . .

[Relapse No. 2] It was about six weeks since I had taken the last morphine. My health in the meantime had not improved to that degree which I thought I had a right to expect. I was free from neuralgic pain it was true, but I was still nervous and irritable, and exceedingly uncomfortable in every way. That cold and clammy perspiration still continued. It seemed to be more profuse than it had been three weeks before. Other symptoms there were too, which along with this, indicated a state of great relaxation of the general system. I saw that tonic remedies were called for, and I took quinine, but without any effect whatever. Mine is one of those constitutions upon which quinine never seems to have any effect. At length the time came when I must go to work, though in no fit condition for it. Shorthand reporting is a pursuit requiring in those who practice it the best condition of physical and mental capacity. The mental faculties which it calls into action are put to the utmost stretch, and the physical health must be such as to give them adequate support. However, the attempt must be made, and I made it. I very soon found that without assistance from some quarter I could not succeed. What was to be done now? I ventured to take a grain of morphine. The effect was marvelous. I could report, now, verbatim, never losing a word. And I could do any amount of labor at transcribing, the drudgery of the stenographer. I now liked to work, the harder and the more of it the better. The morphine had such a bracing tonic effect! . . . I found myself necessitated to take it every second day in order to be able to work, and I was determined not to take it oftener, for I knew that in this way alone could I preserve my freedom. I thought that in the meanwhile, perhaps in two or three weeks, my system might rally, and so become able to work itself out of its relaxed condition when the morphine could be dispensed with.

Here, and here only do I acknowledge guilt in my dealings with morphine: that is, in taking it merely to remove languor of the system, and brace it up sufficiently to enable me to attend to business, at a time when I was not suffering actual pain. Had I had my time fully at my own command I would doubtless have acted differently. But I was the victim of circumstances. Work I must, and in my then condition I could not work. Say, ye cavillers, what in like circumstances would you have done? It seemed as though I had now lost that wholesome fear of morphine which I had once entertained. . . . So I played with morphine as a child plays with fire.

Instead of any improvement taking place in my physical condition, such as I had hoped for, matters only grew worse, and to add to my other difficulties, neuralgic troubles began again to make their appearance about this time. It was not long, under this new condition of affairs, before I found myself compelled to take morphine every day, then twice a day, and also to increase the dose.[19]

19. *Ibid.*, pp. 700–706.

A later relapse is described as follows:

> I bore my suffering as well as I could until the end of the fourth
> day, and then I had to yield. . . . And in all subsequent trials that
> I made, I could never hold out against these gastric symptoms
> beyond the fourth day.[20]

## Summary

In the initial conditioning experience, repeated hundreds of
times as the drug is used to relieve or avoid withdrawal, the patterns of addiction behavior are fixed. These include the user's
realization that he is trapped and has become an addict—a new
and traumatic self-conception that stimulates rebellion and struggle against the grip of a powerful compulsion. The craving for
drugs, generated initially by the threat and the experience of
withdrawal, may be conceived as a basically irrational and sub-
liminal impulse or tendency that is left as a deposit or residuum
from thousands of shots. When the user is taken off drugs, this
basic craving, which has become symbolically elaborated in the
user's psychological make-up, persists as a cortical or conceptual
complex independent of the various chemical and physiological
conditions that are indispensable in its origins. As such, it predisposes the person who has been hooked and is abstaining to
resume use of the drug.

Because the craving is an irrational impulse it impels the person
to do things that reason tells him he should not do and causes
him to be dissatisfied both with being an addict and with being
an abstainer and to switch from one status to the other and back
again in a recurring cycle.

This chapter has been concerned with identifying and describing how the basic drive toward the drug works, behind the scenes
one may say, to push or seduce the abstaining addict back to his
habit. Among the most important of these influences are: the
changed perceptions of the addict which lead him to respond to
virtually all distress as though it were withdrawal distress to be
banished by a fix; the neutralization of memories of the miseries

20. *Ibid.*, p. 707.

of addiction which are relatively remote consequences of taking a shot compared to the invariable satisfactory immediate ones; the rationalizations of the abstainer that life without the drug is dull, that he is better off using it than not, and that he might as well use it because he is stigmatized anyway; the knowledge or beliefs acquired from direct personal experience of the marvelous potency and versatility of the drug; and, finally, the attraction exercised by associations within the drug-using subculture, which, with a few exceptions, provides the only social setting in which full and free communication on all matters associated with the habit is possible without risk to the ego.

CHAPTER

# 7

# A CRITIQUE OF

# CURRENT VIEWS OF ADDICTION

The views of addiction most commonly expressed in both the popular and the scientific literature have not changed significantly for many decades. The main substantial change has been in the vocabularies employed to express them. This is made evident by listing terms that have been used to describe addicts or types of addicts, usually with the assumptions that what is being described is an addiction-prone personality type and that the named attribute has etiological significance. All of the terms that follow are taken from only two studies: that of Terry and Pellens[1] in 1928, which presents older terms taken in some cases from literature of the nineteenth century, and that of Ausubel,[2] published thirty years later: "alienated," "frustrated," "passive psychopath," "aggressive psychopath," "emotionally unstable," "nomadic," "inebri-

1. Charles E. Terry and Mildred Pellens, *The Opium Problem* (New York: Committee on Drug Addictions and Bureau of Social Hygiene, 1928).
2. David P. Ausubel, *Drug Addiction: Physiological, Psychological, and Sociological Aspects* (New York: Random House, 1958).

157

ate," "narcissistic," "dependent," "sociopath," "hedonistic," "child-like," "paranoid," "rebellious," "hostile," "infantile," "neurotic," "over-attached to the mother," "retreatist," "cyclothymic," "con-stitutionally immoral," "hysterical," "neurasthenic," "hereditarily neuropathic," "weak character and will," "lack of moral sense," "self-indulgent," "introspective," "extraverted," "self-conscious," "motivational immaturity," "pseudo-psychopathic delinquent," and finally, "essentially normal."

Views or theories of addiction advanced by different writers can, as a rule, be reliably predicted from knowledge of the in-vestigator's professional and intellectual training and commit-ments. Orthodox Freudians find, in addiction behavior, a confir-mation of Freud's ideas; Adlerians propound Adlerian theories; behavioristic psychologists who are followers of Skinner find that drug addiction fits neatly into the framework of operant condition-ing; sociologists who are followers of Merton emphasize aliena-tion, anomie, and the double-failure hypothesis; statisticians tend to deplore the methodological blunders, connected with sampling and the use of controls, that are committed by the nonstatisticians; biologically trained researchers suggest biological theories and are repelled by the subjectivism and lack of precision of behavioral and psychological studies.

Insofar as this is true, it implies that theories of addiction are based on something other than the facts. If the data serve only to confirm the preexisting ideological positions of the investiga-tors, the resulting controversies are likely to be noisy and futile squabbles not conducive to the formulation and progressive re-finement of theory which is characteristic of genuine science.

On the assumption that the controversy between competing positions stems in large part from the fact that different investi-gators proceed from different and usually unstated methodologi-cal presuppositions, I have tried to state my own fairly explicitly and fully in the foregoing chapters. The comments in this chapter on views which I do not share and which seem mistaken to me are implied by my own methodological assumptions. Thus, I must state that most of the views examined in this chapter are not genuine theories at all from my standpoint, either because they do not purport to be generally applicable to all opiate-type addiction or because they are so formulated that no conceivable evidence to negate them is possible or conceivable. Persons who think of scientific theories in other terms than these will naturally not agree with my evaluations. When a theorist or a critic makes his assumptions explicit, those who disagree are in the position of knowing whether they should discuss the evidence or concern themselves rather with questions of scientific method and logical inference.

## Psychopathy and Addiction

Thirty years ago, in a discussion of drug addiction, E. W. Adams, a well-known British writer on this subject, stated:

It is almost universally agreed now, that running beneath all other causes is an inherent mental or nervous instability of a greater or less degree. That statement may be said to rest upon evidence as convincing as that upon which most of the canons of medicine are based. Addiction can, as will later be seen, be brought about in persons mentally normal to all appearances, if deliberate attempts are made with this object or if their medical advisers unwisely subject them to unduly prolonged narcotic treatment, but such persons will not become addicts of their own accord. Ordinarily, then, addiction is a sign of a mental makeup which is not entirely normal. . . . We shall not go wrong, then, in accepting as a fact the existence of this psychopathic basis in the large majority of the victims of drug addiction.[3]

Numerous other authorities who agree with this conclusion are cited by Adams, and essentially the same views have been expressed by countless writers since that time.

It is at once evident from Adams' statement that it does not qualify as a scientific general theory of addiction because it claims only that *most* addicts who become addicted by voluntarily taking drugs are abnormal in some way and implies that this abnormality occurs more often among addicts than among non-addicts. His statement suggests that the above conclusions may be reversed in the case of those persons who become addicted in

3. E. W. Adams, *Drug Addiction* (London: Oxford University Press, 1937), p. 53.

medical practice without using the drug voluntarily. While he asserts the existence of a psychopathic basis for most voluntary addiction, Adams does not stop to consider whether even this weak conclusion is generally or universally valid. For example, in Eastern countries where folk beliefs hold that opium is an effective remedy for widespread tropical diseases, for sexual impotence, and other complaints and ailments, would voluntary use of opium under such circumstances have the same psychopathic basis? Does such a psychopathic basis exist when the use of the drug is a status symbol, as it has been among upper-class Chinese? Would this idea apply to communities in China and other Eastern countries where it has been reported that it was the custom of virtually all adult males to use opium?

The view expressed by Adams is still widely accepted among students of addiction despite its obvious deficiencies and the wide range of disagreement as to how the alleged psychopathic predisposition or addiction-prone personality is to be described. Some writers in Adams' time and earlier sought to extend the conclusion to all addicts just as contemporary students occasionally do.

This position is, in my opinion, mainly a reflection of a popular conception which long antedates it, that persons with bad compulsive habits are afflicted with "weak wills." A narcotic agent whom I asked why addicts used drugs replied that it was because "they are weaklings." The prevalence of the popular view and the scientific view with which it is in essential agreement is based primarily on frequency of repetition rather than on evidence. Even if it were to be unequivocally confirmed that most addicts are in fact not psychologically normal, little would be gained, since the problem of explaining the mechanisms of addiction would still remain and it would still be necessary to account for the minority, however small, of addicts to whom the description did not apply.

Two of the older studies may be taken as prototypes of this approach. Both were published by competent investigators of excellent standing in their professions, Dr. Lawrence Kolb and Dr. Charles Schultz. As is characteristic of studies in this tradition, both present a classification of addicts as the main grounds for their conclusions. In a study by Kolb, 225 addicts were classified in the following categories: "Normals who are accidentally or necessarily addicted in medical practice (14 per cent). Carefree individuals, devoted to pleasure, seeking new sensations (38 per cent). Definite neuroses (13.5 per cent). Habitual criminals— always psychopathic (13 per cent). Inebriates (21.5 per cent)."[4]

Kolb states that all these addicts became addicted "because of the pleasurable mental satisfaction that the first few doses of the narcotic gave them. The degree of inflation varies in direct proportion to the degree of pathology. It occurred only slightly or not at all in those considered nervously normal, but was very striking in some of the extreme psychopaths."[5]

Concerning the habitual criminal, Kolb asserts: "Habitual criminals are psychopaths, and psychopaths are abnormal individuals who, because of their abnormality, are especially liable to become addicts."[6] He concludes:

> The instability of the various abnormal cases expressed itself in some form of social or psychical reaction that marked them off as different from the average stable individual. They were not necessarily invalids or vicious; some of them were useful citizens and remained so; others were so abnormal as to have been social problems before their addiction, or the use of narcotics with its attendant social and physical difficulties, had seriously reduced their efficiency.
>
> Frank cases of hysteria and psychasthenia were less common than cases that showed biased personality of one kind or another. Psychopathic characters, periodic inebriates, extremely temperamental individuals, and persons who had been problem children were more common than cases with phobias, fits, or pathological fears. A common type among these cases is a psychopath who, with his special deviation of personality, is, in the language of the street, an individual who knows it all and does not care. . . .
>
> The psychopath, the inebriate, the psychoneurotic, and the temperamental individuals who fall easy victims to narcotics have this in common: they are struggling with a sense of inadequacy, imagined or real, or with unconscious pathological strivings that narcotics temporarily remove; and the open make-up that so many of them show is not a normal expression of men at ease with the world, but a mechanism of inferiors who are striving to appear like normal men.[7]

4. Lawrence Kolb, "Types and Characteristics of Drug Addicts," *Mental Hygiene* (1925), 9: 301.

5. Lawrence Kolb, "Drug Addiction in Its Relation to Crime," *Mental Hygiene* (1925), 9: 77.

6. *Ibid.*, p. 88.

7. "Types and Characteristics of Drug Addicts," *op. cit.*, p. 302.

In another study of 119 persons who became addicted in medical practice, Kolb rated only 67 per cent as psychopathic,[8] while in a third study he found that 90 per cent of 210 cases were psychopathic prior to addiction.[9] He summarizes his viewpoint as follows:

It has long been recognized by students of the subject that the addict is generally abnormal from the *nervous* standpoint before he acquires the habit, while some, like Block, assert that normal persons never become habitues. It is probable that Block does not class as habitués persons who, because of certain painful conditions, are necessarily addicted in the treatment of them. If this assertion allows for this exception and is limited in application to countries which like the United States have laws that protect people from the consequences of their own ignorance, its accuracy is supported by my own findings. Ninety-one per cent of this group and eighty-six per cent of a group reported elsewhere by me deviated from the normal in their personalities before they became addicted. . . .

The unstable individuals who constitute the vast majority of addicts in the United States may be divided into two general classes: Those having an inebriate type of personality, and those afflicted with other forms of nervous instability. The various types find relief in narcotics. The mechanism by which this is brought about differs in some respects in the different types but the motive that prompts

8. "Drug Addiction: A Study of Some Medical Cases," *Archives of Neurology and Psychiatry* (1928), 20: 171–83.
9. "Clinical Contribution to Drug Addiction: The Struggle for Cure and the Conscious Reasons for Relapse," *Journal of Nervous and Mental Disease* (1927), 66: 22 ff., quoted by Terry and Pellens, *op. cit.*, p. 617 ff. The lowest percentage of abnormals among addicts that I have been able to ascertain, as reported by a competent authority, is 34 per cent, as reported by R. N. Chopra in "The Opium Habit in India," *Indian Journal of Medical Research* (October, 1935), 23: 357–89. Kolb's 91 per cent is the highest. Other estimates were made by Theodore Riechert, "Die Prognose der Rauschgiftsüchten," *Archiv für Psychiatrie* (1931), 95: 103–126; Hans Schwarz, "Ueber die Prognose des Morphinismus," *Monatschrift für Psychiatrie und Neurologie* (1927), 63: 180–238; H. M. Pollock, "A Statistical Study of One Hundred Sixty-four Patients with Drug Psychoses," *State Hospital Quarterly* (1918–1919), pp. 40–51; Johannes Lange and Emil Kraepelin, as cited by Alexander Pilcz, "Zur Konstitution der Süchtigen," *Jahrbücher für Psychiatrie* (1934), 51: 169 ff; V. V. Anderson, "Drug Users in Court," *Boston Medical and Surgical Journal* (1917), 176: 755–57; Karl Bonhoeffer, "Zur Therapie des Morphinismus," *Therapie der Gegenwart* (1926); 67: 18–22; see also Terry and Pellens, *op. cit.*, index, under "psychopath" and "psychology."

them to take narcotics is in all cases essentially the same. The neurotic and the psychopath receive from narcotics a pleasurable sense of relief from the realities of life that normal persons do not receive because life is no special burden to them. The first few doses, especially if larger than the average medicinal doses, may cause nausea and other symptoms of discomfort, but in the unstable there is also produced a feeling of peace and calm to which they are not accustomed and which, because of its contrast with their usual restless and dissatisfied state of mind, is interpreted as pleasure.[10]

Schultz classified 318 cases of addiction in the following manner:

Unclassified, 42 patients (13.2 per cent); i.e., in 13.2 per cent of the patients treated, little or no evidence could be elicited of psychopathic personality other than the drug addiction *per se*. These cases gave the impression of having possessed and still retaining normal personalities.

Inadequate personalities, 96 patients (30 per cent). While the majority in this group were probably psychopathic types who had been the shiftless black sheep and ne'er-do-wells of their families before using drugs and whose failings may have been accentuated as a result of the addiction, there were some who appeared to have been fairly normal individuals before using drugs, but who went to seed afterwards, from what information was available.

Emotional instability, 65 patients (20 per cent). Here there is a question, in some cases, as to whether the instability was present before or came as the result of the addiction. Undoubtedly, the majority were unstable before using drugs. . . .

There are some types who from their previous histories appear to have been more stable before using narcotics, and in whom the instability was secondary to the use of drugs. (In all observations carried out on these drug addicts, the emotional instability was the most striking feature.) . . .

The following groups appear to have been basically psychopathic. Criminalism, 41 patients (13 per cent). The dominant feature here is seen to be profound egotism combined with complete indifference in regard to ethical issues. The exclusive aim of such an individual is his own pleasure or his own interest. He has neither sentiment of honor nor respect for the truth. His unique pre-occupation is to

10. Quoted by Terry and Pellens, *op. cit.*, pp. 617–23.

escape conviction and punishment. . . .

Paranoid personality, 29 patients (9 per cent). In this type we find conceit and suspicion, and a stubborn adherence to a fixed idea; contempt for the opinions of others, argumentativeness, and a tendency to develop persecutory trends.

Nomadism, 26 patients (8 per cent). The nomadic or wandering tendency is present in most of us to some degree and, as all know, is in certain races so pronounced as to govern their mode of existence and social organization. . . .

Sexual psychopathy, 18 patients (6 per cent), homosexuality. These patients all showed the stigmata and reactions which were characteristic. In addition, many patients showed tendencies to be masochistic; e.g., pricking themselves with pins and needles during treatment or asking for "sterile hypos" after they were off treatment to get a "kick" out of it. This they termed "needlemania." [The followers of Watson and Pavlov might call this a conditioned reflex.]

Thus if we exclude all those in the unclassified and inadequate personality groups, we still have about 56 per cent who appear to have been constitutionally psychopathic.

However, most of those grouped as inadequate personality were probably also basically psychopathic, so that we have between 56 per cent and 87 per cent of the patients who may well have been psychopathic before acquiring the state of drug addiction.[11]

Since the attributes which are said to characterize the various types of addicts in these studies also exist among non-addicts, before one could say with assurance that they were more frequent among drug users it would be necessary to compare addicts with non-addicts from the same social strata, residential and family backgrounds, income level, ethnic background, and so on. However, no control groups were utilized in these two studies.

A more recent investigation by Gerard and Kornetsky,[12] in which a controlled comparison is made, is often cited to support the current versions of the position under discussion. Gerard and Kornetsky used a randomly selected group of 32 adolescent

11. Charles Schultz in "Report of Committee on Drug Addiction to Commissioner of Correction, New York City," *American Journal of Psychiatry* (1930–31), 10: 484.

12. Donald L. Gerard and Conan Kornetsky, "Adolescent Opiate Addiction: A Study of Control and Addict Subjects," *Psychiatric Quarterly* (July, 1955), 29: 457–86.

addicts who were federal probationers or volunteer patients admitted consecutively to the Lexington Public Health Service Hospital. The controls consisted of 23 non-addicts who were acquaintances or friends of known addicts, who were of the same age, ethnic and educational background, who lived in high drug-use census tracts in New York City, and who had "no probationary or institutional record." The search for control subjects began with 91 prospects, of whom all but 23 had to be eliminated for a variety of reasons.

The findings of the study were based mainly upon results obtained from administering the Rorschach and Human Figure Drawings tests, and from a psychiatric interview with each of the subjects in both groups. Evidently because some addict subjects were lost before the study was completed, the authors summarized their psychiatric diagnoses with respect to 30 addicts and the 23 controls as follows.[13]

| Diagnosis | Addicts | Controls |
|---|---|---|
| 1. Overt schizophrenia | 6 | 1 |
| 2. Incipient schizophrenia | 8 | 4 |
| 3. Delinquency-dominated character disorder | 12 | 0 |
| 4. Inadequate personality | 4 | 2 |
| 5. Serious neurotic disturbance | 0 | 6 (26%) |
| 6. Mild neurotic features or "normal" | 0 | 10 (43.5%) |

These results are sharply at variance with those reported by Kolb and Schultz and many other writers in a number of interesting respects. Schizophrenia, for example, which Gerard and Kornetsky report in overt or incipient form in almost half of their addicts, is not mentioned at all by Kolb and Schultz. The latter writers, on the other hand, mention definite neuroses or neurotic-type ailments which Gerard and Kornetsky find only in the controls. All of these studies are alike in at least one respect, namely, that the categories containing the largest number of cases are

13. *Ibid.*, p. 473.

invariably especially nebulous and poorly defined. In Kolb's studies about 60 per cent of the addicts are characterized as carefree individuals devoted to pleasure or as inebriates; Schultz describes 50 per cent of his cases as inadequate personalities or emotionally unstable; Gerard and Kornetsky find that most of their addicts who did not fit under the schizophrenia labels had delinquency-dominated character disorders while no controls did. Since the controls in the latter study were selected on the basis of having no probationary or institutional record, this particular difference was guaranteed in advance by the design of the study and is of no significance. The manner in which the controls were selected suggests that the comparison, besides being one of addicts with non-addicts, was also to a considerable extent a comparison of delinquents and non-delinquents in high delinquency areas.

Gerard and Kornetsky themselves indicate that the size of their sample was inadequate for secure conclusions to be drawn from it. Another serious problem is involved in their interpretations of the Rorschach results, which they found differentiated significantly between addicts and controls and buttressed their conclusions. In a footnote, the authors note that a clinical psychologist who made a blind rating of the Rorschach protocols found no statistically significant differences whatever between the addicts and the controls.[14] This makes one wonder what would have happened if the psychiatric interviews had also been blind, that is, without the interviewer's knowing which subjects were addicted and which not. As Clausen has suggested, it is virtually impossible to interview an addict without tending to attribute to him the personality traits which one's entire training and ideological commitments indicate must be there.[15]

Another classification of addicts has been developed by Ausubel, who regards his scheme as superior to "the widely used Kolb classification."[16] According to Ausubel, there are three basic categories of opiate addiction: (1) "primary addiction in which opiates have specific adjustive value for particular personality defects"; (2) symptomatic addiction in which the use of the drug

14. *Ibid.*, p. 23.
15. John A. Clausen, "Social and Psychological Factors in Narcotics Addiction," *Law and Contemporary Problems* (Winter, 1957), 22: 45.
16. *Op. cit.*, pp. 39–56.

is "only an incidental symptom of behavior disorder and has no adjustive value"; and (3) reactive addiction "in which drug use is a transitory developmental phenomenon in essentially normal individuals influenced by distorted peer groups."[17] The first category of primary addiction includes two subtypes: the inadequate personality and drug use in connection with anxiety and reactive depression states. Symptomatic addiction occurs mainly in "aggressive antisocial psychopaths," or criminals, for whom the drug has no particular adjustive value but is merely incidental in a criminal career. Reactive addiction, according to Ausubel, is essentially an adolescent phenomenon involving mainly "essentially normal boys and girls" for whom the use of drugs "is largely a non-specific aggressive response to the prolonged status deprivation to which adolescents are subjected in our society."[18] This kind of addiction, he says, is usually transitory and self-limiting, with no serious or lasting consequences.

The above description of adolescent addiction is in sharp conflict with that of Gerard and Kornetsky, and the assertion that youthful addiction is a relatively trivial matter, easily overcome and with few serious long-range consequences is simply not true. Speaking of Kolb's inclusion of persons who are accidentally addicted in medical practice, Ausubel dismisses them with the assertion that they are "rare and are not true addicts since their addiction is based chiefly on physical dependence and has little adjustive value in a psychological sense."[19] In support of his classificatory scheme he advances the astonishing argument that parents and teachers who think that anyone can become addicted will be relieved to learn that only those with "very special kinds of personality defects can become truly addicted to drugs."[20]

It is evident that the promulgation of classificatory schemes such as those that have been described has not contributed significantly to the development of theory. While almost all of them recognize the existence of addicts without psychiatric problems and personality defects apart from addiction itself, none offers a rational way of accounting for this. If addiction is contracted

17. *Ibid.*, p. 39.
18. *Ibid.*, pp. 50–51.
19. *Ibid.*, p. 40.
20. *Ibid.*

because of personality defects one may ask why normal persons also become addicted. If the answer is like that of Ausubel, that is, such persons are addicted largely because of the withdrawal symptoms, why should not the same symptoms be sufficient to addict abnormal persons?

Almost all of the writers who, like Ausubel, Kolb, Schultz, and Gerard and Kornetsky, have adopted classificatory schemes in support of the view that addiction is produced by psychiatric or personality problems, have concerned themselves exclusively with American addicts, and have contented themselves by applying their conclusions to "most," "the great majority," or the "bulk" of twentieth century American heroin addicts. Kolb, however, intimated that his conclusions might not be applicable in other countries where laws do not protect individuals against the consequences of their own ignorance as they are presumed to do in the United States. As a matter of fact, of course, which kinds of persons become addicted is a matter that is influenced by patterns of availability, by control policies, by social custom, and by many other factors. The pattern of recruitment in the United States of the twentieth century is vastly different from that of the nineteenth, and both differ drastically from some of those found in European and especially in Asiatic countries.

In their superb survey of the literature of addiction up to 1928, Terry and Pellens evaluated the classificatory schemes that had been proposed, in words that are as relevant today as when they were written:

> In the foregoing, one is struck with the contradictions apparent in the widely varying views expressed as to the types of individuals predominating among chronic opium users. Unless we bear in mind, along with other co-existing factors which will be discussed below, the fact that for the most part each writer was influenced by impressions received from observations on selected cases, we may become confused by the picture presented. For example, terms such as "constitutionally inferior," "degenerate," "vicious," "highly intellectual," "akin to genius," "of the upper social strata," "of the most depraved type," "potential criminals," etc., etc., commonly have been used to indicate type characteristics. All too often the proponent for one type or another loses sight of the fact that his experience has been limited because of certain influencing factors to a selected group.

It is obvious, therefore, that generalizations from such selected and hence quite atypical groups are valueless and prejudicial to a true conception of the real nature of the problem as a whole. . . .

In addition to the foregoing possible misinterpretations on the part of the writers quoted, is it not possible that where individual writers have accorded to certain types a tendency to the use of this drug, effect has been mistaken for cause? Have not these patients, possibly as a result of the situation in which they find themselves—the toxic effect of the drug, disturbed metabolism, fear of discovery and realization that unaided they cannot regain their health—presented temporarily characteristics that were not constitutional with them? In spite of frequently repeated statements that the use of opium and its derivatives causes mental and ethical deterioration in all cases, we are inclined to believe that this alleged effect has not been established. The evidence submitted in support of such statements, in practically every instance coming under our notice, has been secured *after* the development of the addiction and was not based on a knowledge of the individual's condition *prior* to his addiction. In other words, the pre-addict has not been studied, and traits of character, ethical standards, and intellectual capacities based on *post hoc* findings may or may not have a *propter hoc* significance and effects attributable to the influence of the drug quite possibly may be evidence—as also may the taking of the drug—of pre-existing constitutional tendencies. It may be said with equal truth in considering the claims of those who state that certain types of individuals comprise the bulk of chronic opium users, that for one reason or another in the writings of many, "types" as generally understood are not considered as such until extraneous circumstances, possibly even the use of the drug itself, have altered the individual or group in question. In other words, what might be called the original type has come to be something else or attributes or factors not inherent in type delineation have been introduced as type-descriptive. Wherever the truth may lie the evidence submitted in support of the statements appearing in this chapter dealing with type predisposition and with the effect of opium use on mental and ethical characteristics is, in our opinion, insufficient to warrant the opinions expressed. . . . Unfortunately, in an attempt to present a comprehensive picture of the sociologic, constitutional, and other types of individuals involved in chronic opium intoxication, we are handicapped by the fact that there are available few valuable data, but rather in their place we find categoric statements without any presentation of the evidence upon which they are based. For the most part, we have found as data brief series of cases which by reason of the factors determining their selection may not be considered typical of the opium-using population as a whole.

In general, however, it would appear from the data submitted that this condition is not restricted to any social, economic, mental or other group; that there is no type which may be called the habitual user of opium, but that all types are actually or potentially users.[21]

It is difficult to discover in what exact sense the term "normal" is defined by Kolb and others, who take the position that addiction can be explained by the preexisting abnormality of the person who becomes an addict. It is clear, however, that the term is not used in the sense of "average." Kolb, Ausubel, and Schultz admit that normal persons, as they define them, do become addicts, but the implication of their theory is that they should not—that they should show immunity. Apparently some practicing physicians have been more consistent in this matter. Ernst Meyer, a writer who held to the psychopathic theory, tells of cases known to him in which physicians ordered morphine for repeated use with the explanation that there was no danger because of the absence of psychopathic predisposition. Meyer solemnly warns against this practice: "Care in the use of narcotics should still be maintained in spite of the theory that a psychopathic constitution is a necessary basis for the development of a chronic abuse of the drug."[22]

Since all of the so-called character and personality defects which are said to lead to addiction also exist in the general population and are often found in the addict only after he has become addicted, the view being considered appears as an *ex post facto* explanation without practical or predictive value for the physician. Indeed, as Meyer indicated, it is a dangerous doctrine for physicians or anyone else to accept, if its logical implication, that there are some types of persons who are immune to addiction because of normal personality makeup, is accepted and acted upon.

Jöel and Fränkel have sharply criticized this view of addiction as a consequence of psychopathy in terms which are directly

21. Terry and Pellens, *op. cit.*, pp. 513–16.
22. Ernst Meyer, "Ueber Morphinismus, Kokainismus, und den Missbrauch anderer Narkotika," *Medizinische Klinik* (1924), 20: 403–407.

applicable to current positions like those of Ausubel, Gerard, and Kornetsky:

> This conception is wrong in all its details and has dubious consequences. Even disregarding the fact that the concept of psychopathy is so extended today that one can find some psychopathic traits in anyone, the addiction itself is often taken as evidence of degeneracy when psychopathy cannot be otherwise proved. This is, of course, to reason in a circle. Also when it has been demonstrated that these persons have tainted heredities, therapeutically and for prognosis very little has been gained.[23]

If one substitutes "tainted personality" for "tainted heredity" in the above statement, it can be applied without any other change to current theories of the kind under examination.

An American addict, William S. Burroughs, has expressed his views of the idea that there is an addiction-prone personality, in the following blunt language:

> Addiction is an illness by exposure. By and large those who have access to junk become addicts. . . . But there is no pre-addict personality any more than there is a pre-malarial personality, all the hogwash of psychiatry to the contrary. . . . Knock on any door. Whatever answers, give it four half-grain shots of God's Own Medicine every day for six months and the so-called "addict personality" is there![24]

In support of Burroughs' conclusions, it is generally impossible to find any adherent of the addiction-prone personality school who is willing to test his theory on himself—by the six months' test suggested by Burroughs, for example. Clearly if one does not have the special personality attributes necessary for addiction one should be immune. Nevertheless, even with the stimulus of a substantial wager, these investigators refuse to risk the experiment on themselves. This indicates one of three things: (1) they suspect that they may have addiction-prone personalities; (2) they do not know what the type is and do not believe their own theory;

23. Ernst Joël and Fritz Fränkel, "Zur Verhütung und Behandlung der Giftsüchten," *Klinische Wochenschrift* (1925), 4: 1714.

24. William S. Burroughs, "Kicking Drugs: A Very Personal Story," *Harper's Magazine* (July, 1967), 235: 40.

or (3) those who have made the test have become addicted and changed their occupations.

In the older literature of addiction a significant aspect of the attempt to show that addicts constituted a different breed of human beings from non-addicts included the investigation of their genealogical histories. Since such studies are no longer given much attention in the behavioral sciences, I shall content myself by indicating that, when the necessity of controlled comparisons was recognized and applied, virtually all of the claims which had been made concerning the unusual prevalence of hereditary defects in addicts dissolved. The more sophisticated studies that were made seemed to indicate that the hereditary backgrounds of addicts were not significantly different from those of normals, with the possible exception that psychotic conditions of some kinds seemed to be less frequently found in the addict's background.[25]

## Selective Factors in Addiction

The purport of the preceding discussion is not that personality factors do not play any role in the process of becoming addicted. On the contrary, it seems certain that they do and that if there were personality types that could be identified objectively and reliably they would be distributed differently among addicts and non-addicts. However, the same statement would probably be true of the persons who contract venereal disease. One does not speak of a predisposing personality type as a cause of venereal disease, but it would certainly be relevant in a consideration of exposure to the disease. Personality influences may well operate in a similar selective manner in the case of exposure to addiction. However, all the types that exist in the general population also sometimes turn up as addicts and the influence of given personality attributes varies widely in different social settings.

Besides the personality factors there are a great many other kinds of influences that operate selectively with respect to who uses drugs and who does not. Availability of the drug is such an

25. See, for example, Otto Wuth, "Zur Erbanlage der Süchtigen," *Zeitschrift für die Gesamte Neurologie und Psychiatrie* (1935), 153: 502 ff., and Mark Serejski, "Ueber die Konstitution der Narkomanen," *Zeitschrift für die gesamte Neurologie und Psychiatrie* (1925), 95: 130–50.

influence. In the United States high availability exists primarily in two broad areas; one of these is the medical profession, the other, the underworld and the metropolitan slums. Addiction rates are comparatively high in both. Other more indirect influences are those of age, skin color, place of residence, income level, occupation, special events such as going to war or acquiring certain types of diseases, one's associates, and no doubt many others. During the nineteenth century, for example, there were more female than male addicts, the average age of users was much higher than now, Negroes were not over-represented as now, and addiction was distributed fairly evenly in the social classes and may even have been concentrated to a slight extent in the middle and upper strata. Obviously the selective processes at work must have been very different from what they now are, and there is obviously much more involved than personality types.

A study which, like those that have been cited, stresses personality predisposition, but also allows for the other influences of the type noted, is that of Chein and his associates,[26] whose conclusions were based on their well-known investigations of adolescent addiction in New York City slums. Gerard, who co-authored the final published report, presented in it the same classification of addict personality types that he and Kornetsky had previously published.

Chein evidently accepted the general purport of these findings, for he remarks elsewhere that when addicts come to psychiatric attention "they seem to be, without exception, suffering from one or another of a variety of mental disturbances, apart from their addiction."[27] Unlike Gerard and Kornetsky, Chein emphasizes the idea that the spread of drug use is associated with human misery generated by the nature of life in the slums and especially by the nature of family life. Two moods favorable to the spread of the habit are identified: one of pessimism, unhappiness, and futility; the other of mistrust, negativism, and defiance. At the same time

26. Isidor Chein, Donald L. Gerard, Robert S. Lee, and Eva Rosenfeld, *The Road to H: Narcotics, Delinquency and Social Policy* (New York: Basic Books, 1964).

27. Isidor Chein, "The Use of Narcotics as a Personal and Social Problem," in Daniel M. Wilner and Gene G. Kassebaum (Eds.), *Narcotics* (New York: McGraw-Hill, 1965), p. 109.

he observes that only a small percentage of the boys in the areas studied (never more than 10 per cent) become addicted. He thus conceives of the personality disorders which are said invariably to precede and facilitate the addiction as natural consequences of slum life and experiences within the family.

The study by Chein and his associates, it should be recalled, was focused on adolescents in a twentieth-century urban slum. As such, it deals with a specific pattern of recruitment into the ranks of addiction that is prominent in the United States at present, but which does not encompass all existing paths to addiction and which scarcely existed throughout most of the nineteenth century. There are, for example, many European and other metropolitan slums scattered throughout the world which can at least match those of New York and in which addiction rates are probably lower than are those, for example, among physicians. From the very nature of the Chein studies, addiction among physicians, in foreign countries, among hospital patients, in non-slum, non-urban environments, in the upper classes, and in past periods of time, were not taken into account.

The Chein studies, thus, were not, and did not really purport to be, of addicts in general. The conclusions which they generated do not constitute a universally applicable theory of the mechanisms of the addiction process, but are rather descriptions of selective processes, operating within a particular social environment in contemporary American society and applicable to some addicts but not to all and possibly not even to most of them.

## A Psychoanalytic Perspective

While the views of Sandor Radó on addiction have commonly been spoken of as a "theory" of the etiology of drug addiction, it appears that Radó himself regarded them as something other than that. In a 1963 article Radó observed: "though the etiology of narcotic bondage is still unknown, its clinical feature is obviously the victim's craving: if we could stop his craving he would no longer be in bondage."[28] What Radó evidently seeks to do is

28. Sandor Radó, "Fighting Narcotic Bondage and Other Forms of Narcotic Disorders," *Comprehensive Psychiatry* (June, 1963), 4: 160.

to indicate, in psychoanalytic terms, how the craving for drugs is integrated in the motivational structures of the addicted person. Since Radó is not concerned with the origin of the craving, which is the central concern of this study, his views are not directly competitive and are only occasionally of theoretical relevance here.

In an earlier article, Radó suggested that all types of drug craving be regarded as varieties of a single disease which he proposed to call "pharmacothymia." Noting the addict's typical fluctuations in mood between a state of elation or euphoria and one of depression, he characterized the "megalomania of pharmacothymic elation" as a manifestation of narcissistic regression. For many years, Radó says, he could not understand why the addict did not simply quit his habit when continued use of the drug had demonstrated to him that the initial elation disappears and that his hopes concerning it had been delusional: "A patient himself gave me the explanation. He said, 'I know all the things that people say when they upbraid me. But mark my words, doctor, *nothing* can happen to *me.*' . . . The elation had reactivated his narcissistic belief in his invulnerability."

Radó describes the attainment of pleasure from the drug as "an artifical sexual organization which is autocratic and modeled on infantile masturbation. . . . The ingestion of drugs, it is well known, in infantile archaic thinking represents an oral insemination; planning to die from poisoning is a cover for the wish to become pregnant in this fashion. We see, therefore, that after the pharmacothymia has paralyzed the ego's virility, the hurt pride in genitality, forced into passivity because of masochism, desires as a substitute the satisfaction of child bearing."[29]

In the 1963 article, Radó refers to the psychoanalytic doctrine that in the initial experiences of manipulating his own limbs the child comes to believe in his omnipotence and that this is his first self-image or primordial self. The addict's experience of gratification or narcotic grandeur from a fix is said to reactivate the feeling of omnipotence of the primordial self, making the satisfied addict feel like the "omnipotent giant" he had always fundamentally thought he was.[30] Radó concludes that the response of

29. "The Psychoanalysis of Pharmacothymia," *Psychoanalytic Quarterly* (1933), 2: 1–23.
30. *Op. cit.*, pp. 162–63.

narcotic grandeur is elicited only in a small minority of persons who retain a more powerful primordial, omnipotent self than is the case with the vast majority. He notes, however, that some persons who become addicts evidently do not possess this predisposing trait and do not develop narcotic intoxication or experience narcotic grandeur.

From the perspective of the theory concerning the nature and origin of the craving for drugs that has been outlined in previous chapters, it might be expected that this irrational and powerful impulse would be symbolically elaborated by the person subject to its influence and that it would become a pervasive aspect of his personality structure as the latter is viewed by psychiatrists. Radó's interpretation would not be accepted by psychiatrists committed to other ideological positions, and it is hard to see how it could be subjected to any sort of empirical verification. This, however, need not concern us here. The important point to be kept in mind concerning Radó's work is that it is concerned essentially with the consequences of addiction, not with its antecedents. This is the clear import of his own remark that the etiology of addiction is unknown.

### The Pleasure Theory

It is a common belief that opiate addiction is based upon the pleasure or happiness which the drug is supposed to produce. In a sense, this view is incontestable, for obviously the user of drugs obtains satisfactions of some sort or he would not be addicted. The satisfaction of the addict's craving for drugs may itself be called a pleasure. The relief from withdrawal distress which an injection gives may also be so designated. So considered, the assertion that an addict uses drugs because he obtains pleasure or satisfaction from them is merely a tautology.

If one views this theory as a serious attempt at causal explanation it has grave faults. Virtually all addicts maintain, for example, that they feel only "normal" under the influence of the drug after the initial interval when addiction is being established. This contention can scarcely be denied, for, after all, the addict is the final authority on this question of how he feels.

Nevertheless, Ausubel ventures to disagree with the addict about how he feels. Noting that addicts as a group maintain that the kick disappears and that the drug is used, when dependence is fully established, merely to feel "normal," he suggests that they are untruthful. Faced with data that do not conform to his theory, Ausubel alters the data rather than his views by inventing "a lesser residual euphoria, possibly devoid of the original voluptuosity" that always remains. The addict's claim, he argues, "sounds very unlikely when one considers the tremendous cost in money and social prestige, as well as the risk of imprisonment and disgrace involved—all of which could be avoided by simply undergoing the moderate and self-limited physical suffering of withdrawal."[31]

Because addicts have a bad reputation for veracity and because they rarely read or write articles in learned journals, there is little hazard attached to attributing wholly imaginary subjective effects to the drug. Indeed, this is more or less required in the mass media catering to popular tastes, since the general public commonly assumes that the mysterious power of the habit must be based upon an equally mysterious and uncanny pleasure. The writer who in one paragraph describes addicts as living in a state of ecstasy may in the next elaborate on the disaster, disgrace, and misery that addiction entails. Anyone with minimal knowledge of the conditions under which American addicts live could not possibly characterize them as anything but miserable. If they use the drug for pleasure in the usual sense it is certainly not evident in their lives. Obviously, if they were suddenly to begin to act so as to maximize their pleasures and minimize their pains and sorrows, they would all quit their habits.

The idea that the power of the opiate habit rests upon the pleasant state of mind that it engenders shatters upon the fact that there are substantial numbers of addicts who state that they have never experienced euphoria from the drug and the fact that the initial euphoria vanishes either entirely or almost entirely in confirmed addiction. Reports of the absence of any euphoric experiences are particularly common from persons who first begin

31. David P. Ausubel, "The Psychopathology and Treatment of Drug Addiction in Relation to the Mental Hygiene Movement," *Psychiatric Quarterly Supplement* (1948), 22 (2): 219–50.

to use an opiate to relieve severe organic pain, who use it by other than the intravenous route, and who are not members of the addict subculture. Thus, a prominent member of the New York Bar, cited by Bishop in 1921, stated flatly," I have never experienced the slightest pleasurable or sensually enjoyable sensations from the administration of morphine. . . ."[32]

A noted investigator in the field, Abraham Wikler, over a period of many years of research, has come to a conclusion much like mine concerning the inadequacy of the pleasure theory. When the first edition of this book was published in 1947, however, Wikler had a different opinion and dismissed my contention that it was the relief of withdrawal that created the hook in addiction. Subsequently, perhaps in large part because of an experiment that he performed at Lexington in which he permitted an addict inmate to administer to himself the drug of his choice, his views changed. He found that while the addict accepted the opportunity to use drugs with alacrity and anticipatory pleasure, after a few days of use he became morose and unhappy—a fact which showed up not only as direct statements in the interviews but also in the subject's dreams.[33]

The development of Wikler's thinking on this matter is interestingly brought out if one compares his earlier publications with his later ones.[34]

A German physician and ex-addict protested as follows against the notion that an addict uses drugs to produce in himself a pleasant state of mind:

How false it is to say of a drug addict that he takes his injections to produce a "pleasurable state of mind." Good heavens! If people only knew how much misery it causes the addict each time he has to

32. Ernest S. Bishop, *The Narcotic Drug Problem* (New York: Macmillan, 1921), p. 138.
33. Abraham Wikler, "A Psychodynamic Study of a Patient During Self-Regulated Readdiction to Morphine," *Psychiatric Quarterly* (1952), 26: 270–93.
34. For example, Abraham Wikler, *Opiate Addiction: Psychological and Neurophysiological Aspects in Relation to Clinical Problems* (Springfield, Ill., Charles C Thomas, 1953); "On the Nature of Addiction and Habituation," *British Journal of Addiction* (July, 1961), 57: 73–79; "Conditioning Factors in Opiate Addiction and Relapse," in Daniel M. Wilner and Gene G. Kassebaum (Eds.), *Narcotics*, pp. 85–100.

take the drug, they would not say this. True, that the first few injections cause some users to feel stimulated, alert, and so on. However, as soon as tolerance is completely established the euphoria vanishes. When this point is reached, the addict takes his morphine in the same spirit that the prisoner carries his chains. One would then have to use the term "euphoria" to refer to the fact that the distress of abstinence disappears after the injection, but by the same logic any person with a headache could be said to experience euphoria when it disappeared. According to such a standard every normal man spends his whole life in a state of euphoria. . . . And it is entirely false to believe as people do, that addicts use drugs to produce pleasurable sensations. Every addict who hears people talk in these terms, sighs and holds his peace.[35]

Some persons become addicts without ever becoming aware of the euphoric effects of the drug which are alleged to be the cause or basis of addiction. This is often the case when drug users have first used the drug in connection with serious and painful disease or when they were semiconscious or unconscious when they received their first injections. As a German physician correctly observed:

A fundamental fact that must be added here is that the experience of euphoria is by no means a necessary precondition for the development of a craving. In addition to the fact that some people develop a desire for sedatives which never produce euphoria, I am acquainted with morphine users who have never, throughout the long period of their addiction, experienced any euphoria from the drug. In the case of most addicts, whatever pleasurable effects may be experienced are of short duration. Morphine addicts have become addicts after reacting to first injection with dizziness, painful vomiting, and headache, rather than with pleasure.[36]

As in the case of alcoholism, the persons who experience the pleasurable effects of morphine alone are never addicts. The casual or social drinker who drinks a few cocktails is exhilarated

35. Otto Emmerich, *Die Heilung des chronischen Morphinismus* (Berlin, H. Steinitz, 1894), p. 123–4.
36. Fritz M. Meyer, "Ueber einige seltener Vorkommenden Formen von Rauschgiftsucht," *Münchener Medizinische Wochenschrift* (1933), 80: 732–33.

and stimulated by them and suffers few if any bad effects. The chronic alcohol addict, on the other hand, suffers severe after-effects in the form of physical symptoms, and the social effects may be serious as well. Similarly, it is the non-addict who experiences the beneficent effects of morphine with few or none of the evil effects which are so prominent in the case of the addict. The benign effects of morphine are well recognized in medical practice. Whatever unpleasant effects may follow from the medical use of a few injections of opiates are slight, and are in any case usually not recognized by the patient. On the other hand, the opiate addict himself describes the vast evil social and physical consequences that his habit brings upon him.

From the standpoint that emphasizes the pleasures produced by drugs as the key to understanding addiction, a drug such as marihuana should be intensely addictive, since the pleasurable sensations it produces are comparatively pure and uncomplicated by adverse physical consequences, and there is no withdrawal distress. Yet, it is well known that the addictive powers of marihuana and other drugs like it are negligible by comparison. Indeed, these drugs are described as non-addicting.

It is sometimes said that only pathological persons experience pleasure from opiate drugs. This contention is manifestly incorrect, as anyone can find out for himself by talking with acquaintances who have had morphine injections or by talking to a few experienced nurses. Almost all persons who had had morphine injections with whom I discussed the matter described the effects as pleasant, and some found them intensely so. It is usually reported that, if allowances are made for some unpleasant effects with the very first injections, the vast majority of patients experience the initial effects as pleasurable. Retrospective reports of addicts indicate that the initial experiences of addicts cover the entire range of possibilities from those that are intensely pleasurable to those that are decidedly unpleasant. In some cases no effect is noticed.

## Addiction as an Escape

The assertion, which is commonly made, that drug addiction is an "escape mechanism" is evidently based upon the assumption that the drug user's assertion that he feels "normal" is false. It implies that by means of drugs a person can escape from the problems that harass him when he is not using drugs, into a realm of fantasy or pleasurable physical sensations which allow him to forget his inadequacies and his problems. As already indicated, there is no evidence that such a mental state is produced in morphine addicts. There is a great deal of evidence to indicate that it is not. Moreover, the drug user is fully aware of the disastrous effects of his habit, particularly upon his social life. It is therefore difficult to see how the drug habit can be regarded as an escape mechanism, since it does not produce forgetfulness as alcohol does, and since the habit itself constitutes a burden and a problem which is usually more serious than those for which it is alleged to provide an escape. It is true that there may be a parallel between the use of alcohol and the initial use of opiates, and that opiates may be used as an escape device before addiction is established. Morphine as used in hospitals is a potent escape device, enabling patients to escape from intolerable pain, from worry, insomnia, and so on. When addiction is established, however, this effect is no longer present.

## Lower Animals as Addicts

Dr. S. D. S. Spragg described the effects upon chimpanzees of repeated doses of morphine.[37] He claimed that he found unequivocal evidence in the behavior of chimpanzees of a "desire for morphine" and therefore insisted on calling them addicts. He concluded:

> A discussion of the nature of morphine addiction in chimpanzee and man was undertaken, and the thesis was defended that morphine addiction is fundamentally a physiogenic phenomenon, developed according to principles of association. That the "societal" factor (which is usually present in human addiction) is not essential in the development of addiction has been demonstrated by the present results.[38]

Spragg taught his chimpanzee subjects to associate withdrawal distress with the hypodermic injection of morphine. He contended

37. S. D. S. Spragg, "Morphine Addiction in Chimpanzees," *Comparative Psychology Monographs* (April, 1940), vol. 15, no. 7.
38. *Ibid.*, p. 128.

that they exhibited genuine addiction behavior in the following
ways:

> (1) By showing eagerness to be taken from the living cage by the
> experimenter, at the regular dose times or when doses are needed,
> in clear contrast to behavior exhibited when taken from the cage at
> other times; (2) by struggling, under such conditions, to get to the
> room in which injections are regularly given; tugging at the leash
> and leading the experimenter toward and into that room; and ex-
> hibiting frustration when led away from the injection room and back
> to the living cage without having been given an injection; (3) by
> showing eagerness and excitement when allowed to get up on the
> box on which the injections were regularly made, and more or less
> definite solicitation of the injection by eager cooperation in the
> injection procedure or even by initiation of the procedure itself; and
> (4) under controlled test conditions, choosing a syringe-contain-
> ing box (whereupon injection is given) in preference to a food-con-
> taining box.[39]

The choice of food or drugs was offered these chimpanzees
under four conditions: (1) when they were hungry and also in
need of a dose; (2) hungry, but had recently been given an injection of morphine; (3) recently fed, but in need of a dose; and
(4) recently fed and recently injected. Spragg anticipated that
the chimpanzees would choose food under conditions (2) and
(4) and drugs under conditions (1) and (3). His expectations
were fulfilled in the course of the experiment, leading him to the
conclusion that the desire for morphine had been unequivocally
established and that the animals' behavior was essentially like
that of human addicts.

There are a number of serious objections to Spragg's conclusions which make it necessary to reject them. In the first place,
the assertion that the chimpanzees desired morphine injections
involves the fallacy of projecting human attributes onto the animal subjects. On the basis of experimental evidence alone, Spragg
might have concluded that the chimpanzees exhibited a desire to
be pricked with a hypodermic needle. A second objection to
Spragg's conclusions is that hospital patients to whom drugs have

39. *Ibid.*, pp. 59–60.

been given regularly for a short time frequently demand that the injections be continued and object strenuously if they are not. Such patients by no means necessarily become addicted, yet their behavior is essentially like that of Spragg's animals. Hospital patients, under the conditions mentioned above, do not become addicts if they are kept in ignorance. It is also possible to satisfy them by giving them other drugs than opiates. Spragg's assumption that the choices made by the chimpanzees are those which an addict would make under the same conditions is incorrect. American drug addicts, if given the choice of food or drugs when (1) hungry or suffering withdrawal distress, (2) hungry but not suffering withdrawal, (3) not hungry but suffering withdrawal symptoms, and (4) neither hungry nor suffering withdrawal distress, would unquestionably choose drugs under all four conditions provided that the other conditions of the experiment were identical with those imposed upon the chimpanzees. Spragg's results therefore demonstrate an essential difference between the animals and human beings, not a similarity, as Spragg assumes.

Spragg mentions that the chimpanzees did not conform to one of the criteria of addiction as we have defined it, namely, the tendency to relapse. As a matter of fact, however, none of the criteria of our definition were applicable to his chimpanzees.[40]

Subsequent to Spragg's study, there has been a great deal of highly interesting experimental work done on the responses of lower animals to the regular administration of opiates, especially morphine. Allusion has already been made to some of this work in which the gap between human and animal responses to morphine has been further narrowed by the fact that relapse behavior has been induced in lower animals. Some of the investigators in this area speak of their animals as "addicts" and insist or imply that their behavior is essentially identical with that of human addicts.

Such a claim is comparable to a similar claim that is made with respect to so-called homosexuality in lower animals. These conclusions should be regarded as hypotheses to be tested by detailed empirical comparison of the behavior of human and animal sub-

40. For a detailed critique of Spragg's study see A. R. Lindesmith, "Can Chimpanzees Become Morphine Addicts?", *Journal of Comparative Psychology* (April, 1946), 39: 109–117.

jects, and not asserted simply on the basis of systematic information obtained from animal experiments related to a few selected
aspects of human addiction. If a rat that behaves as did some of
those that Nichols[41] trained is to be called an addict, there should
be no sense of anomaly or absurdity in the idea of arresting rats
as violators of the narcotic laws.

The definition of addiction that was developed in an earlier
chapter, and which is much like those proposed by others, included five items which were thought to be characteristic and
common features of addiction behavior. Before lower animals can
be said to exhibit behavior that is identical with that of human
subjects it is reasonable to require that a behavioral comparison
be made on all of these five points. The claim, however, is based
on only one of them, namely, relapse, and even in this case the
evidence presented by Nichols is equivocal. For example, after
the training period had ended and drug intake had been stopped,
the rats did voluntarily choose to drink much more of the morphine, but the amount diminished rather rapidly from the four-
teenth day after withdrawal to the forty-ninth. While Nichols
assumed that the withdrawal symptoms had disappeared, it is
well known that they do not disappear in all human subjects in
49 days but may last as long as four or five months or even longer.
This suggests that the tendency of the experimental rats to drink
the morphine solution may have been linked with residual withdrawal symptoms and may subside as they diminish and disappear. The tendency of human users to relapse because of linger-
ing withdrawal symptoms presents a close parallel, but the human
subjects also relapse after many years of forced or voluntary
abstinence.

If one supposes a hypothetical experiment with human subjects like that performed by Nichols, and supposes that the subjects knew just as little about the drug and what was happening
to them as the rats did, it is certain that no one acquainted with
the behavior of the average American addict would be willing
to say that such subjects were addicts in the same sense. Indeed,
it is well known that morphine-dependent hospital patients who

41. John R. Nichols, "How Opiates Change Behavior," *Scientific American*
(February, 1965), 212 (2): 80–88.

are kept in total ignorance of the drug and of withdrawal distress
sometimes demand injections or "medicine" to relieve withdrawal
symptoms when they are unaware of the nature of the medicine
and of the discomfort they experience. The insistence of the demand tends to be proportional to the severity of the symptoms
and to decline as they subside. If, after a period of time, such a
patient were allowed to have his way, he might well resume the
medication or "relapse" into regular use of the drug. Relapse of
this sort does not constitute addiction in human subjects, since
such patients can still be successfully withdrawn without being
any the worse or the wiser for their experience. Such resumption
of drug use is qualitatively far removed from the superficially
comparable behavior of addicts, and it leads to few or no important long-range behavioral consequences. Such patients also do
not think of themselves as addicts or even suspect that they may
be. This matter of self-conception, which is an integral aspect of
human addiction with vast social and behavioral consequences,
does not, of course, arise in experiments with lower animals,
but clearly it has to be considered before human and animal
responses can be declared to be identical or equivalent.

It is difficult and hazardous to extrapolate to human subjects
findings obtained from observing lower animals in highly con-
trived experimental situations in which human beings are never
placed. Most investigators, in fact, avoid doing this. The difficulties involved in such extrapolation, and in determining what
experimental findings mean, is well illustrated by the differences
between Spragg's and Nichols' findings with regard to relapse.
If rats relapsed for Nichols, why did the chimps not relapse for
Spragg? Another example is provided by the extensive work with
monkeys trained in the self-administration of drugs.[42] In some of
these experiments the caged animals had an apparatus fastened
on their backs that was arranged to permit them to move about
freely and to obtain an injection any time they wished by pressing

42. See, for example, M. H. Seevers, "Opiate Addiction in Monkeys: Methods of Study," *Journal of Pharmacology and Experimental Therapeutics*
(1936), 56: 147, and, by the same author, Chapter 19 in V. A. Drill (Ed.),
*Pharmacology in Medicine* (New York: McGraw-Hill, 1958). Also, T. Thompson and C. R. Schuster, "Morphine Self-Administration, Food-reinforced,
and Avoidance Behaviors in Rhesus Monkeys," *Psychopharmacologia* (1964),
5: 87–94.

a lever. In this situation monkeys routinely take morphine injections regularly to the point of physical dependence and continue the injections over considerable time periods. If they are withdrawn and after a time are put back in the same situation they promptly resume the injections. In general, monkeys show a liking for the same drugs that humans use for kicks and reject the others. The equivocal significance of these experiments with respect to human subjects is suggested by the fact that monkeys go on giving themselves injections of cocaine and other non-addicting drugs in much the same way as they do with morphine, thus obscuring the difference between drugs that produce physical dependence and those that do not. It is hard to imagine a similar experiment with human subjects that would justify a valid comparative judgment.

## Conditioning Theory

As would be anticipated, those investigators who attempt to generalize about both human and lower animal responses to opiates from data secured primarily from observing lower animals usually interpret their findings in terms of the standard concepts of conditioning or reinforcement theory. Since the latter is itself mainly derived from experimental work with lower animals, it is formulated in terms of concepts that are equally applicable to man and animal and characteristically makes no or few allowances for the effect of any of the special attributes or capabilities of human beings which distinguish them from lower animals. Of particular importance to the analysis of opiate addiction is the conditioning theorist's lack of attention to cognitive behavior.

If it is conceded that nearly all human beings are more intelligent than any animal, it may be proposed that it is not unreasonable to expect this to make a difference in the way in which conditioning or reinforcement operates. From what is known about complex human conduct, it is abundantly clear that stimuli and situations affect it primarily as they are understood or interpreted by the subject. The argument that I have developed with respect to the role of withdrawal distress in addiction is simply another instance of this point. So also is the argument that the addicting effect which the relief of these symptoms has depends upon how it is interpreted.

In the process of reformulating my view of addiction as a type or instance of negative reinforcement theory of the operant conditioning variety, Nichols emphasizes that his rats had to initiate action, that they were not passive recipients of the drug, but self-injectors. "Sustained opiate-directed behavior" is established, he reasons, by the repeated reduction of drive (withdrawal) which immediately follows the injections and reinforces the original operant act of taking the first shot. In the human addict, he argues, as I have, that the injections are also used to reduce anticipatory anxiety prior to the actual onset of withdrawal or to avoid withdrawal. Further generalization of the response leads the addict to resort to the fix as a sovereign remedy for almost any distress or anxiety.

Nichols tacitly assumes throughout his discussion that the perceptions of the animal and of the human drug user are largely irrelevant and that the cognitions of the human subject, his knowledge or ignorance of the drug and the distress, and the manner in which he conceives his experiences, are of no critical significance. This is the central point of difference between his position and mine. Nichols explains the absence of relapse in Spragg's chimps as a consequence of their being relatively passive recipients of the drug rather than taking it by themselves, an unconvincing explanation since they did exert themselves considerably to obtain shots when they needed them.

An alternative explanation that seems applicable to both human and animal subjects, and that is consistent with the fact that passive human recipients of the drug do become addicted and that some of those who actively seek it and take it themselves do not, is that the organism's self-initiated actions influence its perceptions or understanding of the situation. The brighter human subject is likely to have acquired sufficient knowledge of drugs so that he grasps the situation even when he is a passive recipient; the animal, on the other hand, because he is not nearly as bright, has difficulty making even some of the most rudimentary associations. The elaborate experimental situations in which animals are enabled to give themselves injections may function as they do simply because they facilitate the learning or grasping of some of the associations or connections between events that are necessary preliminary steps on the path to genuine addiction. These associations are made quickly and almost routinely by most human subjects without artificial aids.

## The "Evil Causes Evil" Fallacy

It is widely and commonly assumed that anything that encourages or facilitates the use of addicting drugs is *ipso facto* evil like the drug habit itself. This frame of mind makes it easy to accept ideas such as that human misery, personality defects, double failure, slum conditions, disorganized family life, and a host of other similar undesirable conditions are contributing factors or "causes" of addiction. Personality traits described as a carefree attitude, willingness to experiment, or as a desire for new experiences and pleasures, are frequently cited as features of the addiction-prone personality and as character or personality defects. The same traits in non-addicts are often admired. The experimental frame of mind which leads young people to try LSD, marihuana, and other drugs also prompts them to become scientists, creative artists, reformers, or innovators. A carefree attitude and an interest in new experience on the part of wealthy businessmen is generally applauded. The search for pleasure, even by chemical means, is a popular national pursuit, as the statistics on alcohol consumption alone are sufficient to indicate.

Another example of the same type is provided by those who, with the advantage of hindsight, reproach the users of drugs who have become addicted for their willingness to violate the law and to take risks. These tendencies are also viewed as personality or character defects. Willingness to take risks, however, is apparent in a large proportion of the population and is a pervasive aspect of living. It is evident, for example, in politics, in international affairs, in marriage, in business and financial operations, in exploration, mountain climbing, sports, racing automobiles and airplanes, and in dozens of other activities and occupations. The persons who accept and even enjoy risk often become heroes if they survive. At another level, millions, by smoking tobacco or drinking alcoholic beverages, seem to accept the accompanying risks. Even the willingness to violate laws is not wholly or absolutely bad, since it has, in the past, often led to innovation and progress.

The "evil causes evil" attitude, by subtly leading people to misconceive the traits, feelings, appearance, actions, and motives of drug addicts causes them to think of drug users as a breed apart from ordinary normal people. The same tendency exists with respect to criminals and prisoners. This is perhaps why one of the most common reactions of the average citizen when he first visits a penitentiary or a place like Synanon where live addicts can be seen and talked to is one of surprise. The prisoners and the addicts, he discovers, are very much like other people, and, like other people, each is different from all the others. Whatever weaknesses, faults, or frailties of character or personality he may note do not surprise or shock him too much because they are already familiar to him, either because he has them himself or because he has observed them among his friends and associates.

The earlier pages of this chapter provide a number of illustrative instances of the fallacy that has been described. Numerous other examples can be found in the popular and scientific literature on addiction, as well as in that on almost any other form of deviant and heavily stigmatized behavior.

# 8

## CONCLUSIONS,

## IMPLICATIONS, PROBLEMS

It has been argued that the power of the opiate habit is derived basically from effects which follow when the drug is removed rather than upon any positive effects which its presence in the body produces. Addiction occurs only when opiates are used to alleviate withdrawal distress, after this distress has been properly understood or interpreted, that is to say, after it has been represented to the individual in terms of the linguistic symbols and cultural patterns which have grown up around the opiate habit. If the individual fails to conceive of his distress as withdrawal distress brought about by the absence of opiates, he does not become addicted, but, if he does, addiction is quickly and permanently established through further use of the drug. Evidence from a wide variety of sources seems uniformly to confirm this conclusion. Data concerning the habit which from other points of view appear paradoxical or contradictory fall into place as logically necessary consequences of the position.

The theory furnishes a relatively simple account of the experience in which the craving for drugs is generated. When this experience is more closely considered, the essential, universal, or common features of addiction can be traced from it in a readily intelligible way. The theory seems to flow from the data and at the same time to make sense of it, even of that part of the data which is constituted by what addicts say. There is, for instance, no need to attribute euphoric effects to the user which the latter denies experiencing, and there is no need for the hackneyed excuse that addicts are unreliable witnesses. In fact, the point of view explicitly developed here can be shown to be implicit in the addict's own special language.

The individual's interpretation of withdrawal distress is a belief or attitude that exists as a cultural and psychological phenomenon. It tends to be imposed upon the addict by his social environment. The crucial fact about it is not is validity, but that the individual, once having accepted it, is subject to influences and social pressures of which he was previously unaware. The attitudes he assumes toward himself are altered. He realizes for the first time that he may be a "dope fiend," and in the privacy of his own thoughts he begins to entertain tentatively that idea of himself and to explore its implications. Further experience with the drug quickly impresses him with the truth of his notion, and he is soon compelled to accept it, though he usually struggles for some time and makes fruitless efforts to free himself. During this time the person is transformed from a non-addict to an addict with all that that implies.

The essential process involved in this transformation and basic to it is a linguistic and conceptual one. It is through the use of the social symbols of language in conversation with himself and with others that the personality changes involved in becoming an addict are initiated and developed. The individual, when he uses the symbols which society provides him, also assumes the attitudes appropriate to those symbols when he applies them to himself. He calls himself a "dope fiend" and gradually hardens himself to the fact that he has become an outcast and a pariah to respectable people. He of necessity seeks the company of other addicts, both because they can help to solve the problems arising out of addiction and because he feels more at home with them. He attempts to quit because he accepts the general public dis-

*pure soc. theory on why the habit is hard to get rid of*

approval of addiction and wishes to remove himself from the pariah category. It is this whole process which George Herbert Mead has described as "taking the role of the generalized other" or assuming toward oneself the attitudes of the group or society in which one lives.[1]

The development of addiction presupposes in the individual a *(1)* complex conception of causality. He must be able to understand *awareness* and believe that the way he feels at a given moment is due to *(2) understanding* the presence in his body of a minute quantity of drugs taken many hours earlier. The effects of morphine are subtle and often difficult to detect. A person who is not aware that he is under the *(3) belief* influence of the drug often thinks that he is perfectly normal. The association between the effects of the drug and the drug itself is therefore a perception which has to be learned. It involves the association of events which occur separately with a considerable time interval between them. The understanding of withdrawal symptoms is even more complex, since it involves grasping the connection between the interruption of a series of injections and the distress that follows several hours later. It also involves reasoning which is contrary to the ordinary. When a person suddenly becomes ill he usually assumes that a foreign substance has been introduced into his body, not that one has been removed.

A person to whom the drug is given without his knowledge does not feel the buoyant sensations because the opiate's effects in small doses are not unusual enough to produce such a response. But it is evident that the buoyancy can be so interpreted to an ignorant user, and, by virtue of this explanation, he can learn to feel buoyed up with a shot. In order that the explanation may acquire meaning, however, the individual must appreciate the causal sequence that associates his sensations at a given moment with a series of preceding injections. It may be concluded, then, that only those to whom the drug's effects can be explained develop addiction. It has been shown that in many cases the beginning of addiction was marked by an addict's or physician's explanation of the significance of the withdrawal distress. On the other hand, patients experiencing withdrawal distress without understanding its connection with opiates, because the connection

1. George H. Mead, "A Behavioristic Account of the Significant Symbol," *Journal of Philosophy* (1922), 19: 160.

was not pointed out, escaped addiction. It may, therefore, be concluded that the immunity of the insane, idiots, and young children who may have taken morphine is based upon a feature common to all, namely, that the meaning of withdrawal symptoms cannot be explained to them.

The inexperienced non-addict fails to recognize the long-range effects of the first injection or to associate them with the immediate effect; hence he neglects, at first, to connect the withdrawal distress with prior use of the drug. Each aspect of opiate usage first appears as an isolated occurrence and is responded to in that way. When the withdrawal distress, the injection, and the drug's effects have been united into a single conceptual scheme, the individual no longer reacts to them separately but sees them as an integrated whole, one reaction implying or symbolizing the others. Withdrawal symptoms signify the need of an injection and are identified with the desire for it. The conceptualization of these events not only puts the various parts into relationship with each other but also relates them to the individual's self and to the culture of the group.

It is evident that the drug addict assumes the group's viewpoint with respect to his experience of withdrawal distress by virtue of the fact that, prior to addiction, he has been a non-addict and a participating member of society. In view of the very use of language symbols, in terms of which the processes of re-evaluation which constitute addiction proceed, the addict necessarily shares the traditional heritage which includes knowledge of, and attitudes toward, the drug habit. Prior to addiction addicts acquire the attitudes of non-addicts, and when they become addicted they must adjust themselves to these attitudes. In other words, as my theory emphasizes, addiction presupposes life in organized society. Children and animals cannot become addicts because they lack the ability to use and respond to the complex linguistic structures which have grown up in human society.

It is interesting to ask at what point a child can become an addict. Infants of 1 or 2 certainly do not become addicted, but a youth of 15 can. At what age does immunity end and why? Only one case which appears to have some bearing on this question was found in the literature of the subject. This involved an infant to whom opiates had been given from birth. Withdrawal symptoms had occurred during the first few days of extrauterine life, the mother having been addicted during pregnancy. The drug was withdrawn gradually when the child was 12 years old, and, as far as is known, he did not exhibit the usual tendency to relapse.[2] It is impossible to form an exact conception of the special factors involved in this case because of the meagerness of the data. The work of R. N. Chopra, who demonstrated that the feeding of opium to infants for the first three years of their lives was unrelated to addiction during adulthood, shows that 3-year-olds cannot be regarded as addicts.[3]

The question may be raised whether the cases in which the drug was continually used from birth do not constitute an exception to the assertion that the addict must belong to a social group before becoming addicted. It is evident, since the 3-year-old cannot be called an addict in our sense of the term, that the child who receives the drug continuously from birth would become an addict only with increasing participation in the culture of his group. The developing concepts of self and of causality and the growing appreciation of and the ability to use language are all involved in the normal development of a child; they are also implicated, as already shown, in the process of addiction.

Jean Piaget, describing some aspects of the mental development of children, writes: "Originally the child puts the whole content of consciousness in the world and draws no distinction between the 'I' and the external world. Above all we mean that the constitution of the idea of reality presupposes a progressive splitting up of this protoplasmic consciousness into two complementary universes—the objective universe and the subjective."[4] Piaget discusses the influence of the progressive differentiation of the subjective and objective upon the child's ideas of physical causality and concludes:

In the course of our studies in child psychology we had expected to fix upon 7–8 as the age before which no genuinely physical explanation could be given of natural phenomena. Our present inquiry

2. Charles E. Terry and Mildred Pellens, *The Opium Problem* (New York: Committee on Drug Addiction and Bureau of Social Hygiene, 1928), pp. 426–27.
3. R. N. Chopra and G. S. Chopra, "The Administration of Opium to Infants in India," *Indian Medical Gazette* (1934), 69: 489–94.
4. Jean Piaget, *The Child's Conception of Physical Causality* (New York: Harcourt, Brace, 1930), p. 242.

entirely confirms this expectation. After 7–8 the more positive forms of causality gradually supplant the others, and we can say that at the age of about 11–12 the evolution is completed. There is therefore, in the domain peculiar to causality, a process of evolution exactly similar to that to which we drew attention in speaking of reality: confusion of the self and the universe, then progressive separation with objectification of the causal sequences. . . . It is only after having assimilated the activity of external bodies to his own muscular activity that the child turns the new-made instrument upon himself and, thanks to it, becomes conscious of his internal experience.[5]

In view of Piaget's description of a child's developing conceptions of causality, the immunity of children to addiction, the apparently permanent cure of a 12-year-old who had been given drugs from birth, and the complete absence of addiction in young persons below the age of ten years or thereabouts, are not accidental circumstances but exactly what one would expect.

It is of considerable interest and significance that, during the last fifteen or so years, there has been considerable experimental work with rats and monkeys that has seemed to a number of investigators to confirm the idea that the hook in opiates is derived from the experience of relief of withdrawal distress, that is, from negative reinforcement. This convergence of views is notable in that it includes persons of very different professional and ideological commitments, such as sociologists, psychologists, and pharmacologists. The experimental findings with lower animals may be summarized with respect to the theoretical position outlined here by saying that they seem to indicate, insofar as animals are capable of responding to opiates as human subjects do, that the similarity is produced by the same basic mechanisms but in a simpler form. In other words, insofar as rats and monkeys can be hooked on drugs, the processes of their becoming so follow the same patterns as in human subjects.

A point of controversy is the question of how far lower animals can go in duplicating human responses. This question is part of the broader question of man's special place in the animal kingdom, his extraordinary intellectual capacities, and his possession of language. Complex human responses, it is argued, are medi-

5. *Ibid.*, p. 286.

ated by language symbols, by ideas or concepts. The significance of a stimulus or situation is not inherent and fixed, but is determined by the way in which it is perceived or conceived. Applied to addiction, these ideas suggest that the effects of drugs on behavior would be expected to depend on how they were understood and interpreted.

Man's possession of language and conceptual thought also enables him to organize and integrate his responses on a more complex level than is the case with lower animals.

Human addiction, unlike the reactions of lower animals, is a cultural or societal phenomenon. It becomes that when the person understands or grasps conceptually what is happening to him and identifies himself as an addict. When the raw biological and pharmacological events are conceptually elaborated they enter into relationships with other conceptual processes, such as conceptions of self and those connected with laws, rules, morality, punishment, and guilt. The complexities of addiction behavior which arise from the cultural nature of man and the fact that he is the only language-manipulating animal are naturally not found in rats and monkeys.

## Addicting and Non-addicting Drugs

The drugs designated as addicting, such as barbiturates, opiates, and alcohol, share the characteristic feature that all produce physical dependence and withdrawal distress. Non-addicting drugs, such as LSD, marihuana, cocaine, and others, do not involve these features. Confusion arises from the fact that there are persons who use non-addicting drugs regularly just as there are persons who use addicting drugs irregularly.

What is implied by the preceding analysis is that the attachments to these two types of substances are qualitatively different and are established in two very different ways. In the case of addicting drugs, we have argued that it is the push of withdrawal distress that fixes the habit; in the case of the non-addicting substances it is the pull of positive pleasure that motivates use. While the opiate addict says he takes the drug to feel normal, the users of LSD and marihuana obviously take these substances to feel other than normal. While opiate addicts under certain circumstances can be deceived about whether they are under the drug's influence, it is inconceivable that an experienced LSD user could take a trip without knowing it or be sent on a trip with a placebo. In the language of reinforcement theory, one may suggest, therefore, that the powerful habits connected with addicting drugs are established by the mechanisms of negative reinforcement, while the weaker habits connected with non-addicting drugs are based on those of positive reinforcement.

From considerations of this kind it is reasonable to suppose that other addictions, such as those involving barbiturates and alcohol, follow the same pattern and involve essentially the same mechanisms as opiate addiction. This point has been made explicitly by Bales with respect to alcoholism.[6] Hebb has argued that there is addiction to food and that the mechanisms that establish this necessary form of addiction may be the same as those of opiate addiction. Withdrawal distress in this case is called hunger. As with opiates, the child is taught to recognize the symptoms and what to do about them. As the individual increases in sophistication, hunger ceases to be the almost purely biological matter that it is at birth and becomes a conceptually and socially controlled process that is linked in intricate ways with other higher cortical functions. As in the case of opium, deprivation or prolonged suffering from hunger and undernourishment intensify the craving and lead to overindulgence when the opportunity offers itself. Just as the symptoms of opiate withdrawal and the desire for opiates are identified with each other by the drug user, so also is the word "hunger" used to refer both to a bodily condition and to a desire for food, which is sometimes linked with the bodily condition and sometimes not.[7]

There are substances like the vitamins, which produce withdrawal symptoms when they are withdrawn, but which do not generate a craving and do not produce an immediately identifiable impact or kick when they are injected. One may speculate that, if the symptoms of severe vitamin deficiency were relieved immediately and dramatically by taking the vitamin, a psychologi-

6. R. F. Bales, *The "Fixation Factor" in Alcohol Addiction* (unpublished doctoral dissertation, Harvard University, 1944).

7. D. O. Hebb, *The Organization of Behavior* (New York: John Wiley, 1949), p. 199.

cal dependence or craving for such substances might be developed. Conversely, if the symptoms of opiate withdrawal vanished only very gradually over a considerable time period after a shot, it may be supposed that no craving would be produced. Speculations of this kind raise questions as to what the timing must be in the relief of distress of this sort for the subject to experience it as euphoria.

### Psychoses and Addiction

The contention that addiction requires a relatively normal cognitive ability sufficient to understand withdrawal symptoms or to grasp a proffered explanation of them implies that full-fledged psychotics with seriously disturbed cognitive processes should be immune to addiction. Pertinent observations by physicians concerning this point may be cited. Sceleth and Kuh, for example, remarked:

> Several hundred patients suffering from the depressed stage of manic depressive insanity were given large doses of opium orally in many instances for periods of from six months to one year. Not one of these patients ever knew what drug he was taking or ever showed any untoward results when it was withdrawn, or in any other way gave evidence of a desire to continue its use. Nor do we recall a single instance recorded in the medical literature of the period during which this form of treatment was administered quite commonly, in which either withdrawal symptoms or a craving for narcotics was reported. This is significant in view of the idea that manic depressive insanity is based on an inherited unstable nervous system.[8]

Dr. Paul Wolff, formerly of Germany, reported the answers to the following question, which was asked of many leading German medical men: "When is the prescription of opium justified?" Three of those who replied referred incidentally to the absence of addiction among psychotics. Dr. Wolff concluded:

> Opium is indispensable in dealing with the fear states of the melancholic individual. But here we make the surprising discovery that

8. Charles E. Sceleth and Sidney Kuh, "Drug Addiction," *Journal of the American Medical Association* (1924), 82: 680.

the continued administration of opium, in the form of opium tincture, during the melancholic mental disturbances, even when continued over a long period of time does not produce drug addiction. That is, it does not, provided the dosage is adapted to the diseased mental state of the patient and provided that the doctor is careful to withdraw the drug at the correct time, as soon as he notes a decrease in the fear tension or excitement of the psychotic patient. In the last three and one-half decades I have seen a number of cases of morphine addiction develop as a consequence of the over-hasty application of morphine in physical distress or disease, but do not recall one single instance in which the administration of scopolaminemorphine during a psychosis led to a craving which lasted beyond the period of the illness.[9]

Dr. Emil Bratz, director of the Berlin Sanitarium, replying to Dr. Wolff's questionnaire, made the following observation on this question, recommending morphine for use in case of depression and for endogenous psychoses:

... but also *only* in endogenous, that is in simple or periodic melancholia arising from a constitutional basis, and even then it should be administered only by an experienced neurologist. Warning must be issued against the administration of opiate preparations in cases of reactive depression in psychopaths—that is, depression in response to the vicissitudes of life. In these cases, it leads with especial ease to the development of addiction.[10]

Professor Karl Bonhoeffer stated:

Opium is indispensable in many cases of endogenous depressions. ... The prescription of opiates for states of depression is unobjectionable also because we know from experience that the depressed persons feel no need for narcotics when the depression has passed away, and practically never become addicts.[11]

9. Paul Wolff, "Wann ist die Verschreibung von Opiaten ärtzlich Begründet?" *Deutsche Medizinische Wochenschrift* (1931), 57: 266. Wolff reported the results of the inquiry in a series of five articles beginning on pages 133, 178, 223, 266, and 318 of the volume cited.
10. *Ibid.*, p. 181.
11. *Ibid.*, p. 223.

These medical opinions clearly suggest that the individual who is isolated from society by certain kinds of mental disease is immune to addiction. It is especially significant that some of the authorities insisted upon the distinction between "endogenous" depressions and those brought about, as Bratz said, by "the vicissitudes of life." The latter, it is indicated, are associated with susceptibility to addiction, the former with immunity.

## Marginal Patterns

Reference has already been made to patterns of drug dependence among patients in medical practice in which the individual does not identify himself as an addict even though he is not altogether ignorant of his actual situation. Between the patient who has no idea what drug he is receiving and knows nothing of withdrawal and physical dependence and one who becomes addicted in the ordinary and usual sense, there is evidently a range of variation which has been inadequately investigated. In the case of the drug-dependent person who defines himself as a medical patient and considers morphine as a "medicine" which he must have to control or alleviate disease symptoms or pain, it appears that there must be something in the objective situation to validate and support this self-conception. Such objective elements may be the actual presence of organic pathology and the very fact that the drug is prescribed by the physician and administered in a medical setting. When such a patient takes the step of administering drugs to himself it seems probable that this tends to undermine and soon destroy his conception of himself as a medical patient. Since the person ordinarily has strong motivations for preferring to be a patient rather than a dope addict, it would be expected that self-deceiving rationalizations would be employed to maintain the former identity whenever possible. By the same token, the person who, in his own mind, has made the switch and knows he is simply an addict would be expected to conceal this fact and prevent others from realizing it.

The settings in which drugs are taken or in which withdrawal distress occurs are known to have profound effects upon the human subject's evaluation of these experiences. Thus, initial euphoric effects are often not noticed when the drug is first taken in a medical setting for medical reasons. An experienced addict, invited to give himself an injection in the police station with several narcotic agents as an audience, is not likely to enjoy the experience. Withdrawal distress appears markedly more severe when the addict kicks his habit in a cell in a jail than when he kicks it in Synanon attended and surrounded by friends who are also addicts. Related phenomena which contribute to the same point are that some of the unpleasant effects associated with the first few trials of the drug, such as dizziness and nausea, come to be highly prized and desired by the addict and that some of the withdrawal symptoms may be evoked in the abstaining addict by suggestions communicated to him. Considerations of this kind indicate that pleasure and pain are elusive, subjective phenomena and that the perception of pain and pleasure may sometimes be considerably modified, neutralized, or even reversed by influences of a conceptual nature derived from the social environment.

It should thus not be surprising that persons who become addicted in medical practice sometimes report that they have never experienced euphoria from the drug. Drug-dependent patients and others who receive opiates for shorter periods no doubt exhibit a wide range of cognitive responses to their situations. A more systematic exploration of this area, with close attention given to the patient's ideas, would be of the greatest interest and importance to the social psychologist concerned with the study of drug effects. The same may be said of experiments with opiates in which placebos are employed. A fuller exploitation of data from these sources would undoubtedly contribute greatly to a more discriminating analysis of addiction than is presently possible.

Extremely interesting and challenging theoretical notions are implicit in the Dole-Nyswander project in New York City in which heroin addicts taken from streets of the city are provided with maintenance doses of methadone, a synthetic equivalent of heroin. The methadone is provided the addict gratis once or twice a day in orange juice in sufficient quantity to maintain body equilibrium and prevent withdrawal distress from appearing. Dole and Nyswander describe what they do in medical terms: they provide "patients" with a "medicine" which "blocks the craving for heroin." The manifestations of heroin addiction are controlled, they argue, much as those of diabetes are controlled by insulin. The program is entirely voluntary and contains no punishment and no threats. The subjects are encouraged to get jobs or to go on to school, and most do.

Under this program the behavior of the subjects changes in a remarkable manner. For example, they begin to speak of their addiction in the past tense, they spontaneously stop talking much about dope and report that they think about it very much less. It appears, in short, that their identity conceptions are changed; they are no longer junkies, but medical patients, and there are corresponding behavioral changes implied by the redefinition. It has been reported repeatedly that there has been no problem in stabilizing the daily dosage of the subjects and that the addict's usual impulse to increase it is either greatly diminished or absent. The subjects seem to act and think like medical patients. Some of the reported effects are no doubt connected with the reduction in anxiety that is associated with having an assured supply of pure drugs made available without any of the usual risks and with much less stigma.[12]

## Cures of Addiction

If the craving for opiates which characterizes addiction is indeed dependent upon withdrawal distress in the manner that has been suggested, the longstanding idea that the problem of narcotics addiction might be solved by the discovery of a non-habit-forming substitute for morphine or heroin is illusory. In a sense, addicts desire the drug because it is habit forming, that is, because it produces physical dependence and withdrawal distress. A drug which did not have such effects could not conceivably be the psychological equivalent of morphine; such an equivalent

12. Vincent P. Dole and Marie E. Nyswander, "A Medical Treatment for Diacetylmorphine (Heroin) Addiction, A Clinical Trial with Methadone Hydrochloride," *Journal of the American Medical Association* (August 23, 1965), 193 (8): 80–84, and by the same authors, "Rehabilitation of Heroin Addicts after Blockade with Methadone," *New York State Journal of Medicine* (August 1, 1966), 66 (15): 2011–17. This description is based in part on my conversations with Dole and Nyswander.

drug would necessarily have to be another habit-forming drug.

One may argue that there are many non-habit-forming substitutes for opiates available at present, if one means by this drugs which produce pleasant sensations but no physical dependence or withdrawal reaction. Marihuana is such a drug, and cocaine is another and a much more powerful one. Neither functions as a substitute for heroin or morphine. The idea of a non-habit-forming substitute for habit-forming drugs, conceived as a solution of the narcotics problem, is comparable to the idea of a non-nutritious substitute for food or a non-liquid substitute for water.

When cures of addiction are discussed, the reference is usually to the process of separating the addict from his drug or to voluntary abstention from use. Little attention is given to the relapse impulse itself, which apparently persists for very long periods of time and probably permanently, in the abstinent addict. This feature of drug addiction is not peculiar to it but is also apparent in other habits. As has been suggested, the cognitive changes that addiction produces as the individual learns from direct experience about the drug and its effects on him may well constitute the most ineradicable feature of the relapse impulse. It is inappropriate to speak of a cure for knowledge. Curing a person of addiction might, in this sense, be compared with curing a person of a college education.

# PART II

# Opiate Addiction as a Social Problem

(Except for minor editorial changes, the next four chapters are reproduced as they appeared in the original edition in 1947. Chapter 13 provides a postscript summarizing the nature of the problem in 1968.)

# 9

## THE PROBLEM

## IN THE UNITED STATES DURING

## THE NINETEENTH CENTURY

Before tracing the development of the narcotics problem in the United States, it is appropriate to consider briefly the broader historical aspects of the problem. Morphine and heroin are derivatives of opium developed during the nineteenth century, but the history of opium itself and of its use by man begins at least several thousand years before the birth of Christ.

Mesopotamia is believed to have been the original home of the opium poppy. The Sumerians, who settled there in 5000 or 6000 B.C., developed an ideogram for opium.[1] This ideogram has been translated as HUL GIL, the HUL meaning "joy" or "rejoicing." Methods of obtaining opium from the poppy were about the same then as they are now. The cultivation of the poppy and the use of

1. Charles E. Terry and Mildred Pellens, *The Opium Problem* (New York, Committee on Drug Addictions and Bureau of Social Hygiene, 1928), p. 55.

opium spread from Mesopotamia to other parts of the ancient world. The Greeks, Romans, Persians, and Egyptians became acquainted with the drug. Homer mentioned it in the ninth century B.C. Arab traders are believed to have introduced it into the Orient, which is now the principal source.[2]

Inasmuch as opium was used as a remedy for human ills even before the Christian era and constituted the main therapeutic agent of medical men for more than two thousand years (through the nineteenth century),[3] it is not surprising that the people of the East, where the poppy is grown, should have suffered more than their share from addiction. Nor is it unusual that for a long time opium addiction was regarded in the West as something peculiar to the Orient.

In 1804, Friedrich Wilhelm Adam Sertürner, a German chemist at Einbeck, discovered in opium meconic acid and an alkaline base which he named *morphium*. This discovery, which marked the beginning of modern alkaloidal medicine, gave great impetus to the development of the type of drug addiction which was to prevail in the West. Other opium alkaloids and derivatives were developed in rapid succession, often in the hope or belief that the new compounds would be free from the habit-forming propensities of previous ones. The climax was reached with the isolation of heroin, or diacetylmorphine, in 1898. This was the last opiate preparation to be hailed by medical men as a non-habit-forming substitute for opium or morphine or as a cure for drug addiction. Heroin turned out to be approximately three times as powerful as morphine (which was more potent than opium) and just as habit-forming.

While Orientals have, in general, persisted in smoking opium or using it orally, another tendency has appeared among them in recent decades as a consequence of efforts made to stamp out smoking. The West, returning favor for favor, has supplied the East with hypodermic needles and with more potent opiates, particularly morphine and heroin. As it becomes more difficult for Chinese addicts to continue their smoking habits it is to be expected that the hypodermic needle will become more popular

2. *Ibid.*, pp. 55–57.
3. *Ibid.*, p. 58.

among them and that they—like the addicts of the United States —will become "vein shooters."

Thomas DeQuincey's *Confessions of an English Opium Eater*, published in 1821, set the style and provided the terms which dominated discussions of opiate addiction for many decades thereafter. DeQuincey drank his opium in the form of laudanum. As a result of his widely read work, addicts were called "opium eaters," regardless of the manner in which they consumed the drug, except that opium smokers were apparently never so designated. The users of morphine, who began to appear in increasing numbers in the 1820's and 1830's, were also referred to as "opium eaters."

It is popularly believed today that most addicts are criminals or derelicts prior to addiction. As we have seen, this impression requires considerable qualification as it applies to contemporary drug users. It is even more inaccurate with respect to the opium eaters of the nineteenth century. In 1889 B. A. Hartwell solicited opinions from druggists in 180 Massachusetts cities concerning the economic and social status of the addicts they knew. Twenty-two per cent of those who replied said addicts were to be found in all classes, another 22 per cent said that the upper classes were principally involved, 3 per cent named the middle classes, and only 6 per cent the lower classes.[4]

Addiction during the nineteenth century, except opium smoking, was not linked up with crime to any appreciable extent. There are a few references to the use of laudanum by prostitutes, but it was not suggested that women became prostitutes because of the drug. The principal stress was placed upon the vice of opium eating among the respectable classes rather than among criminals. W. R. Cobbe said in 1895 that those who drank laudanum, swallowed gum or powdered opium, or used morphine were for the most part intelligent and respectable members of society. He also pointed out that they purchased their supplies of the drug openly and legally in the drugstores.[5]

4. "The Sale and Use of Opium in Massachusetts," *Annual Report of the Massachusetts Board of Health* (1889), 22: 137–58.
5. W. R. Cobbe, *Doctor Judas, A Portrayal of the Opium Habit* (Chicago: S. C. Griggs, 1895), p. 127.

Surveys conducted before the passing of the Harrison Act in 1914 invariably indicated that women addicts outnumbered men by about three to two. For example, in 1878 Orville Marshall found that 62.2 per cent of a sample of 1,313 cases in Michigan were women,[6] and L. P. Brown in 1914 found 66.9 per cent of a group of 2,370 Tennessee addicts to be women.[7] Current statistics based upon samples obtained from law enforcement agencies always show a vast preponderance of males. Other portions of the population in which the incidence of addiction was relatively high, and probably still is, were ex-soldiers and the medical and allied professions.

Addicts experienced no difficulty in obtaining their drugs in those days; in fact, narcotics were almost forced upon them. Not only did the drugstores sell the supplies cheaply and openly, but all kinds of opiate-containing patent medicines were advertised. Thus the addict of the nineteenth century had unlimited sources of supply. He could buy paregoric, laudanum, tincture of opium, morphine, Winslow's Soothing Syrup, Godfrey's Cordial, Mc-Munn's Elixir of Opium, or many other preparations. For a few cents a day he could keep himself loaded. He could even obtain opium by purchasing the so-called cures, widely promoted during the period. Virtually all such remedies contained opiates and were merely examples of quackery.

A narcotics user once flatly asserted to me: "If a junkie tells you he got on to the stuff through his doctor, spit in his eye." The addict of today does not ordinarily become initiated through medical treatment. However, most opium eaters of the last century did, in fact, form the habit through medical treatment or by self-medication. One of the most informative books[8] on drug addiction in the nineteenth century cites more than a hundred cases of addicts who uniformly contracted the habit as a result of medical treatment. Terry and Pellens[9] quote numerous concurring

6. "The Opium Habit in Michigan," *Annual Report of the Michigan State Board of Health* (1878), 6: 61–73.

7. "Enforcement of the Tennessee Anti-Narcotic Law," *American Journal of Public Health* (1915), 5: 323–33.

8. Alonzo Calkins, *Opium and the Opium Appetite* (Philadelphia: J. B. Lippincott, 1871).

9. Terry and Pellens, *op. cit.*, pp. 94–110.

opinions on this point before 1900. Little emphasis was placed on the effects of evil association, and dope peddlers were not mentioned because they were rare or nonexistent.

The public then had an altogether different conception of drug addiction from that which prevails today. The habit was not approved, but neither was it regarded as criminal or monstrous. It was usually looked upon as a vice or personal misfortune, or much as alcoholism is viewed today. Narcotics users were pitied rather than loathed as criminals or degenerates—an attitude which still prevails in Europe.

The sharp contrast between the former public attitude and the present one is well illustrated by the case of the physician who contended in 1889 that it was obviously better to be a drug addict than a drunkard and therefore advocated that chronic alcoholics be cured by transforming them into drug addicts. He published the following statement on this question in a reputable medical journal:

> The only grounds on which opium in lieu of alcohol can be claimed as reformatory are that it is less inimical to healthy life than alcohol, that it calms in place of exciting the baser passions, and hence is less productive of acts of violence and crime; in short, that as a whole the use of morphine in place of alcohol is but a choice of evils, and by far the lesser. To be sure, the populace and even many physicians think very differently, but this is because they have not thought as they should upon the matter.
>
> On the score of economy the morphine habit is by far the better. The regular whiskey drinker can be made content in his craving for stimulation, at least for quite a long time, on two or three grains of morphine a day, divided into appropriate portions, and given at regular intervals. If purchased by the drachm at fifty cents this will last him twenty days. Now it is safe to say that a like amount of spirits for the steady drinker cannot be purchased for two and one-half cents a day, and that the majority of them spend five and ten times that sum a day as a regular thing.
>
> On the score, then, of a saving to the individual and his family in immediate outlay, and of incurred disability, of the great diminution of peace disturbers and of crime, whereby an immense outlay will be saved the State; on the score of decency of behavior instead of perverse deviltry, of bland courtesy instead of vicious combativeness; on the score of a lessened liability to fearful diseases and the lessened

propagation of pathologically inclined blood, I would urge the substitution of morphine instead of alcohol for all to whom such a craving is an incurable propensity. In this way I have been able to bring peacefulness and quiet to many disturbed and distracted homes, to keep the head of the family out of the gutter and out of the lock-up, to keep him from scandalous misbehavior and neglect of his affairs, to keep him from the verges and actualities of delirium tremens and horrors, and, above all, to save him from committing, as I veritably believe, some terrible crime that would cast a lasting and deep shadow upon an innocent and worthy family circle for generation after generation. Is it not the duty of a physician when he cannot cure an ill, when there is no reasonable ground for hope that it will ever be done, to do the next best thing—advise a course of treatment that will diminish to an immense extent great evils otherwise irremediable? . . .

The mayors and police courts would almost languish for lack of business; the criminal dockets, with their attendant legal functionaries, would have much less to do than they now have—to the profit and well-being of the community. I might, had I time and space, enlarge by statistics to prove the law-abiding qualities of opium-eating peoples, but of this anyone can perceive somewhat for himself, if he carefully watches and reflects on the quiet, introspective gaze of the morphine habitué and compares it with the riotous devil-may-care leer of the drunkard.[10]

The consumption of opiates increased enormously, far outdistancing the growth of population, during the last half of the nineteenth century. Since there was relatively little illicit traffic, the following figures on the importation of opiates give a fairly accurate picture of the enormous increase in consumption of this drug during the last four decades of the last century:

| Decades | Opium (in pounds) | Opium Alkaloids (in ounces) |
|---------|-------------------|------------------------------|
| 1860–69 | 110,305 | 588 |
| 1870–79 | 192,602 | 2,296 |
| 1880–89 | 328,392 | 20,212 |
| 1890–99 | 513,070 | 20,193 |

10. J. R. Black, "Advantages of Substituting the Morphia Habit for the Incurably Alcoholic," *Cincinnati Lancet-Clinic* (1889), 22: 537–41.

After 1900 there was a drop in these totals, but it is probable that the illicit traffic was on the increase, since local restrictive legislation was becoming more frequent. In 1909 a federal law was passed prohibiting the importation of opium for smoking. The figures in the above table represent an increased use of opiates in medical practice and in the production of patent medicines as well as an increased prevalence of addiction.

## The Opium Smoker

In contrast with the opium eater, who was regarded simply as the victim of an unfortunate vice, the American opium smoker was typically considered, as H. H. Kane said, "a sporting character." Kane made a careful attempt to trace the development of the habit.

> The first white man who smoked opium in America is said to have been a sporting character named Glendenyn. This was in California in 1868. The second—induced to try it by the first—smoked in 1871. The practice spread rapidly and quietly among this class of gamblers and prostitutes until the latter part of 1875, at which time the authorities became cognizant of the fact and finding, upon investigation, that many women and young girls, as also young men of respectable family, were being induced to visit the dens, where they were ruined morally and otherwise, a city ordinance was passed forbidding the practice under penalty of a heavy fine or imprisonment, or both.[11]

Kane quotes from a letter written by a doctor of Virginia City, Nevada:

> "Opium smoking had been entirely confined to the Chinese up to and before the autumn of 1876, when the practice was introduced by a sporting character who had lived in China, where he had contracted the habit. He spread the practice amongst his class, and his mistress, a woman of the town, introduced it among her *demi-monde* acquaintances, and it was not long before it had widely spread amongst the people mentioned and then amongst the younger class of boys and girls, many of the latter of the more respected class of

11. H. H. Kane, *Opium Smoking in America and China* (New York: G. P. Putnam, 1882), p. 1.

families. The habit grew very rapidly until it reached young women of more mature age, when the necessity for stringent measures became apparent, and was met by the passing of a city ordinance."[12]

Considerable numbers of Chinese arrived in the United States during the 1850's; there were thousands in the West by 1860.[13] It seems incredible, therefore, that no white man should have tried the drug before 1868. An addict who began to smoke opium while he was in the West in 1906 told me that, although he had heard about the account given by Kane, he was disposed to regard it as legend. At any rate, the denizens of the American underworld acquired the habit from the Chinese, who taught them the ritual and the technique and at first supplied the drug. The Chinese influence upon the use of narcotics is evident in many words in the addict's argot.[14]

According to Kane:

The very fact that opium smoking was a practice forbidden by law seemed to lead many who would not otherwise have indulged to seek out the low dens and patronize them, while the regular smokers found additional pleasure in continuing that about which there was a spice of danger. It seemed to add zest to their enjoyment. Men and women, young girls, virtuous or just commencing a downward career, hardened prostitutes, representatives of the "hoodlum" element, young clerks and errand boys who could ill afford the waste of time and money, and young men who had no work to do were to be found smoking together in the back rooms of laundries in the low, pestilential dens of Chinatown, reeking with filth and overrun with vermin, in the cellars of drinking saloons, and in houses of prostitution.[15]

The *San Francisco Chronicle* of July 25, 1881, stated that "the habit in past years, so far as whites are concerned, was confined

12. *Ibid.*, p. 3.
13. See Herbert Asbury, *The Barbary Coast* (New York: Garden City Publishing Co., 1933), chapter 7. Asbury states that in 1852 there were an estimated 22,000 Chinese in California. In 1870 the number was 71,328, according to the U.S. Census. This author gives an excellent picture of San Francisco when opium smoking was introduced.
14. See Glossary.
15. Kane, *op. cit.*, p. 2.

to hoodlums and prostitutes mostly." It added, "Now that there are scores of places where the habit can be contracted in clean rooms in respectable portions of the city, the practice will gradually extend up in the social grade."[16]

The rapidity with which the opium-smoking habit spread was noted by an anonymous writer in *Chambers' Journal* in 1888:

> In 1877 and 1878 when Deadwood, the Metropolis of the Black Hills, one of the richest mining camps ever discovered in the United States, was over 300 miles from the nearest railroad, it was ascertained that the Chinamen had introduced the vice of opium-smoking among the white inhabitants. I was employed at the time as deputy-sheriff, and received instructions to investigate the subject with a view to closing the houses and punishing the proprietors.[17]

Action taken by local authorities was apparently not very effective, for former smokers state that as late as 1910 they were able to travel almost anywhere in the West without taking along either a supply of opium or an opium pipe, depending solely upon the dens that operated in almost all sizeable towns.

The opium smoker of the nineteenth century belonged to an elite underworld group which despised and generally avoided all contact with the hypodermic user or "opium eater" of respectable society. Smokers usually regarded the hypodermic habit as more vicious and difficult to break than the smoking habit. They applied the term "dope fiend" to those who used the drug in some manner other than smoking, but did not apply it to themselves. Their attitudes were indicated by an incident that occurred early in the twentieth century in a New York opium-smoking joint. One of the smokers discovered a hypodermic user in the bathroom giving himself an injection. He immediately reported to the proprietor that there was a "God-damned dope fiend in the can." The offender was promptly ejected.

Unlike opium eating, the smoking habit did not involve contact with the medical profession, for doctors did not prescribe it. Hence, the habit spread solely through contacts with persons who were already addicted, and this is the manner in which drug

16. *Ibid.*, p. 11.
17. "Opium Joints in the Black Hills," *Chambers' Journal* (1888), 65: 654.

addiction in the underworld has continued to spread. A special committee of investigation appointed in 1918 by the Secretary of the Treasury stated: "with respect to the addict of good social standing, the evidence obtained by the committee points to the physician as the agent through whom the habit is acquired in the majority of cases."[18]

It thus appears that the association between addiction and crime in the United States was built up as a consequence of the rapid spread of opium smoking in the underworld during the last decades of the past century. Considerable notoriety and public attention was directed toward this problem. The fact that many thieves and rascals were opium smokers gradually led the public to the belief that all addicts were thieves or rascals and that there was an inherent or necessary connection between the use of opiates and a life of crime. As a matter of fact, the principal reason for the American addict's criminality is not connected with the effects of the drug as such, but rather with the high cost of the drug. In India where there is much addiction but where opium is inexpensive, there is relatively little criminality among addicts.[19]

18. Quoted by Terry and Pellens, *op. cit.*, p. 120.
19. See R. N. Chopra, "Drug Addiction in India and Its Treatment," *Indian Medical Gazette* (1935), 70: 121–31; and Lawrence Kolb, "Drug Addiction in Its Relation to Crime," *Mental Hygiene* (1925), 9: 74–89.

# 10

# FEDERAL ANTI-NARCOTICS

# LEGISLATION

The Harrison Act, passed in 1914, profoundly changed the nature of the narcotics problem in the United States. This law was intended as a revenue and control measure and was not designed to penalize the user of the drug, to whom no direct reference was made. The enforcement of the law was entrusted to the Bureau of Internal Revenue of the U.S. Treasury Department. It was evidently assumed or hoped that by requiring all persons who handled drugs to register with the government and maintain records the flow of drugs would be subject to public control. The act applied equally to cocaine and to opiates and made no distinctions between them. It required all persons who imported, manufactured, produced, compounded, sold, dealt in, dispensed, or gave away any derivative of opium or of coca leaves (cocaine) to register with the Collector of Internal Revenue, to pay special taxes, and to keep records of their transactions. Preparations containing minute quantities of cocaine or of opiates were exempted from the regulations.

Certain of the provisions of Section 1 came to be of crucial importance for the addict. They ran as follows:

> It shall be unlawful for any person to purchase, sell, dispense, or distribute any of the aforesaid drugs except in the original stamped package or from the original stamped package . . . provided, the provisions of this paragraph shall not apply . . . to the dispensing, or administration or giving away of any of the aforesaid drugs to a patient by a registered physician, dentist, or veterinary surgeon or other practitioner in the course of his professional practice, and where said drugs are dispensed or administered to the patient for legitimate medical purposes, and the record kept as required by this Act.[1]

The interpretation of the phrases "legitimate medical purposes" and "in the course of his professional practice" has led to controversy between enforcement agencies and those medical men who insist that prescribing drugs for an addict falls within the legitimate province of the physician.

In Section 2 of the act a similar statement and a similar exception occur:

> It shall be unlawful for any person to sell, barter, exchange, or give away any of the aforesaid drugs except in pursuance of a written order of the person to whom such article is sold, bartered, exchanged, or given. . . . Nothing contained in this section shall apply to the dispensing or distribution of any of the aforesaid drugs to a patient by a physician, dentist, or veterinary surgeon registered under this Act in the course of his professional practice only.[2]

Again in Section 8 the following statement occurs:

> It shall be unlawful for any person not registered under the provisions of this Act . . . to have in his possession or under his control any of the aforesaid drugs . . . provided, that this section shall not apply . . . to the possession of any of the aforesaid drugs which has

1. Taken from the text of the act as given by Terry and Pellens, *The Opium Problem* (New York: Committee on Drug Addictions and Bureau of Social Hygiene, 1928), Appendix VIII, p. 984.
2. *Ibid.*, p. 985.

or have been prescribed in good faith by a physician, dentist or veterinary surgeon registered under this Act.[3]

Some physicians have felt that the phrases "legitimate medical purposes," "professional practice," and "prescribed in good faith" mean that they are entitled to regard addiction as a disease and the addict as a patient to whom they may prescribe drugs to alleviate the distress of withdrawal. English drug laws do interpret addiction in this manner and allow physicians to prescribe drugs for addicts. If the Harrison Act had been interpreted in this manner, American addicts would have been able to buy low-cost legitimate drugs and the illicit traffic in these drugs would probably not have developed. There is virtually no illicit traffic in opiates in England. The Treasury Department has, however, interpreted the Harrison Act to mean that a doctor's prescription for an addict is unlawful, although exceptions are allowed in the case of the aged and infirm addicts for whom withdrawal of the drug might result in death and in the case of addicts suffering from incurable disease.[4] It is specified in this connection that

> physicians will be held accountable if through carelessness or lack of sufficient personal attention the patient secures more narcotic drugs than are necessary for medical treatment, and devotes part of his supply to satisfy addiction.[5]

Anyone who is at all acquainted with addiction knows that this requirement is impractical and cannot possibly be strictly observed.

The Harrison Act has thus made it almost impossible for the addict to obtain drugs regularly from any legitimate source. The doctor's prescription, the drugstore, and patent medicines were eliminated as sources. In their place, to meet the insistent demand for drugs, the illicit traffic grew up. The illicit drug was sold to consumers at prices which were often ten to fifty times higher

3. *Ibid.*, p. 989. See also Chapter 11, pp. 745–806, for a discussion of the implications of this law for the medical profession.
4. *Ibid.*, p. 756. Treasury Decision, No. 2809, March 20, 1919.
5. *Ibid.*, p. 757.

and more during World War I than the price of the legitimate product.

## The Jones-Miller Act

In 1922 in the Jones-Miller Act, Congress provided a fine of not more than $5,000 and imprisonment for not more than ten years for anyone,

> who fraudulently or knowingly imports or brings any narcotic drug into the United States or any territory under its control or jurisdiction, contrary to law, or assists in so doing, or receives, conceals, buys, sells, or in any manner facilitates the transportation, concealment, or sale of any such narcotic drug after being imported or brought in, knowing the same to have been imported contrary to law.[6]

The act also specified that mere possession of the drug was sufficient evidence for conviction unless the defendant could explain the possession to the satisfaction of the jury.[7]

## Social Effects

Some of the effects of the legislation mentioned were, no doubt, desirable; others were definitely undesirable. On the credit side it should be pointed out that for most portions of the population the removal of the drug from open and unrestricted sale and the regulations imposed upon doctors reduced the availability of narcotics and to this degree prevented the spread of the habit. Severe penalties imposed upon addicts and vendors of the drug may also have acted as deterrents. The exorbitant prices charged by illicit dealers also to some extent act as a deterrent to persons who might use the drug if it cost less. No reliable figures are available, however, to indicate whether the number of addicts in the United States has been increasing or decreasing.

Among the undesirable effects of the legislation are the crea-

6. *Ibid.*, Appendix IV, pp. 962–63.
7. *Ibid.*, p. 963.

tion of the illicit traffic, the pauperization and demoralization of addicts, and the stimulation of crime, particularly theft and prostitution. All of these effects follow from the high cost of the illicit drug and from the fact that no legitimate sources of supply are open to most drug users. While it is true that some addicts are criminals prior to addiction, many, perhaps most of them, turn to crime only when the high price of the drug and the danger and inconvenience of maintaining a supply force them to do so. The vast proportion of all the crimes committed by addicts are either violations of the drug laws or theft in order to obtain money to buy the drug.

During the nineteenth century there were many opiate addicts, known as "opium eaters," who were not forced to live in the underworld because of their habits. As has been pointed out, they were usually reasonably respectable members of society, and there is even reason to believe that many of them belonged to upper strata of society. Today, this class has virtually ceased to exist, its former members having been forced into the underworld. Anyone who becomes an addict now finds it extremely difficult and hazardous to maintain his status as a law-abiding person. Since no legitimate sources of the drug are open to him he must take the risk of dealing with peddlers. Once he is caught and sentenced his fate is sealed. He is branded as a criminal. He must thereafter live by his wits whether he wishes to or not.

While the severe restrictions that are placed upon the handling of drugs prevent a part of the population from being exposed to the possibility of addiction, it should be noted that, at the same time, the illicit traffic, called into being by the same regulations, imports and distributes a vast quantity of the forbidden drugs, thus doubly exposing another portion of the population to addiction. The illegal dealer does not keep records or pay taxes on the supplies he handles, and there is nothing to prevent him from giving or selling the drug to anyone he pleases. As a consequence, the spread of the habit in the underworld is not subject to any public control.

There is no doubt that the existence of the illicit traffic in opiates in the United States today is directly dependent upon the enforcement of the Harrison and Jones-Miller acts, which prevent almost all competition between the legal and illegal businesses in narcotics. Prior to 1914 there was some smuggling of opium for smoking, but it was not until some years later, when the Harrison Act began to be seriously enforced, that illicit prices rose and the smuggling of drugs became a really big business.

Another interesting feature of our anti-narcotics legislation is that, whereas it purports to be aimed at the peddler of the drug rather than at the user and does not specifically define the use of drugs as a crime, it does in fact make every addict in the United States a criminal unless he happens to be so old and infirm that withdrawal of the drug would cause death or unless he has an incurable disease. It is possible for a man to be a chronic alcoholic and to drink himself to death without violating the law. It is not possible for an addict to use drugs without violating the law or causing someone else to violate the law. As a consequence of the drug user's vulnerability to arrest, much of the punishment for the violation of the drug laws is handed out to the user of the drug rather than to the peddler. The federal institutions and prisons are filled mainly with the victims of the drug traffic, not with those who profit from the traffic.

The current evil reputation of drug addicts in the United States arises from the peculiar historical development of the problem of addiction in this country. The fact that opium smoking became a fad in the American underworld probably provided the original grounds for the idea that there is an inherent connection between crime and addiction and provided the impetus for anti-narcotics legislation. This legislation in turn reinforced the notion that addicts are necessarily criminals by actually making them that. The agencies which enforce anti-narcotics legislation have become a vested interest in the status quo, and the fact that addicts in most of the other nations of the West are not nearly as criminal as those of the United States has been ignored. In no other country in the world does the opiate addict pay as much for his supply as he does here. This not only accounts for most of the crimes committed by addicts but has also made the United States the most lucrative market in the world for the illicit trafficker. It has also stimulated the cultivation of the poppy in remote portions of the earth.

A competent English observer and medical man commented upon the American situation:

> In the United States of America a drug addict is regarded as a malefactor even though the habit has been acquired through the medicinal use of the drug, as in the case, *e.g.*, of American soldiers who were gassed and otherwise maimed in the Great War. The Harrison Narcotic Law was passed in 1914 by the Federal Government of the United States with general popular approval. It places severe restrictions upon the sale of narcotics and upon the medical profession, and necessitated the appointment of a whole army of officials. In consequence of this stringent law a vast clandestine commerce in narcotics has grown up in that country. The small bulk of these drugs renders the evasion of the law comparatively easy, and the country is overrun by an army of peddlers who extort exorbitant prices from their helpless victims. It appears that not only has the Harrison Law failed to diminish the number of drug takers—some contend, indeed, that it has increased their numbers—but, far from bettering the lot of the opiate addict, it has actually worsened it; for without curtailing the supply of the drug it has sent the price up tenfold, and this has had the effect of impoverishing the poorer class of addicts and reducing them to a condition of such abject misery as to render them incapable of gaining an honest livelihood.[8]

8. Harry Campbell, "The Pathology and Treatment of Morphia Addiction," *British Journal of Inebriety* (1922–23), 20: 147.

# 11

# THE EFFECTS OF WORLD WAR II

Every major war in which the United States has engaged, beginning with the Civil War, has had considerable effect upon the narcotics problem. World War II was not an exception. The Civil War, by popularizing the use of the hypodermic needle in medical practice, and through the none too careful use of opiates for wounded soldiers and for those suffering from such diseases as dysentery, caused an increase in the number of addicts in the United States. The Spanish American War also had a perceptible effect of the same kind but on a lesser scale. World War I again substantially increased the number of addicts, though by this time opiates were being handled with greater prudence and the number of new addicts created by army medication was probably proportionately less than in earlier conflicts. The recent war has had two major effects. In the first place, by disrupting the channels of illegal distribution, it created a drastic shortage of drugs on the internal illicit market and thus reduced the spread of the habit in the civilian population. In the second place, the use of opiates with the army probably increased the number of addicts in the armed forces and also added to the number of those who may be called potential addicts.

## Effects on the Illicit Traffic

The war in Europe disrupted American connections with European sources of illegal drugs, but this was made up for by an increased flow from the Far East. Government supervision of shipping and of foreign travel handicapped the smuggler generally. From the point of view of the local addict, however, the situation became serious only after the beginning of the Pacific war, which cut off supplies from the Orient, particularly from Japan and from territories controlled by Japan. A drastic internal shortage then developed rapidly. Smuggling declined to a record low, illicit prices skyrocketed, and quality deteriorated sharply. Heroin of 1 or 2 per cent purity became common and was sold for as much as from $30 to $50 an ounce. Addicts experienced great difficulty in maintaining their habits and resorted to desperate stratagems and inferior substitutes. A considerable increase in pressure to divert larger quantities of drugs from legitimate to illegitimate channels was noticed. In some cities drugstores began to do a booming business in paregoric, which contains small quantities of opium. This entire picture is clearly portrayed in the annual reports of the Bureau of Narcotics during the war years. The bureau seized the opportunity presented by this situation to tighten its controls, and as a result the illicit traffic was reduced to a record low.

The fact that the Axis controlled a number of the major sources of opium caused that drug to become a strategic item for the Allies. There was, of course, a greatly increased demand for opiates because of the war, and supplies were short, not only on the illicit market but generally. The shortage on the illicit market is indicated by the fact that seizures in the internal trade declined 50 per cent, and that addicts and peddlers increasingly resorted to burglary, robbery, and forgery to obtain supplies.[1]

The sharp rise in illicit prices and correspondingly increased profits apparently encouraged new producers of opium to enter

1. Statement by Elmer Irey reported in the *New York Times,* July 31, 1941, p. 3, col. 2. See also *The Chicago Tribune,* Sept. 13, 1941, on the increased demand for paregoric.

the field to supply American users. The opium poppy can be cultivated in many parts of the world, and it would have been over-optimistic to suppose that new sources of supply would not have appeared to replace the old. During the war years Iran, India, and Mexico became the chief sources for illicit drugs that appeared on the American market. After the German submarine threat in the Atlantic had been brought under control, smugglers were able to reestablish connections with India and Iran and to step up importations from those countries to make up for supplies previously obtained from European countries and from Japan. Although Mexico prohibits the cultivation of the poppy, an increasing tendency is noted in the annual reports of the Bureau of Narcotics for opium of Mexican origin to find its way to American addicts. The Bureau of Narcotics reported in 1944 that there was evidence that the acreage devoted to the clandestine cultivation of the poppy in Mexico was being increased. If the war situation had continued it is probable that a new equilibrium of supply and demand would eventually have been established, and that an increased volume of production in the countries named, and possibly in some other Central American countries, would have lowered illicit prices and improved the quality. The Mexican border and Southern and Atlantic ports became the focus of the smuggling problem during the war.

It is still too early to know what the effects of the termination of the war will be, but the Narcotics Bureau is probably correct in assuming that they will be favorable to an expansion of the illegal business. Having discovered the commercial possibilities of opium production, Central American producers will stay in the business and increase their output unless energetic countermeasures are taken. As trade channels to Europe, China, and Japan are reestablished, supplies from these pre-war sources will again appear to compete with Iranian, Indian, and Mexican opium. It is to be expected that prices will drop, supplies will become more plentiful, dilution will diminish, and the enforcement problems of the Narcotics Bureau will be increased.[2]

Indications that smuggling between China and the United

2. See Gerald Piel, "Narcotics; War Has Brought Illicit Traffic to All-Time Low but U.S. Treasury Fears Rising Postwar Addiction," *Life* (July, 1943), 15: 83–94.

States is already being resumed are available. A United Press dispatch from Shanghai on May 6, 1946, describes countermeasures being taken by Counter Intelligence to prevent the smuggling of drugs out of China.[3] It is pointed out that the profits on a small package of drugs may be 3,000 per cent between China and the United States. Because of the small bulk of opiates the traffic is extremely difficult to control. Many of the persons who transport packages of narcotics are unaware of the fact, since they are paid simply to transport it without being told of its contents. Although American authorities in Japan and China are said to be taking energetic measures to prevent smuggling of narcotics to this country, it must be kept in mind that the vast poppy-producing areas on the continent of Asia are not under American control, and that the detection of illicit shipments of drugs, particularly on merchant ships, is exceedingly difficult if not impossible. The fact that narcotics may be transported on other than American ships to Mexican, Canadian, or other neighboring countries makes the situation doubly difficult.

Chaotic conditions in many parts of the world and flourishing black markets will favor the traffic in drugs. Persons with criminal inclinations or experience who have learned of the profits in the black market may very well turn to the drug traffic, which is probably the most lucrative of all. Current shortages of drugs for medical purposes in Europe may be expected to stimulate the manufacture of morphine. Unsettled conditions will make regulation difficult.

In the Far East, in that part of the continent of Asia occupied by Japan, the number of addicts increased during the war, and the cultivation of the opium poppy was stimulated. The production of opium has become, even more than before, an integral part of the economic structure of many communities. It has become a means of livelihood for many people and an important source of revenue. The millions of addicts in the Far East constitute a huge market and create a powerful demand for opium. As in the past, it is probable that this demand will call forth a large supply, some of which will undoubtedly go to the United States. Unsettled political conditions make it appear highly improbable

3. *Indianapolis Star*, May 6, 1946, p. 4, col. 7.

that any effective means of dealing with the postwar narcotics problem in China will be found very soon. The existence of this situation in China will make our own problem that much more difficult.[4]

## Effects of World War II on Prevalence of Addiction

As has been indicated, the high cost of drugs and their scarcity made it difficult for American users to maintain their habits during the war. Many of them, perhaps most of them, did manage, however, by one means or another to continue their habits. Usually they were compelled to reduce their daily dosage, and sometimes they may have been compelled to abstain, but the ingenuity and persistence of addicts in maintaining their supplies have always amazed those who know them.

The use of inferior substitutes for heroin and morphine was one of the ways in which the attempt to continue the habit was facilitated. Paregoric is such a substitute and can be purchased in small amounts without a prescription. Larger quantities may be obtained by going to several pharmacies, signing a different name at each. It contains a little less than two grains of opium per fluid ounce. American addicts have long been familiar with distillation techniques by means of which some of the nonessential ingredients can be eliminated so that the concentrated residue may be used hypodermically. Sometimes they also drink it straight. I once observed an addict drink an entire water glass of pure paregoric and follow it with a chaser of water. It is relatively easy to purchase paregoric because of its low opium content, and it was, therefore, inevitable that addicts resorted increasingly to it during the stringency of the war years.

The difficulty of obtaining morphine and heroin probably reduced the rate of appearance of new addicts in the American underworld, since available supplies were inadequate even for the old users. It is therefore probable that there was an overall decrease in the number of addicts in this country, although no

4. See Frederick T. Merrill, *Japan and the Opium Menace*, joint publication of the International Secretariat, Institute of Pacific Relations, and the Foreign Policy Association (New York, 1942), for an excellent discussion of the opium problem in China under Japanese occupation.

good statistical evidence is available to prove that this was true. In prewar days, the large quantities of drugs continuously flowing through underworld channels of distribution accounted for a large proportion of the new cases that were constantly appearing. Persons who came in contact with these drugs, or with the peddlers and addicts who handle them, were exposed to addiction. It was relatively simple for the neophyte to obtain heroin or morphine for experimental purposes. The drug was relatively abundant and relatively cheap. The main necessity was to have the proper connection with the underworld. On the other hand, during the war the potential addict or the dabbler found himself crowded out by the fierce competition of old users for an inadequate supply. Some new addicts unquestionably appeared, but their numbers were considerably reduced.

The decline of addiction in the civilian population has, however, no doubt been cancelled, at least in part, by an increase among the members of the armed forces. Opiates were extensively used for the relief of pain and, of necessity, were often in the hands of persons with little or no medical training and with little conception of the danger they represent. Under combat conditions in particular it is impossible to administer morphine with the care that is normally exercised in peacetime medical practice. It is reasonable to suppose that some of the wounded and ill of the armed forces became addicts,[5] and that others were exposed to addiction by experiencing the effects of the drug and might be classed as potential addicts. As demobilization proceeds, ex-servicemen of the types described are beginning to be noticed among those who are arrested for violation of the narcotic laws. It is to be hoped that public sympathy for wounded veterans who acquired their addiction in Army and Navy experience will lead to an examination and overhauling of the assumptions that underlie present enforcement practices. It should be noted that after World War I nothing of this sort occurred. The veteran who became addicted by having been gassed, for example, was treated just like an addicted pimp or shoplifter.

5. One of the first of these cases to come to public attention was that of the late Barney Ross, who volunteered to federal authorities for the cure of a drug habit allegedly contracted at Guadalcanal (Associated Press dispatch, September 12, 1946). See also *New York Times*, Jan. 11, 1947, p. 15, col. 2.

There is, of course, no way of knowing in advance the precise nature of our eventual postwar narcotics problem. It is certain however, that the problem will become more acute and that addicts will appear to be more numerous than was the case during the war. It is possible that the postwar problem will be even more severe than the prewar problem. Unfortunately, available statistics in the United States are not sufficiently reliable, because of the sub rosa character of addiction, to give a dependable index of the number of addicts or of trends.

Some persons will no doubt reason that since war is a time of worry and anxiety, it is to be expected that individuals seeking escape or relief from their worries and fears will resort to drugs more frequently than in time of peace. Though this argument is superficially plausible, it does not take into account the fact that opiates are simply not accessible to most people. Liquor is, and the argument is perhaps applicable to alcoholism. In the case of drugs, however, the dominant statistical determinant of the incidence of addiction is not personal inclination but availability of drugs. Addiction is common in the medical profession for that reason. Addiction declined among civilians in the United States because drugs were exceedingly scarce and difficult to obtain; it probably increased in the armed forces because drugs there were abundant, free, and easy of access. Addiction spreads rapidly in China because the extensive cultivation of the poppy and the large numbers of addicts there make the drug easily obtainable.

CHAPTER

# 12

# NEEDED REFORMS

Many writers have assumed that there is only one basic solution to the opium problem, namely, the limitation, by international agreement, of the amount of opium produced to that just sufficient to meet the medical needs of the world. A number of international conferences have been held for this purpose, but all attempts to secure effective international action on this matter have failed. This failure has been due to the fact that those countries with vested economic interests in the production of raw opium have refused to sacrifice these interests. Since the opium poppy is not cultivated in the United States no such vested economic interest exists here and the American representatives found it relatively easy to assume the proper attitudes of moral superiority toward those nations in which the production or trade in opium was an integral part of the economic structure, forgetting perhaps that the lucrative market for illicit drugs in the United States offers the illegal dealer his best chance for large profits. Unfortunately, there has been so much discussion of international control of this problem that less dramatic and more practical things which we can do for ourselves to put our own house in order have been neglected. It is these measures which we will now discuss.

The most important basic change which is needed in this country is to reinterpret the Harrison and Jones-Miller acts so that the prescription of drugs to an addict by a physician is defined as being within the field of medicine. This would mean that a physician could legally prescribe drugs to an addict, and it would give addicts a legitimate low-cost source of supply. This is the way in which English drug laws are interpreted. No change in the wording of the Harrison Act, and very few changes in the Jones-Miller Act, would be required. All of the regulations, requirements, and penalties specified in these acts to apply to persons who handle drugs could be left untouched. The only change would be that if a physician wished to prescribe drugs to an addict he could do so with complete legality, provided only that he was registered under the act and kept the proper records. It is probable that the Harrison Act was intended to function in this manner in the first place, since it does not specifically prohibit the physician from prescribing for an addict, and since such a prohibition might have been interpreted as an unwarranted interference in the practice of a profession.

At first glance it might seem that such a plan would make opiates more available than they now are and lead to a spread of the habit. Further consideration reveals, however, that the opposite would be the case. In England, where, as has been indicated, doctors do prescribe for addicts, there is much less addiction than in the United States, and there is scarcely any smuggling problem. At present the new addict in this country usually obtains his drugs from illicit sources; under the proposed plan he would have to obtain his supplies from a doctor registered under the Harrison Act. Certainly one would expect medical men to exert more of a restraining influence on the spread of addiction than the underworld peddler does! The reduction or elimination of illegal dealing in opiates would unquestionably remove the greatest source of new addicts now in existence.

August Vollmer, formerly police chief of Berkeley, California, and later professor of police administration at the University of California, and an outstanding authority on police problems, has the following to say about the narcotics problem:

Can the narcotic problem be met intelligently so that it may be controlled and possibly reduced to the point where it need no longer be regarded as a menace to the young men and women of this country, and where drug users will not aggravate the crime conditions, as they do at the present? Stringent laws, spectacular police drives, vigorous prosecution, and imprisonment of addicts and peddlers have proved not only useless and enormously expensive as means of correcting this evil, but they are also unjustifiably and unbelievably cruel in their application to the unfortunate drug victims. Repression has driven this vice underground and produced the narcotic smugglers and supply agents, who have grown wealthy out of this evil practice and who, by devious methods, have stimulated traffic in drugs. Finally, and not the least of the evils associated with repression, the helpless addict has been forced to resort to crime in order to get money for the drug which is absolutely indispensable for his comfortable existence.

The first step in any plan to alleviate this dreadful affliction should be the establishment of Federal control and dispensation—at cost—of habit-forming drugs. With the profit motive gone, no effort would be made to encourage its use by private dispensers of narcotics, and the drug peddler would disappear. New addicts would be speedily discovered and through early treatment, some of these unfortunate victims might be saved from becoming hopelessly incurable.

Drug addiction, like prostitution and like liquor, is not a police problem; it never has been and never can be solved by policemen. It is first and last a medical problem, and if there is a solution it will be discovered not by policemen, but by scientific and competently trained medical experts whose sole objective will be the reduction and possible eradication of this devastating appetite. There should be intelligent treatment of the incurables in outpatient clinics, hospitalization of those not too far gone to respond to therapeutic measures, and application of the prophylactic principles which medicine applies to all scourges of mankind.[1]

Vollmer's proposal goes further than the plan proposed here, since he proposed federal dispensation at cost, probably under the auspices of the Public Health Service. It is possible that this sort of a plan would be necessary at first, but it is believed that in the long run most of the cases could and should be handled by private practitioners. If every addict in the United States became a doctor's patient the average case load would be increased by less than one per doctor. However, since addicts are at present

1. August Vollmer, *The Police and Modern Society* (Berkeley: University of California Press, 1936), pp. 117–18.

concentrated in large cities, temporary clinics might have to be
set up there to handle the immediate problem. As the addicts
secured employment and bettered their economic and social status, these clinics would become less and less necessary, for the
drug user would certainly prefer to patronize a private practitioner rather than to attend a public clinic. The net long-run effect
would be, we believe, to reduce the visibility of the problem and
to bring it under public control through the agency of the Public
Health Service and of the medical profession.

Under this plan the drug addict would, in effect, be given the
same status as the person who drinks alcohol. If the latter does
not steal, destroy property, create public disturbances, assault
someone, or otherwise violate the laws, he is left to his own private devices. Drinking is regarded as a question of private morality, in spite of the fact that drunken persons are in most respects
more dangerous and are much more numerous than drug addicts.
The proposal presented here is simply that addiction to drugs
should be regarded like addiction to alcohol—as a private vice. If
a drug addict steals, kills, or otherwise violates laws he should
be arrested and punished, but he should not be punished simply
because he uses drugs.

Another advantage of the proposed change would be that the
present brutal and unnecessarily cruel methods of handling addicts, to which Vollmer refers, would be eliminated. The addict
would be handled by medical men as a patient; not by policemen
as a pervert and a criminal. It would no longer be possible or
necessary to use drug addicts as informers in order to enforce the
law. In taking these steps the United States would not be ventur-
ing into an unknown field of dangerous experimentation, for the
drug addict in virtually all European countries has been regarded
and treated as a patient for many generations. The United States
would by these measures conform to generally accepted standards
of humanity and decency.

There has been considerable publicity given to the federal hospitals which have been established in the United States by the
Public Health Service to handle and study addicts.[2] It is true that

2. Howard Whitman, "One Up on Narcotics," *Colliers* (Dec. 15, 1945),
116: 82, 86, 88–90.

they represent a step in advance for this country, but Europeans have never attempted to utilize the prison as a means of controlling addiction and have always placed their opiate addicts in the hands of doctors and nurses. The inmates of these hospitals are still prisoners "doing time." In this sense we are still behind European practice.

Under the proposed plan the facilities of the Public Health Service and the Narcotics Bureau would continue to be useful. The narcotics farms could be used as hospitals for addicts or to administer cures to those seeking to free themselves from the habit. The Narcotics Bureau could devote itself more fully to checking on the flow of narcotics through the hands of registered dealers under the Harrison Act. There would also probably be a residual problem involving addicts who were professional criminals who would not conform to the new situation. There would also be the cocaine and marihuana problems to which narcotics agents could devote their energies.

One of the effects of the proposed plan which would, in the long run, be of the greatest importance is that as the illegal traffic dwindled and as more and more addicts came to private physicians reliable information would become available concerning the numbers of addicts in each community. New cases would be detected quickly, and measures could be taken to eliminate foci of infection. Under the present system very little reliable information of a statistical character is available and no one knows how many addicts there are, where they are, or where the new cases come from.

Arthur Woods, formerly New York Police Commissioner and international authority on the opium traffic, appraising the situation in the United States, states:

> Since the passing of the Federal Narcotic Act in 1914, actually thousands of addicts and small peddlers have gone into the Federal prisons, while with but few exceptions the "high financiers" of dope smuggling remain at large. In practice this state of affairs amounts to little more than prosecuting the victims of the traffic and permitting those who reap the large monetary benefits to go untouched.[3]

3. Arthur Woods, *Dangerous Drugs: The World Fight against Illicit Traffic in Narcotics* (New Haven, Conn.: Yale University Press, 1931), p. 62.

Simple justice requires that this situation be corrected. The American people have had an experience with prohibition and from it they have learned that matters of private morality cannot be settled by legislation. The effects of prohibition on drug addiction are substantially the same as they were upon alcohol addiction. As in the case of the bootleg traffic in alcohol, the high financiers of the dope racket can be eliminated only by doing away with prohibition.

It should, of course, not be assumed that any change in the method of handling the narcotics problem will at once or even ultimately eliminate all problems connected with addiction. Many difficult problems would remain, although the situation as a whole might be greatly improved. For example, if the changes recommended here were made, it is probable that some traffic in drugs would continue in the American underworld and that attempts would be made to sell these illicit drugs to addicts to supplement the supplies they were obtaining from medical sources or to enable persons not using the drug to start its use or resume its use. It would, of course, be impossible for illegal dealers to obtain the prices which they now can, and much of the financial incentive would be gone. Nevertheless, there would probably be a problem here and a task for the Narcotics Bureau. Other problems that would remain would be that of attempting to cure as many addicts as possible, and that of guarding against any spread of the habit.

CHAPTER

# 13

# POSTSCRIPT—1968

Since the publication, twenty years ago, of the preceding analysis
and evaluation of the social problem of opiate addiction, the principal changes that have occurred have been that the problem has
become much worse and that the inefficiency, injustice, and
cruelty of the control system have increased and become more
obvious. A rough indication of the magnitude of the increase is
that in 1966 the Federal Bureau of Investigation in the Uniform
Crime Reports lists a total of more than 60,000 drug arrests in
comparison with a 1947 total of about 3,400, with an arrest rate
in 1966 between five and six times that of 1947. Prompted by the
Federal Bureau of Narcotics, the national legislature and state
legislatures have sought to remedy the patent inefficiency of the
system mainly by increasing the rigidity and cruelty of the anti-
narcotics laws. The principles of justice and fair play, it was felt,
had to be sacrificed for the sake of deterrence. The sacrifice was
futile. The new legislation seems to have been based on the assumption that if a given measure of injustice does not produce the
desired social effects the obvious remedy is to have more injustice.

As the narcotics laws have become increasingly punitive, professional and public opinion has largely swung over to an osten-

sibly medical orientation toward the addict. This attitude has manifested itself primarily in expressions of opinion and in the invention of new semantic devices to make old practices seem more palatable; it has not been expressed, at this writing, in any legislation which substantially changes or improves the addict's status with respect to the criminal law. Programs of compulsory civil commitment represent ways of punishing addicts under the guise of treatment; what is new in these programs is the vocabulary rather than the practices. However, it seems probable that the thrust of the ideas in the new words is gradually filtering into the legislative halls and that it will ultimately lead to substantive and basic changes in legal definitions.

The most pronounced and perhaps the most significant change in the narcotics situation during the last three decades may well have been in the area of public opinion. During and immediately before World War II, addiction seems to have been at a low ebb, and the government's policy was challenged only now and then by a few "rear-guard snipers." There were so few of these that the Federal Bureau of Narcotics was able, even with its limited manpower, to exercise a kind of individual surveillance over them. The bureau's line and its manufactured statistics were in the main accepted without question even for some time after the war as narcotics arrest rates rose precipitously year after year. In an effective buck-passing job, the blame for the spread of the habit was first placed on the shoulders of judges, but, as the situation continued to deteriorate, the bureau, its policies, and the punitive system itself were increasingly questioned. Currently, the agencies and officials that constitute "The Establishment" supporting the status quo are generally on the defensive almost everywhere except in a few groups of the far right and in the legislatures. In the latter, the police continue to be viewed as the final authorities on most aspects of the narcotics problem, and it is often argued that all that is required to solve the problem is to increase their freedom of action. The same solution is proposed for virtually all other problems of sin, vice, and crime.

Another indication of the changed climate of opinion is the widespread knowledge in the United States today that most European countries handle addiction as a medical rather than a police problem and that all of them combined probably have a smaller problem than that of New York City alone. Discussion and debate in this area tends to focus on British practices. The American citizen probably has a better understanding of British practices than of American ones. This is because the former are relatively simple and consistent and are reported in a fairly honest and straightforward way with a minimum of the statistical fakery that is traditional in the United States.

During recent years, as has been pointed out by both American and British "establishment" spokesmen, there has been a marked increase in opiate addiction in Britain as well as in other European countries. This has given aid and comfort to the opponents of reform, who argue that it demonstrates that the magnitude of the problem is essentially unrelated to the nature of the control system. Inconsistently, it is then contended that before any changes are made in the American system there should be extensive research and experimentation to determine what the effects of the changes will be. Those who interpret British experience in this manner usually fail to mention that the increased prevalence of addiction in that country, which they take as evidence of the failure of the system, involved an increase in the official totals of addicts from about 350 to something over 900. They also neglect to mention that the contributions that British and other European addicts make to the crime problems in their countries continue to be negligible.

In general the current American situation may be described as one in which agencies and officials with vested interests in the status quo seem to be fighting a delaying action against an overwhelming tide of change. These agencies and officials increasingly feel compelled to adopt the treatment vocabulary and to give lip service at least to the nonpunitive ideals. The growing discrepancy between the professed ideals and the actual practices is becoming more and more noticeable to more and more people. Ultimately this will probably mean that legislators and public officials will have to bring what they do about addicts into a better alignment with what they say about them.

# APPENDIX

# KINDS OF DRUGS AND

# METHODS OF USE

The drugs of addiction that are related to or derived from the twenty or so opium alkaloids are too numerous to be listed, and it would be pointless and tedious to attempt to do so. In addition to the hundreds of compounds derived from opium and its alkaloids, there is a great variety of synthetic drugs that have analgesic effects like those of morphine and which are also addicting. Morphine was the first alkaloid of opium to be isolated (in 1803), and it serves as a standard of comparison because it remains the most satisfactory pain-relieving agent in medical practice.

In the annual report of the Federal Bureau of Narcotics for 1965 (pp. 11–14) 57 kinds of synthetics alleged to be habit forming are listed. Two of these are: (1) pethidine, also known as Demerol or meperidine and by more than forty other names, and (2) methadone, also known as amidone and dolophine. Both are addicting, and both are in reality representatives of families of related drugs with similar molecular structures. Pethidine, the oldest of the synthetic equivalents, which was produced in Germany in 1939, is

accompanied in the bureau's list by 80 other names and methadone by 62—these are alternative names for the drug or the names
of other drugs of the same series.

Opium is obtained by drying the juice from the unripe seed
capsule of the opium poppy or *Papaver somniferum*. Morphine
constitutes about 10 per cent of opium and is mainly responsible
for its physiological effects and its addictive potential. It, its derivatives, and the related synthetics are thus of central relevance
in the consideration of contemporary addiction to the "manufactured drugs" as contrasted with opium as such. Heroin (diacetylmorphine) is the best-known chemical derivative of morphine
and the drug of choice for most American users. It was first produced in 1898. It does not naturally appear as such in opium.
Codeine, which is found in opium, is much less potent than morphine and is a derivative of it. It, like morphine, has numerous
derivatives. It is not popular with addicts but may be used to
maintain addiction when nothing better is available. Drugs of the
morphine type range from a recent derivative known as Bentley's
compound, which is about 10,000 times as powerful as morphine,
to those of the codeine class, which have a relatively slight analgesic and addicting potential. In addition to heroin, the following
drugs are among those that are more potent than morphine:
Dilaudid (dihydromorphinone hydrochloride), Numorphan (oxy-
morphinone hydrochloride), methyldilaudid (metopon hydrochloride), levorphan, a highly addicting member of a family known
as the morphinan series, and phenazocine, a member of a group
known as the benzomorphans. The significant fact concerning
morphine-like compounds, from the addict's point of view, is that
they are interchangeable by substitution for morphine or heroin in
the maintenance of addiction. The drug user is rarely acquainted
with more than a very small percentage of the total range of these
compounds.

Many of the opiate drugs and the related synthetics were proclaimed as non-addicting when they were first introduced. This
was true, for example, of morphine, which was hailed as a substance having all the virtues of opium and none of its defects.
Heroin was similarly characterized as non-addicting and was
sometimes used as a cure for morphine addiction. Demerol, which
was synthesized in 1939, was also originally acclaimed as non-
habit-forming.

Prior to the isolation of morphine, opiate addicts satisfied their habits by smoking opium or by drinking or eating the numerous preparations that contained it. DeQuincey, for example, drank laudanum or tincture of opium. Paregoric is a modern equivalent of laudanum. Addicts sometimes drink it and sometimes boil it down and inject the concentrated residue hypodermically. Pantopon is a mixture of opium alkaloids like that naturally present in opium.

At about the middle of the nineteenth century the hypodermic method of injecting morphine was invented, allegedly by a Scottish physician in Edinburgh. It was at first proclaimed that this method of administration had the double advantage of being more efficient and also non-habit-forming. The use of the hypodermic was widely disseminated in the United States during the Civil War.

American addicts during the latter half of the nineteenth century began to adopt the hypodermic method but at first injected the drug only into the muscles, regarding intravenous injections, which sometimes happened by accident, as dangerous and painful. The technique of "main-lining" or taking intravenous injections, was popularized among users during the twentieth century. It involves the use of an improvised hypodermic outfit which is, from the user's viewpoint, both more efficient and less expensive than the physician's syringe. It consists of a medicine dropper that is fitted into a hypodermic needle. The drug is placed in a small metal container such as a spoon, a bottle top, or the cover of a tobacco can. An appropriate quantity of water is added with the medicine dropper, mixed with the drug, heated with a match or two to dissolve it, and then drawn up into the medicine dropper. A small bit of cotton is used to filter or strain impurities from the solution when it is drawn into the dropper. When the latter is filled to the desired level it is fitted into the hypodermic needle by means of a "collar" or "gasket" and the user is then ready to take his fix.

Preparation for the fix involves, for the usual righthanded addict, tying up the left arm between the shoulder and the elbow so as to distend the veins below that point. When the needle appears to have been inserted into the vein the user may check this fact by noting the appearance of small quantities of blood in the lower part of the medicine dropper. The injection is made by squeezing the rubber bulb of the medicine dropper with the right hand. The needle is then withdrawn and the arm untied. The injections are usually made in the veins on the inside of the arm, but those on the back of the hand may also be used. Similar techniques may be employed to make injections into the veins of the legs. It is reported that an occasional user will make injections directly into the jugular vein when he is unable to locate others (for example, because they have collapsed).

A small number of addicts who object to the intravenous route may use the simpler one of intramuscular injection. Others who dislike the hypodermic method altogether may take their drug in the form of pills or even sprinkle it over their food like salt. In some foreign countries it is reported that suppositories are used. In the Far East, a popular method of heroin use is by inhalation of its fumes when it is heated, on a piece of tinfoil, for example. This particular method is known as "chasing the dragon" from the fact that the relatively heavy fumes are said to form dragonlike shapes in the depressions of the tinfoil.

During the first decades of the century, morphine and heroin competed with each other in the American illicit market, with the latter gradually replacing the former, probably because it is easier to dilute and easier to handle and to conceal as well as being more potent. Since World War II when synthetic equivalents such as methadone and pethidine or Demerol began to be used extensively by physicians, addicts have acquired some acquaintance with these and related drugs which also occasionally turn up in the illicit trade. Under emergency conditions, as already indicated, addicts may resort to a wide variety of inferior substitutes. There are, for example, cough remedies or mixtures, such as terpin hydrate, that contain codeine. Another cough suppressant, Percodan, contains the drug oxycodone hydrochloride, which is more potent than codeine. Addicts in some regions are said to have taken up the use of Darvon (propoxyphene hydrochloride), an analgesic that is not as powerful as codeine and has the disadvantage of producing undesirable side-effects. Under pressure, addicts may also try non-addicting drugs or addicting drugs unrelated to morphine or the opiates, such as the barbiturates, the amphetamines, and others.

While the main methods of taking drugs have been touched

upon, there are others of an emergency type that may be resorted to when the circumstances require it. Thus, a user may gouge or cut a wound in his skin and either inject the solution directly with a medicine dropper or simply put the powdered drug into the wound so that it may be absorbed. If a medicine dropper is at hand and hypodermic needles are not, in prison for example, the hollow end of a sewing machine needle may be inserted into the vein and the injection made by sliding the medicine dropper over it and pressing it against the skin. A user, reporting on his experience with this technique, said that on one occasion when he withdrew the medicine dropper the point of the sewing machine needle had vanished into the vein and was never seen again. Reference should also be made to "sniffing" or "snorting," in which the drug in powdered form is inhaled into the nostrils. Heroin and cocaine were formerly used in this way, and the practice is still encountered.

It seems reasonable to suppose that, as new drugs are produced, other addicting substances not presently known will be found and that some of these, as well as some of those already known to pharmacologists, will become known to addicts. Should the international campaign to restrict the cultivation of the poppy and the production of opium ever begin to show signs of reaching its goal, it seems reasonable to suppose that the natural opiates and heroin which now flow in the world's channels of illicit distribution may be replaced or supplemented by synthetics manufactured in secret illegal laboratories.

# GLOSSARY OF ADDICT ARGOT

About 200 of the following list of approximately 350 expressions in the addict's lingo were collected from Chicago addicts during 1934 and 1935. Dr. David Maurer used these terms in a study of his own and added about forty additional items that were included in the 1947 version of the glossary. Subsequent additions were taken from "A Glossary of Argot in Use at the United States Public Health Service Hospital, Lexington, Kentucky," which was compiled by P. H. Blackley, D. W. Maurer, and J. M. Mead and published at the hospital in 1958. Another significant source was *The Trail of the Poppy* by Charles Siragusa (Edgewood Cliffs, N. J.: Prentice-Hall, 1966).

Most of the terms pertain directly to matters connected with opiate-type drugs, but a sprinkling of others, referring to other kinds of drugs and to common features or concerns of the addict's life not directly associated with drugs, are also included. The list is certainly incomplete and not entirely up to date. It should also be noted that the addict's lingo shades off into and overlaps with other specialized languages of the groups with which users are associated or to which they belong.

A comparison of contemporary argot with that of twenty and more years ago indicates that, while the addict's language has changed and new words and expressions have been invented or have become popular, the change has been much less than is often supposed. There are probably few terms, for example, that appeared in the original glossary that would not still be intelligible to many of the more experienced and sophisticated contemporary users. The extent of a given individual addict's knowledge of the argot is roughly proportional to the degree of his participation in the addict subculture.

*Abb:* An abscess at the point where an injection is made, usually caused by bad drugs or an unsterilized needle.

*Action:* Selling narcotics.

*Around the turn:* To have passed through the severest part of the withdrawal distress, which comes about three days after the last shot. Also, to be *over the hump.*

*Away from one's habit:* To have stopped using drugs. "A fellow still feels pretty rotten when he is only a month away from his habit."

*Bag:* A quantity of illicit drugs in a paper, package, or envelope. See also *Bindle.*

*Bagman:* A peddler. One who sells *bags.*

*Bamboo:* An opium pipe.

*Bang:* Also, *to bang.* An injection of drugs. To be *banging up* is to be giving oneself a shot. Also used as a synonym of *kick,* as in "I get a whale of a *bang* out of the pipe."

*Beat the gong:* To smoke opium.

*Belly habit:* A habit of taking the drug by mouth.

*Bendin' and Bowin':* Full of drugs. See *Loaded.*

*Bernice: Cocaine.* Also *Carrie, Cecil, Charley, Cholly, Corine, Flake, Gold dust.*

*Big man:* The big distributor of drugs. He is usually not an addict, and he seldom goes to jail.

*Big shot connection:* A peddler or dealer who handles relatively large quantities of drugs. Government agents are particularly eager to trap him, but he is wary and elusive. "It isn't the *big shot connection* that does the time in the stir; it's the bird-cage hypes."

*Bindle:* A small amount of drugs done up in a paper. Also *a paper, a deck, a go, a check, a cigarette paper.*

*Bingo:* The pleasure or kicks from an injection.

*Bird-cage hypes:* The poorest class of addicts who have trouble supporting themselves and their habits and live extremely destitute and miserable lives.

*Bird's eye:* A very small quantity of drugs. "When Whitey brought the cap I took a tiny bit, *a bird's eye,* and gave the rest to him.

*Black stuff:* Opium.

*Blank:* Bad or fake dope. Also *dummy, turkey.*

*Blast:* To smoke marihuana.

*Blast party:* Pot party.

*Block:* See *Cube.* Also used to refer to crude bootleg opium.

*Blow a pill:* To smoke opium.

*Blow a shot:* To waste a shot by spilling it or missing a vein.

*Blow the meet:* Not to keep an appointment.

*Blowing:* Taking drugs via the nostrils. Also, *sniffing, snorting.*

*Bo Bo bush:* Marihuana. Also *fu, guage, gash, grass, griefo, hay, joy smoke, love weed, Mary Jane, Mary Warner, mezz, pot, rope, tea, Texas tea, viper's weed, weed,* etc.

*Bombita:* An amphetamine sometimes taken with heroin to enhance the affect.

*Bonaroo:* Good.

*Bonita:* A corruption of the term for milk sugar, which is used to adulterate heroin.

*Boo gee:* Paper used to make the medicine dropper fit snugly into the hypodermic needle.

*Boost:* To shoplift. A common way of making a living among addicts.

*Boots, Boot-and-Shoe dope fiends:* The poorest class of addicts. See *bird-cage hypes.* "The Black Maria picked up about thirty *boots* at the Legion yesterday and took 'em to the band-house."

*Boot:* The kick of an injection. Also, a vein shot in which blood is drawn up into the syringe.

*Booter:* One who takes *boot* shots.

*Boy:* heroin. Also *caballo, crap, doo jee, "H," Harry, horse, junk, schmeck* (or *smack*), *shit, stuff, tecata, white stuff,* etc.

*Break the habit:* To stop using the drug. May also be used as follows: "I *break my habit* in the stomach."

*Brick gum:* Raw opium. Also *leaf gum, mud, gum, brick, leaf.*

*Bring up, back up:* To cause the veins to distend by tying up the arm or leg between the place where the injection is to be made and the heart.

*Brody:* Feigned illness to obtain drugs from a doctor. See *Wing ding.*

*Bug:* To inject coal oil, tobacco juice, or some other noxious substance into oneself to obtain a shot from a doctor; to annoy.

*Buffalo:* A five-year sentence.

*Build up* (one's habit): To increase the daily dosage.

*Bull horrors:* Delusions and hallucinations of pursuit by the police on the part of a cocaine user.

*Bundle:* Twenty-five five-dollar bags of heroin.

*Bunk habit:* One who likes to lie around in an opium-smoking joint is said to have a *bunk habit.*

*Burn:* To pay for narcotics and to be given something else. An informer is *burned* when the police reveal his identity as an informer to the underworld.

*Bust, to bust:* An arrest; the act of arresting someone.

*Buy:* A purchase of drugs to be used as evidence. Also, a peddler.

*Buy money:* Money used to buy drugs.

*"C":* Cocaine. To camouflage a sentence such as "I want some 'C.'" an addict might say, "I'm looking for Charley," or "I want to buy some collars." Also *snow, coke.* See also *Bernice.*

*Candy:* Barbiturates, opiates, or cocaine.

*Canned stuff:* Commercial smoking opium. Also known by the name of the company, as *Lem Kee, Li Young,* etc.

*Cap:* A capsule containing drugs.

*Carry, to, to be carried:* To be supported by drugs. "This shot will *carry* me for six hours." Also *to hold* or *to be held.*

*Cement:* Any kind of drug as it passes into commerce rather than when it is used by addicts.

*Channel, in the:* In a vein. "His veins were so shrunken that he couldn't get it *in the channel.*"

*Charged up:* Under the effects of narcotics. Also *going up, grooving, high, taking a trip, turned on, stoned.*

*Chef:* One who prepares opium for smoking. This is an art and a good *chef* is therefore much in demand. Also *cook.*

*Chicago leprosy:* Abscesses from injections.

*Chinaman, to have a Chinaman on one's back:* To have a drug habit or to be suffering withdrawal distress.

*Chinese needlework:* The handling or use of narcotics.

*Chippy:* One who uses a little bit now and then; same as a *pleasure user.*

*Chuck-horrors:* The addict's state after quitting the habit, when he cannot get enough to eat and will eat anything at any time. It develops after about a week of abstinence. Also *chuck habit, chuckers.*

*Coasting:* The feeling of euphoria produced by a shot during the initial period of use, after a period of abstinence, or by an unusually large dose.

*Coffee-and habit:* A small, irregular habit. See *Chippy.*

*Cokie:* A cocaine user. Also *coke fiend, snow bird, coke bead, cokomo.*

*Cold turkey, to kick a habit cold turkey:* To stop using drugs suddenly without tapering off or without using other drugs for relief.

*Collar:* The material used to make an airtight connection between the medicine dropper and the hypodermic needle. Also, to arrest. See also *boo gee, gasket.*

*Con:* To make contact with a peddler. *"To con for* someone" means to buy drugs for him.

*Connection:* A drug peddler or distributor. "My *connection* was knocked off yesterday." Also, *pusher, shover.*

*Connector:* One who acts as an intermediary between the drug user and a connection.

*Cook:* See *chef.*

*Cooker:* The receptacle in which drugs are dissolved and heated prior to being drawn into the medicine dropper.

*Cotton:* A small piece of cotton through which the drug solution is strained as it is drawn into the medicine dropper. This is done to strain out foreign material which might stop up the needle. An addict who is hard pressed may beg others for their cotton from which he is able to obtain a small amount of drug solution. Hence, to be *using one's cotton* means that the user is having difficulty maintaining a supply. He may also express this idea by saying, *"I'm down to the rinsings."* *"M"* and *"C" Cotton* or the *Cotton brothers* are cottons saturated with morphine and cocaine respectively. "Is Charley Cotton around?" A *cotton habit* is a small habit that may be maintained in part by begging cotton from more prosperous addicts. If an addict has a *cap* but no *joint*, he offers the *cotton* as rental for someone else's *joint*.

*Cop:* To purchase drugs; to admit something.

*Cop a pill:* To smoke opium; to obtain narcotics in tablet form.

*Cop man:* A dealer in drugs; the middleman or go-between in a narcotics transaction.

*Cotics:* Narcotics.

*Crap:* Drugs; inferior or faked drugs.

*Croaker:* A doctor. Also *blood sucker*.

*Crock:* An opium pipe.

*Cube:* A cube of morphine containing a grain or two and about the size of small dice. Also *block*.

*Cut:* To adulterate drugs. Morphine, which usually is sold in cubes, is adulterated before being put up in cubes. Heroin, which is sold in powdered form, can be cut more readily.

*Cutered pill:* A strong and unpalatable pill obtained when the bowl of the opium pipe becomes too hot or too full of yenshee.

*Cuttin' up:* Cutting the wrists to persuade a doctor to give an injection of drugs.

*Deadwood:* An addict arrested directly by a narcotics agent rather than through the intervention of a stool pigeon.

*Dirty:* Having illicit drugs in one's possession. Also *heeled* or *holding*.

*Dolly:* Dolophine, a synthetic opiate equivalent.

*Dope fiend:* A drug addict. Also *gowster, junker* or *junkie, smecker, hop-head, user, cookie,* etc.

*Dope hop:* A term for drug addict sometimes used in prison.

*Do-popper:* A needle addict.

*Dreck:* Heroin. German word meaning mud, filth, or excrement.

*Dripper:* An eye dropper or medicine dropper which forms an indispensable part of the addict's hypodermic outfit. "The *dripper* leaked and I blew the shot." Also *dingus, dinghizen, fake, fake-a-loo.*

*Drive in:* To deliver drugs to an imprisoned addict.

*Dugout:* An addict who has come to the end of his resources. Also, one who eats a great deal, for example, an addict with the *chuckers* or *chuck-horrors.*

*Dummy:* Bad or fake dope.

*Dutch route:* Suicide.

*Dynamite:* Unusually powerful or pure drugs.

*Eater:* An addict who takes drugs by mouth.

*Eights:* One-eighth of an ounce of (adulterated) heroin. Also, tablets containing an eighth of a grain of the narcotic.

*Embroidery:* Scars on the arms from repeated intravenous injections. Also, handling or using drugs. See *Chinese needlework.*

*Engine:* Outfit for smoking opium.

*Eye-opener:* The first injection of the day, sometimes taken before getting out of bed. The effects of this injection are particularly marked because the drug has worn off during the night and the addict often wakes up sick.

*Fiend:* A term of disparagement applied to addicts who have less than usual control over their habits.

*Figure eight:* A feigned spasm or illness designed to induce a doctor to administer an injection. Also *wing-ding.*

*Finger-of-stuff:* A finger stall filled with drugs to protect them from dampness and to facilitate smuggling. A condom may also be used. An addict may swallow a quantity of drugs before entering prison and recover it later with the use of these containers.

*Fit:* A hypodermic outfit.

*Five-cent bag:* A five-dollar bag of illicit heroin.

*Fix, to fix:* The act of taking drugs. "Let's stop in the hotel and *fix.*" Also means to take enough drugs to relieve abstinence symptoms, as in "I drank enough paregoric to halfway *fix* me." Also *to get one's yen off,* or *to get the habit off.*

*Flash:* The immediate physical impact of a shot, especially an intravenous one. Also *tingle.*

*Flea powder:* A non-narcotic sold as a narcotic. Also drugs of very poor quality. Also *garbage, lemonade.*

*Flipper, to flip:* To be knocked unconscious by a shot of drugs; to inform. See also *hot shot.*

*Floating:* Under the influence of narcotics.

*Fold up:* To quit using drugs. Also, *to be washed up, to be off, to be caught up, to be on the up-and-up.*

*Frame, frame for:* The deception of a physician in order to obtain drugs.

*Freak:* A user who likes to play with the needle. See *needle yen.*

*Fun, foon:* An opium pill.

*Fuzz:* Police.

*Gap:* To yawn and salivate, especially because of withdrawal.

*Gapper:* An addict during the initial stages of withdrawal.

*Gasket:* See *Boo gee, collar.*

*Gazer:* Federal narcotics agent. Also *whiskers, fuzz.*

*Gee fat:* The lining of an opium pipe.

*Gee rags:* Used to make the bowl of an opium pipe fit snugly into the saddle.

*Geeze:* Heroin or narcotics.

*Geezer:* A small shot.

*Get off on:* To take drugs regularly.

*Get the habit off:* To take drugs at the regular time or to relieve withdrawal symptoms.

*Give the chatter:* To talk to or answer questions asked by officials.

*Giving birth:* A difficult bowel movement. See *Yenshee baby.*

*Go:* To take drugs.

*God's Own Medicine, G.O.M.:* Opiates. This term is also used by members of the medical profession.

*Gonger:* Opiate derivates.

*Goods:* Drugs. A term used by dealers. Also *merchandise.*

*Gow:* Narcotics.

*Gowster:* A user.

*Grasshopper:* A marihuana smoker.

*Green ashes, green mud:* Ashes left from incompletely burned opium.

*Grocery boy:* A hungry addict not particularly in need of drugs.

*Gun:* A hypodermic outfit or *joint.*

*Gutter:* An addict who uses drugs intravenously. Also, the veins themselves.

*"H":* Heroin. "Jake is putting out a lot of *"H"* and some *"C."*

*Habit:* Addiction to drugs or abstinence symptoms. "My *habit* is coming on and I lost my joint."

*Hang up:* To quit using or selling drugs.

*Hard stuff:* The more powerful drugs such as heroin and cocaine as contrasted with marihuana.

*Harpoon:* The hypodermic needle. Also *spike, point, Bay State, nail, luer.*

*High:* To be excessively full of drugs. Also *lit up, geed up, polluted, full of poison, steppin' high, leaping, leapin' and stinkin', purring, purrin' like a cat.*

*High-hat:* A large pill of smoking opium. Also *fire-plug.*

*Hip, to be on the:* To be smoking opium.

*Hit the gow, hit the stuff:* To be addicted.

*Hit:* The effects of a shot as they are first noticed. "That shot was dynamite; it *hit* me like a ton of bricks."

*Hitch up the reindeers:* To be preparing to use cocaine. Also *to go for a sleigh ride.*

*Hocus:* The drug in solution.

*Holding:* To have drugs to sell on one's person.

*Hooked:* To be addicted or to have used drugs long enough so that when one stops the withdrawal symptoms will appear.

*Hoosier fiend:* An inexperienced or ignorant addict or an ex-workingman who has become addicted.

*Hop:* Smoking opium. Also *grease, skamas, gow, tar.* Also opiates in general.

*Hop-head:* Originally used to designate opium smokers only but now used for addicts in general.

*Hop joint:* A place where opium is smoked. Also *lay-down joint.*

*Hop toy:* An opium container.

*Horn, to:* To inhale narcotics into the nostrils.

*Hot shot:* An injection of poison in place of the drug. "The son-of-a-bitch is a stool. Give him a *hot shot.* Give him some strychnine."

*Hype, hypo:* An addict who uses a hypodermic needle. Also *jabber, hypo smecker.* A *hypo* is also a hypodermic injection.

*Ice-tong doctor:* An illegal practitioner who sells drugs.

*In action:* Actively peddling drugs.

*In front of the gun:* Pushing narcotics. The pusher is supposed to take the rap and protect his dealer when he is caught.

*In paper:* Narcotics smuggled into prison in letters, postcards, etc.

*In the sack:* The peddler is *in the sack* when he makes a sale to a police officer and is sure to be arrested.

*Iron cure:* To kick the habit cold turkey in a jail or prison cell. Also, the *steel and concrete cure.* In the old Chicago Bridewell Prison, where addicts were supposed to work in the quarry during the withdrawal period, it was often the *quarry cure.*

*Jab:* To use drugs hypodermically. "I've smoked and I've *jabbed.*"

*Jaboff:* The feeling of exhilaration immediately following a *vein-shot.*

*Jackoff shot, jack a fix:* A deliberate playing with the needle and drawing blood into the medicine dropper while taking a shot. See *needle fiend, verification shot.*

*Jam:* An overdose. Trouble with the law.

*Jammed up:* Overloaded with drugs.

*Jobbed:* Framed.

*John:* One who does not use narcotics. See *square, straight.*

*Joint:* A hypodermic outfit usually improvised by fitting a medicine or eye dropper into a hypodermic needle. A receptacle such as a spoon or the top of a tobacco can in which the drug is heated and dissolved is also included. Also *lay-out, factory, machinery, gun, artillery, the works, the business, the bizz.* A *joint* may also be an opium den or an opium smoking outfit. Also, a marihuana cigarette.

*Jolt:* An injection or its effects.

*Jones:* A habit.

*Joy pop:* A shot taken for the fun of it by a non-addict who usually intends not to get hooked.

*Joy stick:* An opium pipe. A marihuana cigarette.

*Junk:* Opiates. Also *stuff, dope, gow, geeze, smeck, dreck, hocus, gee, cotics, mo-jo, medicine, shit,* etc.

*Junker:* Formerly the preferred term among users for an addict.

*Junk hog:* One who uses excessive quantities of drugs when he has the opportunity.

*Junkie:* A drug addict. Also *gowster, dope fiend, hop-head, smecker, user, gow-head, cookie, dope-hop, yenshee quay.*

*Keep the meet:* A meeting of a peddler and his customer.

*Keyster plant:* A finger stall with drugs in it concealed in the rectum.

*Kick-back:* Relapse into the habit after a period of abstinence.

*Kicking the gong around:* Smoking opium. Also *laying on the hip.*

*Kick the habit:* To stop using drugs. "They threw me into a cell in the clink and I kicked her cold turkey."

*Knocker:* A person who is opposed to the use of drugs.

*Lamp habit:* One who likes to see the lamp used in smoking opium lit constantly is said to have a *lamp habit.*

*Laugh and scratch:* To use drugs. Refers to the itching sensation often produced by opiates, especially when taken intravenously in large amounts. "Doc and I picked up a piece of stuff and *laughed and scratched* most of the night."

*Lay-down joint:* A place where one can go to smoke opium. Also *hop-joint* or *lay-down.*

*Laying on the hip:* The act of smoking opium. Also *kicking the gong around, kicking it around, puffing, rolling the log.*

*Lemon:* Inferior quality heroin or a non-narcotic fraudulently substituted for it.

*Lemon bowl, orange bowl:* The bowl of an opium pipe, the lower part of which is made of a scraped out lemon or orange.

*Lent:* Japanese fibrous opium introduced on the West coast.

*Line shot:* A vein shot.

*Lipping the dripper:* To test the medicine dropper by sucking the air out of it and causing it to stick to one's lips.

*Lipton tea:* Poor quality drugs.

*Loaded:* Full of drugs.

*Lobby-gow, lobb:* One who hangs around and runs errands.

*Long-tailed rat:* Applied to stool pigeons.

*"M":* Morphine. Almost any word beginning with this letter of the alphabet may be employed to refer to morphine. An addict might say, "I am waiting for Martha," and any other user would understand that he was waiting for a delivery of morphine.

*Machinery:* The paraphernalia used in taking a shot.

*Main-line:* A vein. Also used as a verb, meaning to inject intravenously. "If you can *main-line* a cube of the stuff I put out, you can have it. It will be on the house."

*Make a spread:* To lay out the equipment used in taking a fix.

*Manita:* Sugar of milk used to adulterate or *cut* heroin.

*Margin men:* Dealers or runners who have no money invested in the goods but use some other person's bank roll. They risk their liberty rather than their money.

*Mark a connection:* To take note for future reference of an individual who is selling drugs.

*McCoy:* Chemically pure drugs. "This stuff costs a lot but it is the real *McCoy*."

*Medicine:* The drug.

*Meet:* An appointment. "I have a *meet* with a connection to score."

*Merchandise:* Illicit narcotics, usually heroin.

*Mick:* To give a person a *Mickey Finn*.

*Mickey, Mickey Finn:* A drink that knocks out the victim, or a powerful laxative.

*Miss Emma:* Morphine.

*Monkey:* A habit. "I have a *monkey* on my back." This usually means that the person is sick from lack of drugs. Also *to have a Chinaman on one's back*.

*Morf:* Morphine.

*Mount Shasta, to be from:* To be addicted.

*Mouse:* An informer.

*Mouth habit:* An oral habit.

*Mr. Fish:* A user who voluntarily gives himself up to the authorities in an effort to break his addiction; a volunteer or a newcomer in an institution.

*Nail:* Hypodermic needle.

*Narco:* Narcotics detective.

*Narcotic bulls, narcotic coppers:* Narcotics officers.

*Needle fiend:* One who has a hypodermic drug habit. Also *hype.* Also refers to the addict who likes to play with the needle, to prick himself with it, or to receive sterile injections after he is off the drug. This desire is referred to as a *needle yen.*

*Needle shy:* To be squeamish about inserting the needle or about watching the process.

*Needle trouble:* To have trouble with the needle, for example, to have it stopped up or broken off. The use of the cotton prevents needle trouble.

*O.D.:* An overdose.

*Oil-burning habit:* A big habit.

*Off:* Not using drugs.

*On:* Using drugs.

*On ice:* In jail.

*Out in front:* Paying for drugs before delivery.

*Overcharged:* A larger dose than needed to maintain the habit.

*Pack one's keyster:* To conceal a quantity of drugs in the rectum or vagina. A condom may be used.

*Panic:* A scarcity of drugs, usually produced by the arrest of big peddlers. "The heat's on. Connection blowed up. There's a *panic* on."

*Panic man:* An addict in desperate need of drugs and suffering abstinence symptoms.

*Paper:* A quantity of drugs wrapped in paper.

*PG:* Paregoric. Used by addicts as a poor substitute for heroin or morphine. It may be taken straight or boiled down and injected hypodermically.

*Picked up:* Under the influence of a recent injection.

*Pick up:* An injection. "He didn't feel right because he missed his morning *pick up*."

*Piece:* An ounce of drugs or any relatively large quantity. Also *O.Z.* or *O.* A *piece* man thus is one who deals in relatively large amounts.

*Pill:* Opium as it is consumed in the bowl of the pipe. Also *yen-pok.*

*Pin shot:* An injection made by using a pin or other sharp instrument to make a wound into which the end of the medicine dropper is inserted directly. Also *penitentiary shot.*

*Pinyen:* Opium.

*Pitch:* To sell narcotics in small amounts.

*Plant:* A concealed supply of drugs or equipment for using them.

*Playing around:* When an addict who has not been using drugs for a time takes a shot now and then with the intention of not allowing himself to become readdicted, he is *playing around.* "I know a man who works in the City Hall who used to be hooked on the pipe and has *played around* for ten years." Also *dabble.*

*Playing the nod:* To doze or go to sleep from overindulgence.

*Pleasure user, pleasure smoker:* Persons who have never been addicted, who use the drug occasionally only. Most of these persons become addicted. The occasional use of drugs in this manner is referred to as *three-day habit, weekend habit, chicken-shit habit, ice cream habit, Saturday-night habit, chippy habit.*

*Point shot:* An injection of drugs made with the broken point of a hypodermic needle or a sewing machine needle. The point is inserted into the vein or skin, and the medicine dropper is slipped over it and held against the skin while the injection is made.

*Poison:* Opiates and cocaine; an informer.

*Poison Act:* The Harrison Narcotic Act of 1914.

*Pop, to pop:* A shot, to take a shot.

*Powdered bread:* Money dusted with luminous powder used by the police to make purchases from peddlers.

*Push, to push shorts:* To peddle small quantities of drugs. Also, *to shove* or *to pitch.* "Go and score from Jim, he's *pushing* for me."

*Ration:* The addict's regular dose, the size of which depends upon how long he has been using drugs and how high he has built up his habit.

*Register:* Allowing the blood to appear in the lower portion of the medicine dropper as an injection is being made to indicate that the needle is in a vein.

*R.F.D. dopehead:* An addict who travels about in rural areas and small towns and gets his drugs from local doctors.

*Right croaker:* A physician who will sell or give an addict drugs. Also known as a *croaker* who will *sail, turn, write scrip,* or give one *a reader.*

*Right guy:* An addict who will not act as an informer when arrested.

*Rolling stuff, to be:* To be transporting narcotics.

*Rooster brand:* Cheap bootleg opium refined from yenshee or green ashes.

*Satch:* To saturate any absorbent material with a drug solution. Drugs may be smuggled into prison by saturating a piece of paper, drying it out, and writing a note on it. Some addicts make it a practice to saturate a portion of their clothing so that in case they are arrested they will have an emergency supply. A quantity of drugs so concealed is a *satch.*

*Scoffing:* Taking the drug orally. Also *mouth habit.*

*Score:* To buy drugs. Also to *connect,* or *make a connection.*

*Score dough:* Money with which to buy drugs. "I had a guy on the send for me and he ran off with my *score dough.*"

*Scrip:* A prescription for narcotics. Also *reader.* "I wrote *scrip* so long that I actually began to think I was a doctor."

*Self-starter:* An addict who voluntarily goes to an institution to quit his habit. See *Mr. Fish.*

*Send:* To produce euphoria. *To be on the send:* To buy drugs for someone else.

*Set, set of works:* Instruments for taking a shot.

*Shit:* Narcotics. See *Junk.*

*Shoot:* To inject hypodermically. Also *to fix, to jab, to put poison in one's arm.* "The boys are beginning to *shoot* sodium amytal on the coast."

*Shooting gallery:* A place where users meet to take shots.

*Short go, short piece:* A small quantity of drugs for the money.

*Shot:* An injection of drugs. Also *jolt, pop, pick-up, fix, prod, bang, bing, bingo, jabpop, prop, geezer.*

*Shot up:* Under the influence; scarred arms from abscesses and injections.

*Shove:* To sell drugs.

*Sixteenth:* One-sixteenth of an ounce.

*Skin shooter:* One who uses the drug intramuscularly rather than intravenously.

*Smokers:* Opium smokers. Also *pipes, pipe fiends, gowsters, hop-heads, yenshee boys.*

*Sneeze, sneeze down:* To hold an addict without charges while persuading him to act as an informer or to supply information useful to the police.

*Sniffer, snifter:* One who sniffs powdered drugs into the nostrils. Also *blowing.* Because penalties are now being imposed for the possession of a hypodermic needle some addicts are resorting to this technique which used to be a popular method of taking heroin.

*Speed ball:* A combination of cocaine and morphine in a single injection.

*Spoon:* A small quantity of heroin.

*Spread the joint:* To get a hypodermic outfit ready for use.

*Square, Square John:* A non-addict.

*S.S.:* A shot into the skin.

*Stem:* Of an opium pipe. "My good old pipe and stem! Good God! How I love them!"

*Stick:* The pipe used in smoking opium. Also *gonger, log, bamboo, dream stick, saxophone.* Also marihuana cigarette.

*Stomach habit:* An oral habit.

*Stoned:* Under the influence.

*Stool pigeon:* An addict or peddler who gives information to narcotics agents to assist them in making arrests, or who provides evidence against other peddlers or addicts by making purchases from a peddler with marked money supplied to him by the narcotics agent. An undercover narcotics agent is not a stool pigeon.

*Straight:* A user's feeling of well-being after a shot. A non-user or *square.*

*Student:* One who is trying drugs or who has difficulty establishing a habit.

*Suey-pow:* A wet sponge used to cool off the bowl of the opium pipe.

*Sugar:* Narcotics.

*Sugar cubes:* Large cubes of bulk morphine.

*Take off:* To take a shot.

*Tar:* Smoking gum opium.

*Tie up:* To distend one's veins, usually of the left arm, by applying an improvised tourniquet.

*Tie rag:* The handkerchief, towel, or cloth used as a tourniquet in tying.

*Tomcat:* An improvised hypodermic made with part of a sewing machine needle.

*Tools:* Paraphernalia for making an injection.

*Torture chamber:* An institution in which drugs are not available.

*Toy:* A small box of opium.

*Tracks:* Scars from injections.

*Train arrived:* Narcotics smuggled into prison. Also *trained nurse.*

*Trey:* A three dollar bag of narcotics, usually heroin.

*Trolley:* The secret contraband distribution system within a prison.

*Turkey:* A capsule or package supposed to contain narcotics but actually containing chalk or some other non-narcotic substance.

*Turn:* To consent to do business with someone. "A big peddler won't *turn* for a bird-cage hype."

*Turn in, turn up:* To inform; to betray to the police.

*Turn on:* To take drugs. To introduce someone to drug use.

*Twisted:* Under the influence of narcotics.

*Twister:* Used either as the equivalent of *wing ding, speed ball,* or to refer to the physical spasms of withdrawal.

*Under the gun:* Under police observation.

*Up and down the lines:* The damage to and discoloration of the veins from intravenous injections.

*Vein shooter:* One who takes the drug intravenously. Also *main-liner, main line shooter, gutter.* The act of intravenous injection is known as *going into the sewer, in the line,* or *taking it main.*

*Verification shot:* A fix during which blood is drawn up into the dropper to verify that the needle is in the vein.

*V.S.:* A vein shot.

*Wake up:* The first injection of the day.

*Wasted:* Under the influence; arrested as a peddler.

*Whiskers:* Law enforcement agents.

*White, Dr.:* A camouflaged reference to drugs. "I'm sick and only *Dr. White* can help me."

*White nurse:* Drugs.

*Wing ding:* A simulated set of symptoms or a deliberately induced poisoning or injury which is supposed to cause a physician to prescribe or administer an injection of morphine. Also *twister, meter, brody.*

*Witch hazel:* Heroin.

*Works:* Instruments used in taking an injection. Also government agent or undercover man.

*Writing:* A letter or note on paper saturated with drugs. Also refers to the writing of prescriptions for addicts by doctors and others.

*Wrong:* Untrustworthy, an informer.

*Yen:* The desire for narcotics or the abstinence symptoms. The term is used mainly for the desire for the drug during abstinence distress. It would be incorrect for a non-addict to say that he had a *yen* for a shot.

*Yen-hock:* A large needle used to prepare opium for smoking.

*Yenshee:* The ash residue which forms inside the bowl of an opium pipe. It can be re-cooked and smoked again, although it is usually mixed with fresh drugs because it is bitter by itself.

*Yenshee baby:* A difficult bowel movement after a period of constipation induced by the use of opiates.

*Yenshee boy:* An opium smoker.

*Yenshee gow:* An instrument used to clean the bowl of an opium pipe.

*Yenshee quay:* An opiate addict. Formerly used only to refer to opium smokers.

# SELECTED BIBLIOGRAPHY

ADAMS, E. W. 1937. *Drug Addiction*. London: Oxford University Press.

——. 1933. "Some Unusual Forms of Drug Addiction," *British Journal of Inebriety*, 31: 1–15.

——. 1935. "What is Addiction?" *British Journal of Inebriety*, 33: 1–11.

ALEXANDER, JOSEPH G. 1894. "Lotus Eating and Opium Eating," *Contemporary Review*, 66: 337–50.

ALKSNE, H. 1960. "Hospital Treated Adolescent Drug Users: A Follow-up Study," *Health News*, 37: 10–19.

AMERICAN MEDICAL ASSOCIATION. Council on Mental Health. 1957. "Report on Narcotic Addiction," *Journal of the American Medical Association*, 165: 1707–13, 1834–41, 1968–74.

AMSLER, CÄSAR. 1935. "Ueber Gewöhnung an narkotische Gifte und Entwöhnung davon, insbesondere ueber Morphingewöhnung und Entwöhnung," *Wiener Klinische Wochenschrift*, 48: 815–18.

ANDERSON, V. V. 1917. "Drug Users in Court," *Boston Medical and Surgical Journal*, 176: 755–57.

ANSLINGER, H. J. 1954. "British Narcotic System," Correspondence, *Journal of the American Medical Association*, 156: 789.

——, and W. OURSLER. 1962. *The Murderers*. New York: Farrar, Straus and Cudahy.

————, and WILLIAM F. TOMPKINS. 1953. *The Traffic in Narcotics.* New York: Funk and Wagnalls.

ARLEN, H. W. 1962. "The Treatment and Rehabilitation of Drug Addiction," *American Journal of Orthopsychiatry,* 32: 316–17.

AUSUBEL, DAVID P. 1948. "The Psychopathology and Treatment of Drug Addiction in Relation to the Mental Hygiene Movement," *Psychiatric Quarterly Supplement,* 22 (2): 219–50.

————. 1958. *Drug Addiction: Physiological, Psychological and Sociological Aspects.* New York: Random House.

BALES, R. F. 1944. *The Fixation Factor in Alcohol Addiction: An Hypothesis Derived from a Comparative Study of Irish and Jewish Social Norms.* Unpublished doctoral dissertation, Harvard University.

BALL, JOHN C. 1965. "Two Patterns of Narcotic Drug Addiction in the United States," *Journal of Criminal Law, Criminology and Police Science,* 56: 203–11.

————. 1967. "The Reliability and Validity of Interview Data Obtained from 59 Narcotic Drug Addicts," *The American Journal of Sociology,* 72 (6): 650–54.

————, and M. P. LAU. 1966. "The Chinese Narcotic Addict in the United States," *Social Forces,* 45 (1): 68–72.

BEACH, H. D. 1957. "Morphine Addiction in Rats," *Canadian Journal of Psychology,* 11: 104–12.

BECKER, HOWARD S. 1953. "Becoming a Marihuana User," *American Journal of Sociology,* 59: 235–42.

————. 1963. *Outsiders: Studies in the Sociology of Deviance.* Glencoe, Ill.: The Free Press.

BEECHER, HENRY K. 1959. *Measurement of Subjective Responses.* New York: Oxford University Press.

BELL, F. MCKELVEY. 1911. "Morphinism and Morphinomania," *New York Medical Journal,* 93: 690–92.

BERRY, L. H. 1951. "Medical Counseling Clinics for Young Narcotic Addicts," *Journal of the American Medical Association,* 147: 1129–32.

BIBERFELD, JOHANNES. 1916. "Zur Kenntnis der Morphingewöhnung. II, Ueber die Specifizität der Morphingewöhnung," *Biochemische Zeitschrift,* 77: 283–97.

BISHOP, ERNEST S. 1921. *The Narcotic Drug Problem*. New York: Macmillan.

BLACK, J. R. 1889. "Advantages of Substituting the Morphia Habit for the Incurably Alcoholic," *Cincinnati Lancet-Clinic* (N.S.), 22 (1): 537–41.

BLOCK, SIEGFRIED. 1916. "Drug Habitués," *New York Medical Journal*, 101: 405–407.

BLOEDORN, W. A. 1917. "Studies of Drug Addicts, *United States Naval Medical Bulletin*, 11 (3).

BONHOEFFER, KARL. 1926. "Zur Therapie des Morphinismus," *Therapie der Gegenwart*, 67: 18–22.

BROWN, L. GUY. 1931. "The Sociological Implications of Drug Addiction," *Journal of Educational Sociology*, 4: 358–69.

BROWN, L. P. 1915. "The Enforcement of the Tennessee Anti-Narcotic Law," *American Journal of Public Health*, 5: 323–33.

BROWN, THORVALD T. 1961. *The Enigma of Drug Addiction*. Springfield, Ill.: Charles C Thomas.

BROWN, WILLIAM. 1931. "Prevention and Treatment of Drug Addiction," *British Medical Journal*, 1 (for 1931): 495–97.

————. 1935. "Psychology in Relation to Alcohol and Drug Addiction," *British Journal of Inebriety*, 33: 61–65.

BURKHART, R. 1883. "Zur Pathologie des chronischen Morphiumvergiftung," *Deutsche Medizinische Wochenschrift*, 9: 33–35.

BURROUGHS, WILLIAM S. 1967. "Kicking Drugs: A Very Personal Story," *Harper's Magazine*, 235 (1406): 39–42. (*See* W. Lee.)

California Department of Justice, Bureau of Criminal Statistics. *Drug Arrests and Dispositions in California*. (Annual.)

CALKINS, ALONZO. 1871. *Opium and the Opium Appetite*. Philadelphia: J. B. Lippincott.

CAMPBELL, HARRY. 1922–23. "The Pathology and Treatment of Morphia Addiction," *British Journal of Inebriety*, 20: 147–61.

CASRIEL, DANIEL H. 1963. *So Fair a House: The Story of Synanon*. Englewood Cliffs, N.J.: Prentice-Hall.

CAVOIR, NORMAN, RICHARD L. KURTZBERG, and DOUGLAS S. LIPTON. 1967. "The Development and Validation of a Heroin Addiction Scale with the MMPI," *The International Journal of the Addictions*, 2 (1): 129–38.

CHAPMAN, K. W. 1957. "Narcotic Addiction: Part 4," *Modern Medicine*, 25: 192–214.

CHEIN, I. 1956. "Narcotics Use among Juveniles," *Social Work*, 1: 50–60.

————. 1965. "The Use of Narcotics as a Personal and Social Problem." In Daniel M. Wilner and Gene G. Kassebaum (Eds.), *Narcotics*. New York: McGraw-Hill.

————, DONALD L. GERARD, ROBERT S. LEE, and EVA ROSENFELD. 1964. *The Road to H: Narcotics, Delinquency and Social Policy*. New York: Basic Books.

———— and EVA ROSENFELD. 1957. "Juvenile Narcotics Use," *Law and Contemporary Problems*, 22 (1): 52–68.

CHESSICK, R. D. 1960. "The 'Pharmacogenic Orgasm' in the Drug Addict," *Archives of General Psychiatry*, 3: 545.

————, DAVID H. LOOF, and HAZEL G. PRICE. 1961. "The Alcoholic-Narcotic Addict," *Quarterly Journal of Studies on Alcohol*, 22: 261–68.

CHOPRA, G. S., and PARAMJECT SINGH CHOPRA. 1965. "Studies on 300 Indian Drug Addicts with Special Reference to Psychosociological Aspects, Etiology and Treatment," *Bulletin on Narcotics*, 17 (2): 1–9.

CHOPRA, R. N. 1928. "The Present Position of the Opium Habit in India," *Indian Journal of Medical Research*, 16: 389–439.

————, and J. P. BOSE. 1931. "Psychological Aspects of Opiate Addiction," *Indian Medical Gazette*, 66: 663–66.

————, and G. S. CHOPRA. 1934. "The Administration of Opium to Infants in India," *Indian Medical Gazette*, 69: 489–94.

————. 1932. "The Opium Habit in the Punjab," *Indian Journal of Medical Research*, 20: 545–64.

————. 1933. "Morphine Habit in India," *Indian Medical Gazette*, 68: 368–70.

————. 1935. "Drug Addiction in India and Its Treatment," *Indian Medical Gazette*, 70: 121–31.

————, and K. S. GREMAL. 1927. "The Opium Habit in India: An Analysis of 100 Cases Amongst the Sikh Population of Calcutta," *Indian Journal of Medical Research*, 15: 57–65.

CLAUSEN, JOHN A. 1957. "Social and Psychological Factors in Narcotics Addiction," *Law and Contemporary Problems*, 22: 34–51.

CLOWARD, RICHARD A., and LLOYD E. OHLIN. 1960. *Delinquency and Opportunity*. Glencoe, Ill.: The Free Press.

COBBE, W. R. 1895. *Doctor Judas: A Portrayal of the Opium Habit*. Chicago: S. C. Griggs.

"Collision Course on Treatment of Narcotic Addicts?" 1962. Editorial, *New York Medicine*, 18: 559–61.

COPELAND, R. S. 1920. "The Narcotic Drug Evil and the New York City Health Department," *American Medicine*, 26 (1): 17–23.

CORNELL, C. (as told to) 1952. "My Son Is a Dope Addict," *Saturday Evening Post*, 224 (30): 20–21, 77–79, 80–81, 84.

CROTHERS, T. D. 1902. *Morphinism and Narcomanias from Other Drugs*. Philadelphia: W. B. Saunders.

————. 1915. "Medical Colleges Responsible for Many New Spirit and Drug Addicts," *Medical Record*, 88: 437–39.

CROW, CARL. 1940. "Dope, Japan's New Weapon," *Reader's Digest*, 36 (3): 31–34.

CROWLEY, R. M. 1939. "Psychoanalytic Literature on Drug Addiction and Alcoholism," *Psychoanalytic Review*, 9: 39–54.

DAI, BINGHAM. 1937. *Opium Addiction in Chicago*. Shanghai: Commercial Press.

DANA, CHARLES L. 1918. "The Problem of Drug Addiction," *Medical Record*, 93: 177.

DANSAUER, FRIEDRICH, and ADOLF RIETH. 1931. "Ueber Morphinismus bei Kriegsbeshädigten," *Arbeit und Gesundheit: Schriftenreihe zum Reichsarbeitsblatt*, no. 18. Berlin: Reimar Hobbing.

DAVID, ERICH. 1925. "Ueber die Ursachen der so häufigen Ruckfälligkeit nach der Morphinentwöhnung," *Zeitschrift für die Gesamte Neurologie und Psychiatrie*, 99: 475–84.

DAVIS, W. M., and J. R. NICHOLS. 1962. "Physical Dependence and Sustained Opiate-Directed Behavior in the Rat: A Preliminary Report," *Psychopharmacologia*, 3: 139.

DEMOTT, B. 1962. "The Great Narcotics Muddle," *Harper's Magazine*, 224 (3): 46–54.

DENEAU, G. A., D. A. MCCARTHY, and M. H. SEEVERS. 1959. "Physical Dependence and Liability Studies in the Monkey," Addendum

1, Minutes 20th Meeting, Committee on Drug Addiction and Narcotics, National Research Council, Washington, D.C., National Academy of Sciences, Jan. 10–11.

DeQuincey, Thomas. 1930. *The Confessions of an English Opium-Eater*. London: J. M. Dent.

Dole, Vincent P., and Marie E. Nyswander. 1965. "A Medical Treatment for Diacetylmorphine (Heroin) Addiction—A Clinical Trial with Methadone Hydrochloride," *Journal of the American Medical Association*, 193 (8): 80–84.

————. 1966. "Rehabilitation of Heroin Addicts after Blockade with Methadone," *New York State Journal of Medicine*, 66 (15): 2011–17.

*Drug Addiction: Crime or Disease?* 1961. Interim and Final Reports of the Joint Committee of the American Bar Association and the American Medical Association on Narcotic Drugs. Bloomington: Indiana University Press.

"Drug Addiction: The Second Report of the Interdepartmental Committee" (Lord Brain, chairman). 1966. *The International Journal of the Addictions*, 1 (1): 131–46.

Dupouy, Roger. 1912. *Les opiomanes; mangeurs, buveurs et fumeurs d'opium*. Paris: Alcan.

Duranty, Walter. 1943. "Opium Smoking," *Atlantic Monthly*, 171 (2): 106–13.

Duvall, H. J., B. Z. Locke, and L. Brill. 1963. "Follow-up Study of Narcotic Drug Addicts Five Years after Hospitalization," *Public Health Reports*, 78: 185–93.

*Duties of Doctors and Dentists under the Dangerous Drugs Act and Regulations* (1956), Dangerous Drugs 101 (6th Ed.), London: Her Majesty's Stationery Office.

Earle, C. W. 1880. "The Opium Habit: A Statistical and Clinical Lecture," *Chicago Medical Review*, 2: 442–46, 493–98.

Eaton, Virgil G. 1888. "How the Opium Habit Is Acquired," *Popular Science Monthly*, 33 (September): 663–67.

Ebin, David (Ed.). 1961. *The Drug Experience*. New York: Orion Press.

Eddy, Nathan B., H. Isbell, M. H. Seevers, and H. Halbach. 1965. "Drug Dependence: Its Significance and Characteristics," *Bulletin of the World Health Organization*, 32: 721–33.

EHRHARDT, H. 1959. Drug Addiction in the Medical and Allied Professions in Germany," *Bulletin on Narcotics*, 11 (1): 18–26.

ELDRIDGE, WILLIAM B. 1962. *Narcotics and the Law*. Chicago: American Bar Foundation.

EMMERICH, OTTO. 1894. *Die Heilung des chronischen Morphinismus*. Berlin: H. Steinitz.

ERLENMEYER, ALBRECHT. 1926. "Zur Theorie und Therapie des Morphinismus," *Zeitschrift für die Gesamte Neurologie und Psychiatrie*, 103: 705–18.

————. 1887. *Die Morphiumsucht*. (3rd ed.) Munich: Heuser.

ESSIG, C. F. 1964. "Addiction to Nonbarbiturate Sedative and Tranquilizing Drugs," *Clinical Pharmacology and Therapeutics*, 5: 334–43.

FAUCHER, LOUIS. 1910–11. "Contribution a l'étude du rêve morphinique et de la morphinomanie." Thesis, University of Montpellier, No. 8.

FINESTONE, HAROLD. 1957. "Cats, Kicks and Color," *Social Problems*, 5 (7): 3–13.

————. 1957b. "Narcotics and Criminality," *Law and Contemporary Problems*, 22 (1): 69–85.

FORT, JOEL P., JR. 1954. "Heroin Addiction among Young Men," *Psychiatry*, 17: 251–59.

FRASER, H. F. 1957. "Tolerance to and Physical Dependence on Opiates, Barbiturates, and Alcohol," *Annual Review of Medicine*, 8: 427.

FREEDMAN, A. M. 1962. "Response of Adult Heroin Addicts to a Total Therapeutic Program," *American Journal of Orthopsychiatry*, 32: 314–15.

————. 1965. "Treatment of Drug Addiction in a Community General Hospital," *Comprehensive Psychiatry*, 4 (3): 199–207.

————, CLIFFORD J. SAGER, EDWIN L. RABINER, and RICHARD E. BROTMAN. 1963. "Response of Adult Heroin Addicts to a Total Therapeutic Program," *American Journal of Orthopsychiatry*, 33: 890–99.

GAMSO, R. R., and P. MASON. 1958. A Hospital for Adolescent Drug Addicts," *Psychiatric Quarterly* (Supp.), 32–33 (1): 99–109.

GERARD, DONALD L., and CONAN KORNETSKY. 1955. "Adolescent Opiate Addiction: A Study of Control and Addict Subjects," *Psychiatric Quarterly*, 29: 457–86.

————. 1954. "Adolescent Opiate Addiction: A Case Study," *Psychiatric Quarterly*, 28: 367–80.

GLASER, FREDERICK B. 1966. "Narcotic Addiction in the Pain-Prone Female Patient, I. A Comparison with Addict Controls," *International Journal of the Addictions*, 1 (2): 47–60.

Great Britain. 1961. *Drug Addiction, Report of the Interdepartmental Committee*. London: Her Majesty's Stationery Office (The Brain Report I).

Great Britain. 1966. Interdepartmental Committee on Drug Addiction, Second Report. "Drug Addiction in the United Kingdom," *Bulletin on Narcotics*, 18 (2): 23–28 (The Brain Report II).

Great Britain. 1926. Ministry of Health, Report, Departmental Committee on Morphine and Heroin Addiction (The Rolleston Report).

GREEN, T. C. 1960. "The Incidence of Drug Addiction in Great Britain and Its Prevention," *Proceedings of the Royal Society of Medicine*, 53: 921–25.

GRIFFIN, LEPEL. 1894. "The Lotus Eater," *Nineteenth Century*, 35: 513–22.

HALL, MARGARET E. 1938. "Mental and Physical Efficiency of Women Drug Addicts," *Journal of Abnormal and Social Psychology*, 33: 332–45.

HAMBURGER, ERNEST. 1964. "Barbiturate Use in Narcotic Addicts," *Journal of the American Medical Association*, 189 (5): 366–68.

HESS, ALBERT G. 1965. *Chasing the Dragon*. New York: The Free Press of Glencoe.

HILDEBRAND, FRITZ. 1926. "Gewöhnung an Genuss und Rauschgifte," *Klinische Wochenschrift*, 5: 1755.

HISCHMANN, A. 1912. *Die Opiumfrage*. Berlin: Leonard Simon.

HOWE, H. S. 1955. "A Physician's Blueprint for the Management and Prevention of Narcotic Addiction," *New York Journal of Medicine*, 55: 341–49.

————. 1957. "An Alternative Solution to the Narcotics Problem," *Law and Contemporary Problems*, 22: 132–37.

HUBBARD, S. DANA. 1920. "Some Fallacies Regarding Drug Addiction," *Journal of the American Medical Association,* 74: 1439–41.

HUXLEY, A. 1954. *Doors to Perception.* New York: Harper.

ISBELL, HARRIS. 1963. "Historical Development of Attitudes Toward Opiate Addiction in the United States." In Seymour M. Farber and Roger H. L. Wilson (Eds.), *Conflict and Creativity,* New York: McGraw-Hill.

————, SOL ALTSCHUL, C. H. KORNETSKY, A. J. EISENMAN, H. G. FLANARY, and H. F. FRASER. 1950. "Chronic Barbiturate Intoxication," *Archives of Neurology and Psychiatry,* 64 (7): 1–28.

————, and H. F. FRASER. 1950. "Addiction to Analgesics and Barbiturates," *Journal of Pharmacology and Experimental Therapeutics,* Part II, 99: 355–94.

————, and WALTER M. WHITE. 1953. "Clinical Characteristics of Addictions," *American Journal of Medicine,* 14 (5): 558–65.

JAFFE, JEROME H., and LEON BRILL. 1966. "Cyclazocine, a Long Acting Narcotic Antagonist: Its Voluntary Acceptance as a Treatment Modality by Narcotics Abusers," *International Journal of the Addictions,* 1 (1): 99–123.

JANDY, E. C., and MAURICE FLOCH. 1937. "Narcotic Addiction as a Factor in Petty Larcency in Detroit," *Bureau of Governmental Research, Detroit,* report no. 145.

JERMULOWICZ, Z. W., and MAG. A. TURNAU. 1962. "Control and Treatment of Drug Addicts in Israel," *Bulletin on Narcotics,* 24 (2): 11–18.

JÖEL, ERNST, and FRITZ FRÄNKEL. 1925. "Zur Verhütung und Behandlung der Giftsüchten," *Klinische Wochenschrift,* 4: 1713–18.

————. 1926. "Zur Pathologie der Gewöhnung. II, Ueber Gewöhnheit und psychische Gewöhnung," *Therapie der Gegenwart,* 67: 60–63.

JOSSELYN, E. E. 1887. "An Analysis of Twelve Cases of the Morphia Habit," *Medical Register,* 1: 195–98.

JOUET, DANIEL. 1883. "Étude sur le morphinisme chronique." Thesis, University of Paris.

KALANT, ORIANA, J. 1966. *The Amphetamines, Toxicity and Addiction.* Toronto: University of Toronto Press.

KAKU, SAGATARO. 1924. *Opium Policy in Japan.* Geneva: A. Kundig.

KANE, H. H. 1880. *The Hypodermic Injection of Morphia.* New York: C. L. Berminghan.

————. 1882. *Opium Smoking in America and China.* New York: G. P. Putnam.

KEELEY, L. E. 1890. *Opium, Its Use, Abuse, and Cure, or, From Bondage to Freedom.* Dwight, Ill., L. E. Keeley.

KING, A. 1958. *Mine Enemy Grows Older.* New York: Signet Books.

KING, EDGAR. 1916. "The Use of Habit-Forming Drugs by Enlisted Men," *Military Surgeon,* 39 (3, 4): 273–81, 380–84.

KING, R. G. 1957. "Narcotic Drug Laws and Enforcement Policies," *Law and Contemporary Problems,* 22: 113–31.

————. 1953. "The Narcotics Bureau and the Harrison Act: Jailing the Healers and the Sick," *Yale Law Journal,* 62: 736–49.

KOENIG, H. 1914. "Die Prognose des Morphinismus," *Berliner Klinische Wochenschrift,* 51: 1061–64.

KOLB, LAWRENCE. 1927. "Clinical Contribution to Drug Addiction: The Struggle for Cure and the Conscious Reasons for Relapse," *Journal of Nervous and Mental Diseases,* 66: 22–43.

————. 1962. *Drug Addiction: A Medical Problem.* Springfield, Ill., Charles C Thomas.

————. 1928. "Drug Addiction: A Study of Some Medical Cases," *Archives of Neurology and Psychiatry,* 20: 171–83.

————. 1925. "Drug Addiction in Its Relation to Crime," *Mental Hygiene,* 9: 74–89.

————. 1925. "Pleasure and Deterioration from Narcotic Addiction," *Mental Hygiene,* 9: 699–724.

————. 1925. "Types and Characteristics of Drugs Addicts," *Mental Hygiene,* 9: 300–13.

————, and A. G. DuMEZ. 1924. "The Prevalence and Trend of Drug Addiction in the United States and Factors Influencing It," *Public Health Reports,* 39: 1179–1204.

LARIMORE, GRANVILLE W., and HENRY BRILL. 1960. "The British Narcotic System: Report of Study," *New York State Journal of Medicine,* 60: 107–15.

LARNER, J. (Ed.). 1964. *The Addict in the Street,* New York: Grove Press.

LASKOWITZ, D. 1961. "The Adolescent Drug Addict," *The Journal of Individual Psychology,* 17: 68–69.

————. 1967. "The Phenomenology of Doriden (Glutethimide) Dependence among Drug Addicts," *The International Journal of the Addictions*, 2 (1): 39–52.

LAUBENTHAL, F. (Ed.). 1964. *Sucht und Missbrauch*. Stuttgart: Georg Thieme Verlag.

LAYARD, JAMES C. 1874. "Morphine," *Atlantic Monthly*, 33: 697–712.

League of Nations. 1930. *Report of the Commission of Inquiry into the Control of Opium Smoking in the Far East*, I. Geneva, Switzerland: League of Nations.

LEE, W. [Pseud., William S. Burroughs]. 1963. *Junkie*. New York: Ace Books.

LEHMANN, H. E. 1963. "Phenomenology and Pathology of Addiction," *Comprehensive Psychiatry*, 4 (3): 168–180.

LEVINSTEIN, EDOUARD. 1880. *Die Morphiumsucht*. Berlin: Hirschwald.

LICHTENSTEIN, P. M. 1914. "Narcotic Addiction," *New York Medical Journal*, 100: 962–66.

LIGHT, A. B., E. G. TORRANCE, W. G. KARR, EDITH G. FRY, and W. A. WOLFF. 1929. *Opium Addiction*, Chicago: American Medical Association.

LINDESMITH, ALFRED R. 1938a. "The Argot of the Underworld Drug Addict," *Journal of Criminal Law and Criminology*, 29 (2): 261–78.

———— 1938b. "A Sociological Theory of Drug Addiction," *American Journal of Sociology*, 43 (4): 593–613.

————, and JOHN H. GAGNON. 1964. "Anomie and Drug Addiction." In Marshall Clinard (Ed.), *Anomie and Deviant Behavior*. New York: The Free Press of Glencoe.

———— 1940. "Dope Fiend Mythology," *Journal of Criminal Law and Criminology*, 31 (2): 199–208.

———— 1940b. "The Drug Addict as a Psychopath," *American Sociological Review*, 5 (6): 914–20.

———— 1946. "Can Chimpanzees Become Morphine Addicts?" *Journal of Comparative Psychology*, 39 (2): 109–17.

———— 1947. *Opiate Addiction*. Bloomington, Ind.: Principia Press.

———— 1965a. *The Addict and the Law*. Bloomington, Ind., Indiana University Press.

————. 1965b. "Problems in the Social Psychology of Addiction." In Daniel M. Wilner and Gene G. Kassebaum (Eds.), *Narcotics*. New York: McGraw-Hill.

LONG, R. H. 1959. *The Physician and the Law*. (2d ed.) New York: Appleton-Century-Crofts.

LUDLOW, FITZHUGH. 1867. "What Shall They Do To Be Saved?" *Harper's Magazine*, 35: 377–87.

MAIER, H. W. 1933. "Zur Klinik der Toxicomanien," *Schweizer Archiv für Neurologie und Psychiatrie*, 30: 380–94.

MAPOTHER, EDWARD. 1931. "A Discussion of the Prevention and Treatment of Drug Addiction," *British Journal of Inebriety*, 29: 13–19.

MARKS, JEANETTE. 1928. "The Opium Habit," *British Journal of Inebriety*, 24: 74–79.

MARSHALL, ORVILLE. 1878. "The Opium Habit in Michigan," *Annual Report of the Michigan State Board of Health*, 6: 61–73.

MARTIN, ERNEST. 1893. *L'Opium, ses Abus, Mangeurs et Fumeurs d'Opium, Morphinomanie*. Paris: Société d'Éditions Scientifiques.

MARTIN, W. A., and C. W. GORODETZKY. 1967. "Cyclazocine, an Adjunct in the Treatment of Narcotic Addiction," *International Journal of the Addictions*, 2: 85–94.

MASTERS, F. J. 1896. "The Opium Traffic in California," *Chautauquan News*, 15: 54–61.

MATTISON, JANSEN B. 1894. "Morphinism in Medical Men," *Journal of the American Medical Association*, 23: 186–88.

————. 1885. *The Treatment of Opium Addiction*. New York: G. P. Putnam.

MAURER, DAVID W. 1936. "The Argot of the Underworld Narcotic Addict," *American Speech*, 11: 116–27.

————. 1938. "The Argot of the Underworld Narcotic Addict: Part II," *American Speech*, 13: 179–92.

————, and VICTOR H. VOGEL. 1962. *Narcotics and Narcotic Addiction*. (2d ed.) Springfield, Ill., Charles C Thomas.

Mayor's Committee on Marihuana. 1944. *The Marihuana Problem in the City of New York*. Lancaster, Pa., Jacques Cattell Press.

MCIVER, JOSEPH, and GEORGE E. PRICE. 1916. "Drug Addiction: Analysis of One Hundred and Forty-Seven Cases at the Philadelphia General Hospital," *Journal of the American Medical Association*, 64: 476–80.

McPHERSON, GEORGE E., and J. COHEN. 1919. "A Survey of One Hundred Cases of Drug Addiction Entering Camp Upton, New York, via the Draft, 1918," *Boston Medical and Surgical Journal*, 180: 636–38.

MERRILL, FREDERICK T. 1942. *Japan and the Opium Menace*. New York: International Secretariat, Institute of Pacific Relations, and Foreign Policy Association.

MEYER, ALAN S. (Ed.). 1952. *Social and Psychological Factors in Opiate Addiction: A Review of Research Findings Together with an Annotated Bibliography*. New York: Columbia University Press.

MEYER, ERNST. 1924. "Ueber Morphinismus, Kokainismus, und den Missbrauch anderer Narkotica," *Medizinische Klinik*, 20: 403–407.

MEYER, FRITZ M. 1928. "Ein Beitrag zum Morphinismus und zu der Behandlung nach Kahle," *Deutsche Medizinische Wochenschrift*, 54: 1369–70.

————. 1933. "Ueber einige seltener vorkommenden Formen von Rauschgiftsucht," *Münchener Medizinische Wochenschrift*, 80: 732–33.

————. 1936. "Einige zahlenmässige Ergebnisse an 90 Morphinkranken," *Zeitschrift für die Gesamte Neurologie und Psychiatrie*, 154: 499–506.

MICHELSEN, TWAIN. 1940. "Lindesmith's Mythology," *Journal of Criminal Law and Criminology*, 31: 373–400.

MORHOUS, EUGENE. 1953. "Drug Addiction in Upper Economic Levels: A Study of 142 Cases," *West Virginia Medical Journal*, 49: 189–90.

MORTON, S. T. 1885. "An Experience with Opium," *Popular Science Monthly*, 27: 334–39.

MOSELEY, ARNOLD. 1959. "The Addict's Bag of Tricks," *Journal of the Oklahoma State Medical Association*, 52: 309–10.

MURTAGH, J. M., and S. HARRIS. 1959. *Who Live in Shadow*. New York: McGraw-Hill.

New York Academy of Medicine, Committee on Public Health. 1953. *Conferences on Drug Addiction among Adolescents*. New York: Blakiston.

———. 1955. "Report on Drug Addiction," *Bulletin of the New York Academy of Medicine*, 31: 592–607.

———. 1963. "Report on Drug Addiction—II," *Bulletin of the New York Academy of Medicine*, 39: 417–73.

———. 1965. "Report on Drug Addiction—III," *Bulletin of the New York Academy of Medicine*, 41 (7): 825–29.

NICHOLS, JOHN R. 1963. "A Procedure Which Produces Sustained Opiate-Directed Behavior (Morphine Addiction) in the Rat," *Psychological Reports*, 13 (3): 895–904.

———. 1965. "How Opiates Change Behavior," *Scientific American*, 212 (2): 80–88.

———, and W. M. DAVIS. 1959. "Drug Addiction II. Variation of Addiction," *Journal of the American Pharmaceutical Association*, Scien. Ed., 48: 259.

———, HEADLEE, C. P., and H. W. COPPOCK. 1956. "Drug Addiction, I, Addiction by Escape Training," *Journal of the American Pharmaceutical Association*, Sci. Ed. 45: 788–91.

NOLAN, D. W. 1881. "The Opium Habit," *Catholic World*, 33: 827–35.

NYSWANDER, MARIE. 1956. *The Drug Addict as a Patient*. New York: Grune and Stratton.

O'DONNELL, JOHN A. 1964. "A Follow-up of Narcotic Addicts: Mortality, Relapse and Abstinence," *American Journal of Orthopsychiatry*, 34: 948–54.

———. 1963. "A Post-Hospital Study of Kentucky Addicts—A Preliminary Report," *Journal of the Kentucky State Medical Association*, 61: 573–77; 604.

———. 1966. "Narcotic Addiction and Crime," *Social Problems*, 13: 374–85.

———. 1965. "The Relapse Rate in Narcotic Addiction: A Critique of Follow-up Studies." In *Narcotics*, Daniel M. Wilner and Gene G. Kassebaum (Eds.), New York: McGraw-Hill.

———, and JOHN C. BALL (Eds.). 1966. *Narcotic Addiction*. New York: Harper and Row.

OLTMAN, JANE E., and SAMUEL FRIEDMAN. 1964. "Twenty Years of Drug Addiction," *Diseases of the Nervous System*, 25: 90–96.

OSTROMISLENSKY, IVAN. 1935. "Morphinism," *New York Medical Record*, 141: 556–60.

————. 1936. "Relapses in Morphine Addiction," *Clinical Medicine and Surgery*, 43: 74–78.

PARTINGTON, J. E. 1940. "The Comparative Mental Efficiency of a Drug Addict Group," *Journal of Applied Psychology*, 24: 48–57.

PARTRIDGE, MAURICE. 1963. "Drug Addiction in Great Britain," *Comprehensive Psychiatry*, 4 (3): 208–13.

PAYNE, E. GEORGE. 1931. *The Menace of Narcotic Drugs*. New York: Prentice-Hall.

PESCOR, MICHAEL J. 1938. "A Statistical Analysis of the Clinical Records of Hospitalized Drug Addicts," *Public Health Reports*, Supplement No. 43. Washington, D.C.: U.S. Government Printing Office.

————. 1941. "Prognosis in Drug Addiction," *American Journal of Psychiatry*, 97: 1419–33.

————. 1942a. "Physician Drug Addicts," *Diseases of the Nervous System*, 3: 2–3.

————. 1942b. "Time Element in the Treatment of Drug Addiction," *American Journal of Psychiatry*, 99: 435–38.

PETTEY, GEORGE E. 1913. *Narcotic Drug Diseases and Allied Ailments*. Philadelphia: F. A. Davis.

PIEL, GERALD. 1943. "Narcotics: War Has Brought Illicit Traffic to All-Time Low but U.S. Treasury Fears Rising Postwar Addiction," *Life*, 15: 82–94.

PILCZ, ALEXANDER. 1934. "Zur Konstitution der Süchtigen," *Jahrbücher für Psychiatrie*, 51: 169.

POHLISCH, KURT. 1931. "Die Verbreitung des chronischen Opiatsmissbrauchs in Deutschland, ermittelt auf Grund eines vom Reichsgesundheitsamt zusammengestellten und geprüften Materials," *Monatschrift für Psychiatrie und Neurologie*, 79 (1): 1–32.

POLLOCK, H. M. 1918–19. "A Statistical Study of One Hundred Sixty-Four Patients with Drug Psychoses," *State Hospital Quarterly*, 4. Utica, N.Y. 40–51.

QUINN, W. F. 1961. "Narcotic Addiction—Medical and Legal Problems with Physicians," *California Medicine*, 94: 214–17.

RADÓ, SANDOR. 1933. "The Psychoanalysis of Pharmacothymia," *Psychoanalytic Quarterly*, 2: 1–23.

————. 1956. *Collected Papers*, Vol. 1 (1922–55), New York: Grune and Stratton.

————. 1957. "Narcotic Bondage: A General Theory of the Dependence on Narcotic Drugs," *American Journal of Psychiatry,* 114: 165–70.

————. 1963. "Fighting Narcotic Bondage and Other Forms of Narcotic Disorders," *Comprehensive Psychiatry,* 4 (3): 160–67.

RASOR, ROBERT W. 1958. "Narcotics Addicts: Personality Characteristics in Hospital Treatment." In Paul H. Hoch and Joseph Zubin (Eds.), *Problems of Addiction and Habituation.* New York: Grune and Stratton.

RAY, MARSH B. 1961. "The Cycle of Abstinence and Relapse among Heroin Addicts," *Social Problems,* 9: 132–40.

RAYNOR, G. F., and H. E. BAUER. 1935. "A New Treatment for Drug Addiction: Preliminary Clinical Report on Use of Rossium," *Medical Record,* 142: 139–42.

REICHARD, J. D. 1946. "Some Myths about Marihuana," *Federal Probation,* 10: 15–22.

REMONDINO, P. C. 1896. "The Hypodermic Syringe and Our Morphine Habitués," *Medical Sentinel,* 4: 4–7.

"Report of the Mayor's Committee on Drug Addiction to the Honorable R. C. Patterson, Jr., Commissioner of Correction, New York City," 1930–31. *American Journal of Psychiatry,* 10: 433–588.

RIECHERT, THEODORE. 1931. "Die Prognose der Rauschgiftsüchten," *Archiv für Psychiatrie,* 95: 103–26.

ROSENBLOOM, JOSEPH R. 1959. "Notes on Jewish Drug Addicts," *Psychological Reports,* 5: 769–72.

RUBINGTON, EARL. 1967. "Drug Addiction as a Deviant Career," *International Journal of the Addictions,* 2 (1): 3–20.

RUSSEL, PASHA T. W. 1931. "Drug Addiction in Egypt," *British Journal of Inebriety,* 29: 60–65.

SANDOZ, C. EDOUARD. 1922. "Report on Morphinism to the Municipal Court of Boston," *Journal of Criminal Law and Criminology,* 13: 10–55.

SCELETH, CHARLES E. 1916. "A Rational Treatment of the Morphine Habit," *Journal of the American Medical Association,* 66: 860–62.

————, and SIDNEY KUH. 1924. "Drug Addiction," *Journal of the American Medical Association,* 82: 679–82.

SCHASRE, ROBERT. 1966. "Cessation Patterns among Neophyte Heroin Users," *International Journal of the Addictions,* 1 (2): 23–32.

SCHNEIDER, KURT. 1933. "Süchten," *Deutsche Medizinische Wochenschrift*, 59: 1423–26.

SCHUR, EDWIN M. 1962. *Narcotic Addiction in Britain and America: The Impact of Public Policy*. Bloomington: Indiana University Press.

SCHWARZ, HANNS. 1927. "Ueber die Prognose des Morphinismus," *Monatschrift für Psychiatrie und Neurologie*, 63: 180–238.

————. 1932. "Weitere Untersuchungen zur Prognose des Morphinismus," *Monatschrift für Psychiatrie und Neurologie*, 84–85: 257–60.

SCOTT, FREDERICK GILBERT LAUGHTON. 1930. *The Morphine Habit and Its Painless Treatment*. London: Lewis.

SEEVERS, M. H. 1954. "Adaptation to Narcotics," *Federation Proceedings*, 13: 672–84.

————. 1962. "Medical Perspectives on Habituation and Addiction," *Journal of the American Medical Association*, 181 (2): 92–98.

————, and G. A. DENEAU. 1963. "Physiological Aspects of Tolerance and Physical Dependence." In W. S. Root and F. G. Hoffman (Eds.), *Physiological Pharmacology*, New York: Academic Press.

————, and L. A. WOODS. 1953. "The Phenomena of Tolerance," Symposium on Drug Addiction, *American Journal of Medicine*, 14: 546–57.

SEREJSKI, MARK. 1923. "Ueber die Konstitution der Narkomanen," *Zeitschrift für die Gesamte Neurologie und Psychiatrie*, 95: 130–50.

"SIGMA" (pseud.). 1868. "Opium Eating," *Lippincott's Magazine*, 1: 404–12.

SIMMEL, E. 1948. "Alcoholism and Addiction," *Psychoanalytic Quarterly*, 17: 6–31.

SLOCUM, M. A. 1925. "Morphine: Its Use before and after Operations," *Journal of the American Medical Association*, 84: 1264–67.

SMITH, GENE M., CHARLES W. SEMKE, and HENRY K. BEECHER. 1962. "Objective Evidence of Mental Effects of Heroin, Morphine and Placebo in Normal Subjects," *Journal of Pharmacology and Experimental Therapeutics*, 136 (1): 53–58.

SOLLIER, PAUL. 1903. "Hystérie et morphinomanie," *Revue Neurologique*, 11: 855.

SOLOMON, DAVID (Ed.). 1966. *The Marihuana Papers*. Indianapolis: Bobbs-Merrill.

SPRAGG, S. D. S. 1940. "Relations between Intelligence and Morbid Addictions," *Yearbook of the National Society for the Study of Education*, 39: 285–90.

―――. 1940. "Morphine Addiction in Chimpanzees," *Comparative Psychology Monographs*, Vol. 15. Baltimore: Johns Hopkins Press.

STANLEY, L. L. 1919–20. "Drug Addictions," *Journal of Criminal Law and Criminology*, 10: 62–70.

―――. 1915–16. "Morphinism," *Journal of Criminal Law and Criminology*, 6: 586–93.

―――. 1917–18. "Morphinism and Crime," *Journal of Criminal Law and Criminology*, 8: 749–56.

STRAUSS, ERWIN. 1920. "Zur Pathogenese des chronischen Morphinismus," *Monatschrift für Psychiatrie und Neurologie*, 47: 80–97.

TAKMAN, J. 1961. "An Epidemiological Study of Narcotic Use among Stockholm Adolescents," *Proceedings of the 3d World Congress of Psychiatry*. Montreal: McGill University Press.

TAYLOR, NORMAN. 1949. *Flight from Reality*. New York: Duell, Sloan and Pearce.

TERRY, CHARLES E. 1927. *A Further Study and Report on the Use of Narcotics under the Provisions of Federal Law in Six Communities in the United States of America for the Period of July 1, 1923, to June 30, 1924*. New York: Bureau of Social Hygiene.

―――, and MILDRED PELLENS. 1928. *The Opium Problem*. New York: Committee on Drug Addictions in collaboration with the Bureau of Social Hygiene.

―――, J. W. COX, and MILDRED PELLENS. 1927. *Report to the Committee on Drug Addictions on the Legal Use of Narcotics in Detroit and Environs for the Period of July 1, 1925, to June 30, 1926*. New York: Bureau of Social Hygiene.

THOMPSON, TRAVIS, and CHARLES R. SCHUSTER. 1964. "Morphine Self-Administration, Food-Reinforced, and Avoidance Behaviors in Rhesus Monkeys," *Psychopharmacologia*, 5: 87–94.

TREADWAY, W. L. 1930. "Further Observations on the Epidemiology of Narcotic Drug Addiction," *Public Health Reports*, 45: 541–53.

―――. 1929. "Report of the Departmental Committee on Morphine and Heroin Addiction to the Ministry of Health: Review," *Public Health Reports*, 44: 1239–41.

_____. 1930. "Some Epidemiological Features of Drug Addiction," *British Journal of Inebriety,* 28: 50–54.

TROCCHI, A. 1961. *Cain's Book.* New York: Grove Press.

TU, TSUNGMING. 1951. "Statistical Studies on the Mortality Rates and the Causes of Death among the Opium Addicts in Formosa," *Bulletin on Narcotics,* 3: 9–11.

TURANO, ANTHONY M. 1935. "Punishment for Disease," *American Mercury,* 36: 207–215.

United States. Treasury Department. Bureau of Narcotics. Annual Reports. 1930–. "Traffic in Opium and Other Dangerous Drugs." Washington, D.C.: U.S. Government Printing Office.

VOGEL, VICTOR H. 1937. "Clinical Studies of Drug Addiction: IV. Suggestibility of Narcotic Addicts," *Public Health Reports,* Supplement No. 132.

_____, HARRIS ISBELL, and KENNETH W. CHAPMAN. 1948. "Present Status of Narcotic Addiction," *Journal of the American Medical Association,* 138: 1019–26.

VOGEL, V. H., and DAVID W. MAURER. 1954. *Narcotics and Narcotic Addiction,* Springfield, Ill.: Charles C. Thomas.

VOLKMAN, RITA, and DONALD R. CRESSEY. 1963. "Differential Association and the Rehabilitation of Drug Addicts," *American Journal of Sociology,* 69 (2): 129–42.

VOLLMER, AUGUST. 1936. *The Police and Modern Society.* Berkeley: University of California Press.

WEEKS, JAMES R. 1961. "Self-Maintained Morphine 'Addiction'—A Method for Chronic Programmed Intravenous Injections in Unrestrained Rats," *Federation Proceedings,* 20: 397.

_____. 1962. "Experimental Morphine Addiction: Method for Automatic Intravenous Injections in Unrestrained Rats," *Science,* 138 (3537): 143–44.

_____. 1964. "Experimental Narcotic Addiction," *Scientific American,* 210 (3): 46–52.

_____, and R. JAMES COLLINS. 1964. "Factors Affecting Voluntary Morphine Intake in Self-Maintained Addicted Rats," *Psychopharmacologia,* 6: 267–79.

WHISSON, MICHAEL G. 1965. *Under the Rug: The Drug Problem in Hong Kong.* Hong Kong: Hong Kong Council of Social Service.

White House Conference on Narcotic and Drug Abuse, September 27–28, 1962. *Proceedings*. Washington, D.C.: U.S. Department of Justice.

WHOLEY, C. C. 1912. "Morphinism in Some of Its Less Commonly Noted Aspects," *Journal of the American Medical Association*, 58: 1855–56.

WIKLER, ABRAHAM. 1948. "Recent Progress in Research on the Neurophysiologic Basis of Morphine Addiction," *American Journal of Psychiatry*, 105 (5): 329–38.

―――. 1952. "A Psychodynamic Study of a Patient During Self-Regulated Readdiction to Morphine," *Psychiatric Quarterly*, 26: 270–93.

―――. 1953. *Opiate Addiction: Psychological and Neurophysiological Aspects in Relation to Clinical Problems*. Springfield, Ill.: Charles C Thomas.

―――. 1955. "Rationale of the Diagnosis and Treatment of Addiction," *Connecticut State Medical Journal*, 19 (7): 560.

―――. 1961. "On the Nature of Addiction and Habituation," *British Journal of Addiction*, 57 (2): 73–79.

―――. 1965. "Conditioning Factors in Opiate Addiction and Relapse." In Daniel M. Wilner and Gene G. Kassebaum (Eds.), *Narcotics*. New York: McGraw-Hill.

―――, and R. W. RASOR. 1953. "Psychiatric Aspects of Drug Addiction," Symposium on Drug Addiction, *American Journal of Medicine*, 14: 566–70.

WILLCOX, WILLIAM H. 1933. "Medico-legal Aspects of Alcohol and Drug Addiction," *British Journal of Inebriety*, 31: 131–44.

―――. 1926. "The Prevention and Arrest of Drug Addiction," *British Journal of Inebriety*, 24: 1–8.

WILLIAMS, EDWARD H. 1922. *Opiate Addiction: Its Handling and Treatment*, New York: Macmillan.

WILLIAMS, H. S. 1938. *Drug Addicts Are Human Beings*. Washington, D.C.: Shaw.

WILNER, DANIEL M., and GENE G. KASSEBAUM (Eds.). 1965. *Narcotics*. New York: McGraw-Hill.

WINICK, CHARLES. 1962. "Maturing Out of Narcotic Addiction," *Bulletin on Narcotics*, 14: 1–7.

————. 1961. "Physician Narcotic Addicts," *Social Problems*, 9: 174–86.

————. 1959–60. "The Use of Drugs by Jazz Musicians," *Social Problems*, 7: 240–53.

————, and MARIE NYSWANDER. 1961. "Psychotherapy of Successful Musicians Who Are Drug Addicts," *American Journal of Orthopsychiatry*, 13: 622–36.

WISSLER, ALBERT. 1931. *Die Opiumfrage: Ein Studie zur weltwirtschaftlichen und weltpolitischen Lage der Gegenwart*. Jena: Gustav Fischer.

WOLFF, PAUL. 1933. "Alcohol and Drug Addiction in Germany," *British Journal of Inebriety*, 31: 141–71.

WOODS, ARTHUR. 1931. *Dangerous Drugs: The World Fight Against Illicit Traffic in Narcotics*. New Haven: Yale University Press.

WUTH, OTTO. 1934. "Ueber Morphinismus," *Medizinische Klinik*, 30: 956–58.

————. 1935. "Zur Erbanlage der Süchtigen," *Zeitschrift für die Gesamte Neurologie und Psychiatrie*, 153: 495–505.

YABLONSKY, LEWIS. 1965. *The Tunnel Back: Synanon*. New York: Macmillan.

ZIMMERING, PAUL, JAMES TOOLAN, RENATE SAFRIN, and S. BERNARD WORTIS. 1952. "Drug Addiction in Relation to Problems of Adolescence," *American Journal of Psychiatry*, 109 (3): 272–78.

————. 1951. "Heroin Addiction in Adolescent Boys," *Journal of Nervous and Mental Diseases*, 114: 19–34.

ZINBERG, NORMAN E., and DAVID C. LEWIS. 1964. "Narcotic Usage: A Spectrum of a Difficult Medical Problem," *New England Journal of Medicine*, 270 (19): 989–93.

# INDEX

Adams, E. W., 159–60, 267
Addicting and non-addicting drugs, 197–99
Addiction defined, 3, 49–52, 64–67
Addiction-prone personalities, 107, 157–72
Addicts, attitudes of, 6–7, 11–12, 34–35, 40–44, 137–38, 141–45; interviewing of, 5–7; medical, 41–42, 54–56, 58–62, 116–19, 167, 201–203, 210–12
Alcoholics Anonymous, 51
Alcoholism, 4, 26, 38, 79, 179, 181, 188, 198, 211–12, 236
Alexander, J. G., 267
Alkaloids, opiate, 4, 208, 243–44
Alksne, H., 267
Altschul, S., 275
Ambivalence of user, 132
Amsler, C., 33, 267
Analytic induction, 20–21
Anderson, V. V., 162, 267
Animals as addicts, 9, 125–27, 181–86
Anomie, 158, 173–74
Anslinger, H. J., 267

Argot, theoretical significance of, 100–103
Arlen, H. W., 268
Asbury, H., 214
Associations and relapse, 148–50
Ausubel, D. P., 157, 166–68, 170, 171, 177, 268
Availability, influence of, 148–50, 231, 234
Avoidance and escape behavior, 74
Awareness of addiction, 92–94

Bales, R. F., 198, 268
Ball, J. C., 268, 280
Bancroft, W. D., 133–34
Barbiturates, 198
Bauer, H. E., 282
Beach, H. D., 126, 268
Becker, H. S., 24, 148, 268
Beecher, H. K., 25, 268, 283
Bell, F. M., 47, 268
Berry, L. H., 268
Biberfeld, J., 65, 268
Biological aspects of addiction, 65–66
Bishop, E. S., 178, 269

Black, J. R., 212, 269
Blackley, P. H., 249
Block, S., 162, 269
Bloedorn, W. A., 269
Bonhoeffer, K., 162, 200, 269
Boredom of abstainer, 146–48
Bose, J. P., 36, 270
Brain, W. R. (Lord Brain), 272
Braithwaite, R. B., 19
Bratz, E., 200, 201
Brill, H., 276
Brill, L., 272, 275
British control system, 234, 241
Brotman, R. E., 273
Brown, L. G., 79, 269
Brown, L. P., 210, 269
Brown, T. T., 269
Brown, W., 269
Burkhart, R., 269
Burroughs, W. S., 171, 269

Calkins, A., 57, 110, 145, 210, 269
Campbell, H., 223, 269
Casreil, D. H., 269
Causal analysis, 12–15, 16–22
Causal process and variables, 13
Causality, concept of, as precondition
    of addiction, 194–97
Cavoir, N., 269
Chapman, K. W., 270, 285
Character deterioration in addiction,
    40, 43–44
Chein, I., 48, 173–74, 270
Chessick, R. D., 270
Chimpanzees, experiments with,
    181–83
China, opium problem in, 208–209
Chinese opium smokers in U.S.,
    214–15
Chopra, G. S., 270
Chopra, P. S., 270
Chopra, R. N., 36, 42–43, 120, 162,
    195, 216, 270
Chotzen, F., 26
Civil commitment program, 240
Class status of nineteenth-century
    addicts, 209

Clausen, J. A., 166, 271
Cloward, R. A., 271
Cobbe, W. R., 209, 271
Cocaine, 4, 79–80, 100, 197, 204,
    217
Cocteau, J., 130, 138
Codeine, 244
Cognition, role of, 8–9, 57–59, 72–
    83, 120–22, 144–45, 187–88,
    192–97, 201–203
Cohen, J., 278
Collins, R. J., 285
Commission of Inquiry into the Con-
    trol of Opium Smoking in the
    Far East, League of Nations,
    277
Conditioning theory, 186–88
    See also Negative reinforcement;
    Operant conditioning; Positive
    reinforcement
Conwell, Chic, 5
Copeland, R. S., 271
Coppock, H. W., 280
Cornell, C., 271
Council on Mental Health, A.M.A.,
    267
Cox, J. W., 284
Craving, source of, 7–8
Cressey, D. R., 285
Crime and addiction, 216, 220–23
Crothers, T. D., 58, 89–90, 135, 271
Crow, C., 271
Crowley, R. M., 271
Crucial instances of addiction, 15,
    69–72, 123–25
Cures, cold turkey, 143–44; desire
    for, 132–38; gradual reduction,
    143–44; see Relapse impulse

Dai, B., 125, 271
Dana, C. L., 271
Dansauer, F., 48, 52, 54–55, 63, 90,
    108, 124, 137, 271
David, E., 146–47, 271
Davis, W. M., 271–80
Deluxe dosage, 90
Demerol, 243

DeMott, B., 271
Deneau, G. A., 271, 283
Departmental Committee on Morphine and Heroin Addiction (Rolleston Report), 121, 274
Dependence, physical, 67; psychological, 55–58, 67, 83–90
DeQuincey, T., 90, 209, 245, 272
Determinism, 12–13
Dewey, John, 13
Dilaudid, 244
Dole, V. P., 91, 202–203, 272
Dolophine, 243
Dosage, average, 59–62; increase of, 59, 62–63, 90–92
Double failure hypothesis, 158
Drill, V. A., 185
Drug balance, 32
Drug use vs. addiction, 48
Dumez, A. G., 276
Dupouy, R., 43, 90, 110, 272
Duranty, W., 272
Duvall, H. J., 272

Earle, C. W., 272
Eaton, V. G., 117–18, 272
Ebin, D., 272
Eddy, N. B., 272
Effects of drugs, beneficial, 43
   direct and indirect, 39–44
   initial, 24–28, 105–107
   reversal of, 31–39, 78
Ehrhardt, H., 273
Eisenman, A. J., 275
Eldridge, W. B., 273
Emmerich, O., 178–79, 273
Erlenmeyer, A., 7–8, 32, 47, 59, 78, 273
Escape theory, 180–81
Essig, C. F., 273
European drug control programs, 240–41
Evil-causes-evil fallacy, 188–89
Experimental logic, 13–22, 123–25
Experiments with lower animals, 125–27

Falsification of theory, 97, 123
Farber, S. M., 275
Faucher, L., 28, 81–82, 108, 110, 111, 273
Federal Bureau of Narcotics, 226–27, 239–40, 243
Federal Bureau of Prisons, 5
Finestone, H., 273
Fix, Techniques of, 245–46
Flanary, H. G., 275
Floch, M., 275
Fort, J., 273
Fränkel, F., 79, 107, 170, 171, 275
Fraser, H. F., 273, 275
Freedman, A. M., 273
Freud, S., 158
Friedman, S., 280
Fry, E. G., 29–30, 86–88, 277

Gagnon, J. H., 277
Galilean vs. Aristotelian science, 18–19
Gamso, R. R., 273
Gerard, D. L., 48, 164, 166, 167, 168, 171, 173, 270, 274
Germany, addiction in, 59–62
Glaser, F. B., 115–16, 274
Gorodetzky, G. W., 278
Green, T. C., 274
Gremal, K. S., 120, 270
Griffin, L., 274

Habituation vs. addiction, 47–49, 54–67
Halbach, H., 272
Hall, M. E., 274
Hamburger, E., 274
Harris, S., 279
Harrison Act, 64, 119, 210, 217–19, 221, 223, 234, 237
Hartwell, B. A., 209
Headlee, C. P., 280
Hebb, D. O., 198
Heredity of addicts, 171–72
Heroin, 208, 244
Hess, A. G., 274
Hildebrand, F., 274

Hischmann, A., 274
Hoch, Paul H., 282
Hoffman, F. G., 283
Honeymoon period, 25
Hooked, 101–103
Howe, H. S., 274
Hubbard, S. D., 276
Hunger as addiction, 198
Hunter, John, 145
Huxley, A., 275
Hypochondria of abstainer, 143
Hypodermic use of drugs, 245–46
Hypotheses of study, 7–9

Illicit traffic, 221–23, 225–30
Immunity to addiction, 24, 103–104
Impact effects, 33–34, 38, 40, 91
Indian addicts, 42–43, 119–20
Induction, 20–21
Infants, physically dependent, 195
Inhalation techniques, 246
Initial experiences with drugs, types
    of, 105–107
Interview techniques, 5–7
Intravenous injection, 33–34, 245–
    47
Irey, E., 226
Irrationality of craving, 74, 131–32
Isbell, H., 272, 275, 285

Jaffee, J. H., 275
Jandy, E. C., 275
Jermulowicz, Z. W., 275
Jöel, E., 79, 107, 170, 171, 275
Jones, Broadway, 5, 6, 140, 141
Jones-Miller Act, 220–21, 234
Josselyn, E. E., 275
Jouet, D., 47, 110, 275
Joy popper, 103

Kalant, O. J., 275
Kaku, S., 275
Kane, H. H., 132, 133, 213–15, 275–
    76, 277
Karr, W. G., 29–30, 39, 86–88
Kassebaum, G. G., 53, 126, 173, 178,
    270, 278, 280, 286
Keeley, L. E., 136, 276

Keynes, J. M., 21
King, A., 276
King, E., 276
King, R. G., 276
Koenig, H., 276
Kolb, L., 26–27, 41, 42, 59, 60, 62,
    107, 134, 160–62, 165, 166, 167,
    168, 170, 276
Kornetsky, C., 164, 165, 166, 167,
    168, 171, 173, 274, 275
Korsakoff's psychosis, 26
Kraepelin, E., 100, 162
Kuh, S., 199, 282
Kurtzberg, R. L., 269

Lambert, A., 111
Lange, J., 162
Language, role in addiction, 192–94
Larimore, G. W., 276
Larner, J., 276
Laskowitz, D., 276–77
Lau, M. P., 268
Laubenthal, F., 277
Laudanum, 119, 209
Layard, J. C., 56, 150–54, 177
Lee, R. S., 48, 173, 270, 277
Lee, W., 277
Legewie, B., 56, 78
Lehmann, H. E., 277
Levinstein, E., 47, 59, 277
Lewin, K., 18–19
Lewis, D. C., 116, 287
Lichtenstein, P. M., 277
Libermann, H., 110
Light, A. B., 29–30, 40, 86–88, 277
Lindesmith, A. R., 183, 277–78
Lipton, D. S., 269
Locke, B. Z., 272
Long, R. H., 278
Loof, D. H., 270
LSD, 26, 38, 79–80, 188, 197–98
Ludlow, F., 278

McIver, J., 278
McPherson, G. E., 278
Maier, H. W., 278
Mapother, E., 278

Marginal patterns, 112–16, 201–203

Marihuana, 4, 24, 79–80, 100, 180, 197, 204

Marks, J., 278

Marshall, O., 210, 278

Martin, E., 278

Martin, W. A., 278

Mason, P., 273

Masters, F. J., 278

Mattison, J. B., 110, 278

Maurer, D. W., 249, 278, 285

Mayor's Committee on Marihuana, 278

Mayor's Committee on Drug Addiction, 35, 37, 55, 76, 134, 164, 282

Mead, G. H., 13, 193

Mead, J. M., 239

Medical profession, legitimate practice, 218–19; opinions of opiates, 142, 145; precautions to prevent addiction, 112, 116, 120–22

Merrill, F. T., 229, 279

Merton, R., 158

Methadone, 243

Methadone maintenance experiment, 91–92, 202–203

Meyer, A. S., 279

Meyer, E., 170, 279

Meyer, F. M., 179, 279

Mexico, opium production in, 227

Michelsen, T., 279

Morhous, E., 279

Morphine, 142, 208, 243

Morton, S. T., 144–45, 279

Moseley, A., 279

Motivation in addiction, 16–17, 83–84

Murtagh, J. M., 279–80

Needle-shy users, 34

Negative evidence, functions, 9–11, 13, 17–22

Negative reinforcement, 9, 95, 125–27, 197–99

Neutralization, 135

New York Academy of Medicine, 279

Nichols, J. R., 125, 126, 184, 185, 187, 271, 280

Nineteenth-century drug use, 116–19, 150–54, 207–217

Nolan, D. W., 118–19, 280

Non-addicting substitutes for opiates, 203–204

Normality, of addict, 26, 34–39; concept of, 170

Nyswander, M. E., 91, 202–203, 272, 280, 286

O'Donnell, J. A., 51, 53, 280

Ohlin, L. E., 271

Oltman, J. E., 280

Operant conditioning, 125

Opium, 244

Opium eaters, 209

Opium smoking in the U.S., 208–209, 213–16

Orskey, S., 75

Ostromislensky, I., 44, 280–81

Oursler, W., 267

Pain-prone female patients, 115–16

Papaver somniferum, 244

Paregoric, 226, 229, 245

Partington, J. E., 281

Partridge, M., 281

Payne, E., 281

Pellens, M., 8, 26, 27, 32, 33, 40, 56, 59, 78, 90, 99–100, 111, 112, 117, 147, 157, 162, 163, 168, 170, 195, 207, 210, 216, 218–20, 284

Personality as selective factor; see Addiction prone personality

Pescor, M. J., 281

Pethidine, 243–44

Pettey, G. E., 281

Pharmacothymia, 175

Physical dependence; see Dependence

Physical effects of habit, 39–41

Physicians, addiction among, 108, 149

Piaget, J., 195–96

Piel, G., 221, 281

Pilcz, A., 161, 281

Placebo effects, 11, 25, 34–39, 114

Pleasure theory, 176–80

Pleasure user, 103

Pohlisch, K., 48, 59–62, 108–109, 281

Pollock, H. M., 162, 281

Positive reinforcement, 9, 79–80, 197–99

Price, G. E., 278

Price, H. G., 270

Primary addiction, 166–67

Pseudo-withdrawal symptoms, 131–32

Psychoanalytic view of addiction, 174–76

Psychoneurotics, 121

Psychopathy, as cause of addiction, 157–72

Psychoses, and addiction, 26–27, 165–66, 199–201; treated with opiates, 199–201

Public Health Service, 6, 236–37

Public opinion, changes in the U.S., 240–41

Pure induction, 21

Queré, F. S., 110

Quinn, W. F., 281

Rabiner, E. L., 273

Radó, S., 174–76, 281–82

Rasor, R. W., 282, 286

Rationalizations of addicts, 150–54

Rats as addicts, 125–27, 184–86

Ray, M. B., 148, 282

Raynor, G. F., 282

Reactive addiction, 166–67

Reform proposals, 234–37

Reichard, J. D., 282

Relapse, in lower animals, 126, 184–85; rates, 52–54

Relapse impulse, 50–54, 130–32, 138–55

Remondino, P. C., 121, 282

Reichert, T., 162, 282

Rieth, A., 48, 52, 54–55, 63, 90, 108, 124, 137, 271

Ritchie, A. D., 13

Root, W. S., 283

Rosenbloom, J. R., 282

Rosenfeld, E., 48, 173, 270

Ross, Barney, 230

Rubington, E., 282

Russel, P. T. W., 282

Safrin, R., 287

Sager, C. J., 273

Sampling, 5, 12

Sandoz, C. E., 27, 31, 76, 132–33, 282

Sceleth, C. E., 111, 119, 282

Schasre, R., 113–14, 282

Schneider, K., 283

Schultz, C., 35–37, 55–56, 76, 133, 134, 143–44, 160–66, 168, 170

Schur, E. M., 283

Schuster, C. R., 185, 284

Schwarz, H., 162, 283

Scientific theory, 9–10

Scott, F. G. L., 283

Seevers, M. H., 185, 271, 272, 283

Selective factors, 172–74

  See also Addiction prone personalities

Self conceptions, of addicts, 63–64, 96, 137, 148, 185; of medical patients, 115–16, 201–203

Self confidence in spread of habit, 74–75

Self experimentation, 28, 81–82, 107–112

Semke, C. W., 283

Serejski, M., 172, 283

Sertürner, F. W. A., 208

Sex ratio among addicts, 173, 210

"Sigma," 56–57, 88, 283

Simmel, E., 283

Siragusa, C., 249
Skinner, B. F., 125, 158
Slocum, M. A., 283
Smith, G. M., 283
Social effects of anti-narcotic laws, 220–23
Sollier, P., 27, 283
Solomon, D., 284
Spragg, S. D. S., 65, 181–83, 185, 187, 284
Stanley, L. L., 69–70
Statistical method, 12, 13–14, 18–19
Strauss, E., 124, 284
Subculture of addiction, 149–50
Sutherland, E. H., 5, 140, 141
Symptomatic addiction, 166–67
Synanon, 51, 189, 202
Syringe, as symbol, 121-22

Takman, J., 284
Taylor, N., 284
Terry, C. E., 8, 26, 27, 32, 33, 40, 48, 56, 59, 78, 90, 99–100, 111, 112, 117, 147, 157, 162, 163, 168, 170, 195, 207, 210, 216, 218–20, 284
Thompson, T., 185, 284
Tobacco habit, 131
Tompkins, W. F., 268
Toolan, J., 287
Torrance, E. G., 29, 30, 40, 86–88, 277
Treadway, W. L., 284–85
Trocchi, A., 285
Tu, T., 285
Turano, A. M., 285
Turnau, M. A., 275

Universals, 18–21

Variables, 13

Vogel, V. H., 278, 285
Volkman, R., 285
Vollmer, A., 234–36, 285

War, effects of, 225–31
Weeks, J. R., 126, 285
Whisson, M. G., 285
White, W. M., 275
White House Conference on Drug Abuse, 286
Whitman, H., 236
Wholey, C. C., 111–12, 286
Wikler, A., 126, 178, 286
Willcox, W. H., 109–110, 286
Williams, E. H., 286
Williams, H. S., 286
Wilner, D. M., 53, 126, 173, 178, 270, 278, 280, 286
Wilson, R. H. L., 275
Winick, C., 286–87
Wissler, A., 287
Withdrawal distress, craving and, 7–8
    dangers, 76–77
    described, 28–31
    first experiences with, 98–100
    recognition of, 37, 78–83
Wolff, P., 122, 199–200, 277, 287
Wolff, W. A., 29–30, 86–88
Woods, A., 237, 287
Woods, L. A., 283
Wortis, S. B., 287
Wuth, O., 172, 287

Yablonsky, L., 287
Yen, 102–103

Zimmering, P., 287
Zinberg, N. E., 116, 287
Znaniecki, F., 20–21
Zubin, J., 282